D1203132

BACTERIAL ANATOMY

Other Publications of the
Society for General Microbiology

THE JOURNAL OF GENERAL MICROBIOLOGY
(Cambridge University Press)

MECHANISMS OF MICROBIAL PATHOGENICITY
FIFTH SYMPOSIUM OF THE SOCIETY
(Cambridge University Press)

AUTOTROPHIC MICRO-ORGANISMS
FOURTH SYMPOSIUM OF THE SOCIETY
(Cambridge University Press)

ADAPTATION IN MICRO-ORGANISMS
THIRD SYMPOSIUM OF THE SOCIETY
(Cambridge University Press)

THE NATURE OF VIRUS MULTIPLICATION
SECOND SYMPOSIUM OF THE SOCIETY
(Cambridge University Press)

THE NATURE OF THE BACTERIAL SURFACE
FIRST SYMPOSIUM OF THE SOCIETY
(Blackwell's Scientific Publications Limited)

BACTERIAL ANATOMY

SIXTH SYMPOSIUM OF THE
SOCIETY FOR GENERAL MICROBIOLOGY
HELD AT THE
ROYAL INSTITUTION, LONDON
APRIL 1956

CAMBRIDGE

Published for the Society for General Microbiology

AT THE UNIVERSITY PRESS

1956

LIBRARY
SIENA HEIGHTS COLLEGE
ADRIAN, MICHIGAN

PUBLISHED BY
THE SYNDICS OF THE CAMBRIDGE UNIVERSITY PRESS
London Office: Bentley House, N.W. 1
American Branch: New York
Agents for Canada, India, and Pakistan: Macmillan

Printed in Great Britain at the University Press, Cambridge
(Brooke Crutchley, University Printer)

QR
1
.S623

CONTRIBUTORS

BIRCH-ANDERSEN, A., Statens Seruminstitut, Copenhagen.

BISSET, K. A., Department of Bacteriology, University of Birmingham.

BRADFIELD, J. R. G., Cavendish Laboratory, Cambridge.

DeLAMATER, E. D., Department of Physiology, University of Pennsylvania, Philadelphia, U.S.A.

ELLIOTT, C. G., Department of Genetics, University of Glasgow.

HANNAY, C. L., Science Service Laboratory, Department of Agriculture, London, Ontario, Canada.

HUGHES, W. H., Wright-Fleming Institute, St Mary's Hospital, London.

MAALØE, O., Statens Seruminstitut, Copenhagen.

McQUILLEN, K., Department of Biochemistry, University of Cambridge.

MITCHELL, P., Department of Biochemistry, University of Cambridge.

MOYLE, JENNIFER, Department of Biochemistry, University of Cambridge.

ROBINOW, C. F., Department of Bacteriology and Immunology, University of Western Ontario, Canada.

SALTON, M. R. J., Department of Biochemistry, University of Cambridge.

STOCKER, B. A. D., Lister Institute of Preventive Medicine, London.

THORNE, C. B., Camp Detrick, Frederick, Maryland, U.S.A.

TOMCSIK, J., Institute of Hygiene and Bacteriology, University of Basel.

WEIBULL, C., Biokemiska Institutionen, Uppsala Universitet, Uppsala, Sweden.

37315

CONTENTS

EDITORS' PREFACE

The fifteen articles in this volume represent papers which will be discussed at the Sixth Symposium of the Society for General Microbiology in London in April 1956.

The Editors wish to thank the Staff of the Cambridge University Press for their admirable co-operation and help which have made publication of the book possible in time for it to be considered by members of the Society before the Symposium.

E. T. C. SPOONER

B. A. D. STOCKER

*London School of Hygiene and Tropical Medicine
and Lister Institute of Preventive Medicine
    March 1956*

CELLULAR ORGANIZATION IN BACTERIA

K. A. BISSET

Department of Bacteriology, University of Birmingham

INTRODUCTION

Control of cytological methods

So far as can be determined by the evidence at present available, living organisms are divisible into three main groups in respect of the structure and mechanism of their cells. First, the viruses, which may not have a single origin, and which lack many of the usual attributes of cells; so much so, that some authorities doubt their claim to be living organisms in their own right. Secondly, the blue-green algae; these possess a more conventional cellular organization but are exceptional in that they show no signs of ever having possessed flagella. They have a nucleus, but its structure and mode of division have not been satisfactorily described. Thirdly, the flagellate cells, including numerous forms which have long since modified or discarded their flagella, but which show obvious signs of relationship with and descent from flagellates. This very large and important group includes green plants, animals, fungi and also bacteria. All its members, including bacteria, resemble one another closely in the main characters of their cellular organization; but each of the major subdivisions enumerated has certain details of structure and behaviour peculiar to itself. It is the purpose of this introductory paper to consider the peculiarities of bacteria in this respect.

Most of the components believed to exist in the cells of the other members of the flagellate group have at various times been claimed for bacteria also. And in nearly every case the point has been a subject of dispute.

It need not be assumed, however, that the interpretation of cytological appearances is so entirely subjective that no means of coming to a firm decision in such disputed issues is to be found. The tests which can be applied are simple and obvious enough. The first of these is indeed so obvious that, like other obvious things, it is very frequently overlooked; it is that any hypothesis which seeks to explain a particular appearance or set of appearances must be compatible, not only with these, but with all available information from other sources. And as a corollary, it should not be forgotten that where evidence from two or more sources is in agreement, the validity of any single source which produces conflicting results must reasonably be regarded as suspect.

The second test which can be applied to cytological evidence is a *sine qua non* of every kind of experimental work, but its application to this type of study is not infrequently misunderstood, and in consequence neglected. This is the use of controls. Control of experimental method is no less applicable to cytology than in any other field. Any staining procedure or microscopical examination must be regarded as an experiment and treated as such. The cytologist of ordinary experience does not now credit any refractile body with the possession of a distinct cortex and medulla, simply because it gives such an appearance at certain optical foci; nor does he believe a structure to be uniform throughout because it chances to stain in this manner with a single strong dye. Similarly, at a slightly less elementary level of reasoning, it is now generally accepted to be true that neither the straightforward transfer to bacteria of the methods which have produced fundamental evidence concerning other types of cytological material, nor the attempt to base cytological interpretations upon routine bacteriological staining methods have produced more than a minimum of useful evidence concerning the morphology of bacteria. The effect of this knowledge should have been a realization that all technical methods can be regarded, at best, as necessary evils, to be considered guilty of misrepresentation until they are proved innocent by the use of controls.

The form which controls must take in this sort of work is not as difficult to conceive as it might appear to be from an examination of the statements of those investigators who have neglected to employ them, or who have failed to take due cognizance of the evidence which they provide.

The effect of a technique upon an organism can be checked in at least two ways: by comparison of its effects upon a variety of similar and more or less dissimilar organisms, and by comparison of the effects of different techniques upon the same organism.

One of the studies which was most influential in encouraging the present revived interest in the fine structure of bacteria, that of Robinow (1945), made admirable use of both types of control. By contrast, other authors have gone so far as to make a virtue of the practice of concentrating upon a single method, applied to a single subject, and indeed to solitary, and apparently rather exceptional individual organisms among the cultures examined. This point of view cannot be too deeply deplored.

In a series of recent papers by several different authors upon the cytology of staphylococci and other related cocci, some excellent examples can be found both of the application of controls and of the results of failing to do so. Where controls have been properly used, the results achieved independently, indeed almost simultaneously, by different methods, are in reasonably close accord. Where controls were neglected or misapplied, the almost incredible divergence between these claims concerning the morphology of so well-known a micro-organism as the staphylococcus is of itself an adequate commentary upon their reliability.

One of the most interesting of these papers was published by Webb & Clark (1954). These careful workers, who deserve every credit for the manner in which they check and reinvestigate their own findings, applied the control of comparative staining methods and described septate cocci with two or four cells, each cell containing a small nucleus. Their technique for demonstrating the nucleus consisted of staining with crystal violet and differentiating with nigrosin. But when stained in this manner some of the larger cocci appeared as if each contained a single large nucleus. However, the use of the second type of control, by applying the same method to a large bacillus (first by the present writer and subsequently by Clark & Webb, 1955), showed that these rod-shaped bacteria then appeared with a long central stained area, and showing very little sign of the cell divisions or other structures visible by other techniques. Thus the stained centre and cleared periphery of some of the larger cocci was perhaps explained, in that the effect of the nigrosin was to differentiate only the outer layers of the organism. And I am informed that subsequent work in the same laboratory, by the use of a different type of nuclear stain, has revealed from four to six nuclei in some of the larger cocci (Clark, personal communication, 1955). The general picture is thus in close accord with that obtained by the present writer (Bisset, 1954a) (see also Pl. 1, figs. 3, 4 in this paper).

Similarly, Wigand & Peters (1954) have so correlated the apparently divergent results of different enzymic treatments of cocci, at different ages, as seen by classical, phase-contrast and electron microscopy, that their evidence is in excellent accord with other available information. In contrast, Dawson & Stern (1954), examining electron micrographs of crushed cell walls of staphylococci, were led to believe that these organisms consisted of a single cell, dividing by a constrictive ingrowth. They used no controls of any sort. In this case, in view of the well-known fact that the penetrative powers of the electron beam through such material are not at all great, the obvious requirement was that the same technique should have been applied to other bacteria of known complex structure, in order to check its efficacy in the demonstration of cell boundaries. The lack of such controls invalidates the claim of these conclusions to stand up against descriptions of a much higher degree of cellular subdivision based upon other, mutually corroborative, techniques. The conclusion to be drawn from a comparison of these different sources of information is that only the most mature septa, already on the point of fission, were demonstrated by Dawson & Stern on this occasion.

On the other hand, Bradfield (1954) compared the results of his technique of staining electron-transparent sections of bacteria upon a variety of species. But his interpretations would certainly have been greatly clarified had he controlled this promising but untried method in the complementary manner, by the use of parallel preparations employing some more familiar technique or techniques. Bradfield's conclusions, as they stand, have very little in common with those from any other source. He regards the staphylococcus as containing a central nucleus with multiple but amitotically dividing chromosomes.

An equally divergent view of the staphylococcal nucleus was that of Krieg (1954), who examined living material by fluorescent microscopy, and described a single comma-shaped chromosome in each coccus, dividing longitudinally and separating by a rotatory movement at cell division. Once more, the same method had been employed upon other bacteria, but the results of this control were ignored. In so well-known a species as *Bacterium coli*, for example, some cells appeared to contain a fine spiral thread; others showed nothing. The ordinary, vegetative, rodlets were not demonstrated, and this should have cast suspicion upon the universality of the potentialities of the technique. A control of this type was also available from internal evidence in the illustrations of the cocci themselves, since only about 10 % of these showed any 'nuclear structures' at all. The parallel-preparation type of control was not employed, but was available, in the work of Bisset & Hale (1953a), who showed that cocci of this type almost always contain four or more cells, separated by cross-walls. Taking these two types of control properly into account it is obvious that even in those cocci from which Krieg drew his conclusions only the contents of one or two component cells had been stained, and that these represented Krieg's 'nuclei'.

An entirely different type of claim was made by DeLamater & Woodburn (1952), who produced appearances in such cocci which they stated to be mitotic spindles. In this case the controls were applied by other workers; Bisset (1954a) and Clark & Webb (1954) made parallel preparations showing that, in this and in other comparable cases, each 'mitotic figure' comprised the contents of several distinct cells.

It is worthy of emphasis that those of the foregoing studies from which conclusions were drawn that were mutually corroborative, and therefore almost certainly accurate, were by no means all performed by the use of the same methods (although the present writer (Bisset, 1954*a*) attempted to use and compare as many of these as possible in order to resolve the discrepancies), but these corroborative studies resembled one another in that proper use was made of controls of the types described; and it was this which ensured their reliability, irrespective of method.

In the assessment of conflicting claims in a relatively new subject such as bacterial cytology, it is essential not only to consider which interpretation is capable of explaining all the appearances described, but to reject those that explain only those sources of evidence upon which they are based, and disregard all others. It is also important to recognize which interpretation is most in accordance, not so much with the state of affairs in cells in general, as with that state most typical of the bacteria themselves.

Bacteria do indeed possess a number of characters which they share with other protista and, in addition, like all the main groups of living things, they have their own peculiarities whereby they may be recognized.

REPRODUCTION IN BACTERIA

It is probably safe, by this time, to assume that that part of the description of bacteria which defines them as reproducing exclusively by 'simple' fission is so outdated as to require no further comment, although it continues to be enshrined in the publications sanctioned by various semi-official bodies.

In fact, bacteria reproduce by the fission or budding of single cells and filamentous syncytia, by the fragmentation of septate filaments, by the formation of more or less spore-like cells, and by the release of tiny motile gonidia, as well as by the more enigmatic L-forms (Pl. 1).

The production of spore-like cells is widely agreed to include a sexual or autogamous process of some kind, and the nuclear activity by which it is accompanied is distinctly different from that of vegetative reproduction (Bisset, 1955*a*). It has occasionally been suggested that the formation of gonidia and of L-forms also includes a sexual process (Löhnis & Smith, 1916; Stempen & Hutchinson, 1951).

More elaborate sexual mechanisms have also been claimed to exist in bacteria, but these claims have either been directly disproved or have failed to be confirmed. Cytological and genetical evidence agree that sexuality, where it occurs in bacteria, entails a relatively simple nuclear fusion.

There is nothing exceptional in the reproduction of bacteria. Different types of bacteria show considerable variations in their degree of evolutionary adaptation, but the main trends of development are parallel with, and in every way comparable to, those found in other members of the flagellate group.

The vegetative stages of most types of bacteria divide by 'simple' fission, but since the fissile unit, the rod or coccus, is not always a single cell, but may consist of any number of cells from two or three to a dozen or more (Pl. 1), fission is by no means synonymous with cell division. A recent and original demonstration of the cell membranes of *Bacillus megaterium* by Newton (1955) shows the very great extent to which this type of bacillus may be subdivided into relatively tiny cells.

The question is largely a matter of timing as between cell division and fission. Sometimes they coincide, sometimes the latter lags behind the former and a multicellular unit arises (Pl. 1, figs. 1–5; Text-fig. 1 A, B). In the present context, however, it is cell division which requires more immediately to be considered.

DIVISION OF THE NUCLEUS

In the division of the bacterial nucleus a question of timing also arises, and is of more fundamental importance to the problem of cellular organization. This is the co-ordination of cell division and nuclear division. Obviously, if this is exact each cell contains a single nuclear unit; if cell division lags behind then multinucleate cells will arise. Both conditions occur quite commonly among bacteria (Pl. 1, figs. 1–5; Text-fig. 1C).

The mechanism of nuclear division in bacteria has now been demonstrated with such clarity (Pl. 1, fig. 5) and the cytological and genetical pictures have achieved such complete correlation that it is difficult to allow much room for alternative explanations (Text-figs. 2, 3).

It is an axiom of cytogenetics that the hereditary factors in a dividing nucleus must be so arranged that each is fully represented in both daughter nuclei. That is to say, they must be arranged in linear form, so that the splitting of the rod or string serves to divide each unit along its length. Although it is theoretically possible for them to be in the form of a plate or disk, dividing parallel to its main plane, yet this is mechanically much less simple, and certainly does not usually occur.

The string of genes in most types of cell is, of course, the chromosome, and the processes of mitosis ensure that these divide in concert and that the daughter cells obtain a full equipment of daughter chromosomes. Diploid nuclei contain chromosomes in similar but not identical pairs; and in equational division of the nucleus, each member of the pair splits and is represented in the daughter nucleus.

The bacterial nucleus in its simplest form consists of a single chromosome-like rod, dividing lengthwise (Pl. 1, fig. 5; Text-fig. 2). Although these rods very often lie in pairs, these are not true diploid pairs, but recently divided sisters. Each goes eventually to a different cell. Thus

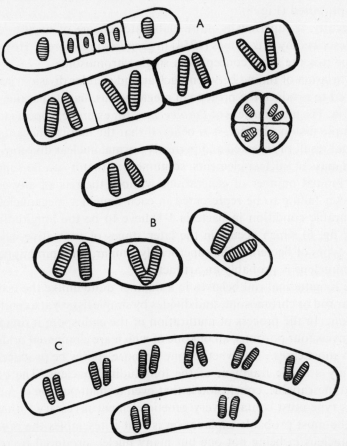

Text-fig. 1. Timing in nuclear and cell division. A, cell division proceeds more rapidly than fission, producing multicellular rods and cocci. B, cell division, fission and nuclear division keep pace. C, nuclear division proceeds more rapidly than cell division, giving rise to multinucleate filaments.

division of the nucleus is not equational but reductional. A true mitosis is not required and almost certainly does not occur. The blepharoplast (Pl. 1, fig. 9), which provides the centriole in some types of protista, takes no part in the division of the bacterial nucleus. The claims of DeLamater (1951, 1954 and numerous other papers) to prove the existence of a classical mitosis in bacteria have been analysed elsewhere

(Clark, Galyen & Webb, 1953; Hale, 1954; Delaporte, 1954; Bisset, 1953*a*, 1954*a*).

The single, reductionally dividing chromosome is now acceptable to geneticists (e.g. Ryan & Wainwright, 1954) after a period in which various hypotheses for which there exists no cytological support whatever had been proposed (Fig. 3).

Recently, a superficially more elaborate scheme of nuclear division was described by Fitz-James (1954) in germinating spores. However, in essence it is the same concept of a single chromosome.

A variation of timing between nuclear and cellular division, such as is believed to produce the protozoan meganucleus, has its parallel among bacteria. The meganucleus of *Paramecium*, for example, appears to divide by simple fission. In fact, it is believed that the mature meganucleus is the final result of repeated and perfectly normal nuclear divisions, and is thus a mass of nuclear elements, so numerous that it can be subdivided for a limited number of generations without the risk of any essential character failing to be represented in each daughter meganucleus. The comparable condition in bacteria I believe to be the longitudinal rod (Pl. 1, fig. 6) which occurs in the later stages of vegetative culture of many types of bacteria. The superficially similar, fine spiral appearance of the nucleus is probably an artifact.

The longitudinal rod behaves in a manner quite unlike the transverse nuclear rod or chromosome and divides by simple fission at a central constriction. In the process of maturation of the endospore it divides into as many as four portions, all but one of which are eliminated or degenerate, in most cases. But whether one or more spores be produced, each has only a single fragment of the longitudinal nucleus. The obvious, indeed inescapable, conclusion is that even a small portion of a nucleus of this type must contain every genetic element necessary for survival. And the most probable explanation is that it resembles the protozoan meganucleus in being not one but many nuclei, produced by repeated nuclear divisions in anticipation of cell division. The same process may be, and probably is, stimulated or abetted by sexual or autogamous nuclear fusions (Bisset, 1955*a*). Very probably the rod consists of a large number of parallel transverse rods, each a full functional nucleus (Text-fig. 2). Thus, even a small part of the entire rod is capable of providing adequate nucleation for an entire cell. It is widely believed (see Bisset, 1955*a*, for literature) that the formation of the vesicular resting nucleus from this rod form entails a reduction process.

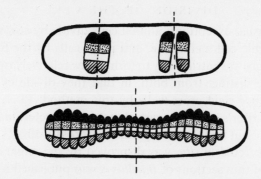

Text-fig. 2. Division of the nucleus; the genetic units are represented by the differently hatched and stippled sections of the chromosome-like nuclear rod. In the upper figure, the longitudinal division of the normal vegetative nucleus ensures that these are equally represented in the daughter nuclei. In the lower figure, the apparent transverse division of the long type of nucleus (cf. also Pl. 1, fig. 6) is explicable in terms of a polyploid constitution, whereby all genetic units are already present in both of the dividing portions, as in the protozoan meganucleus.

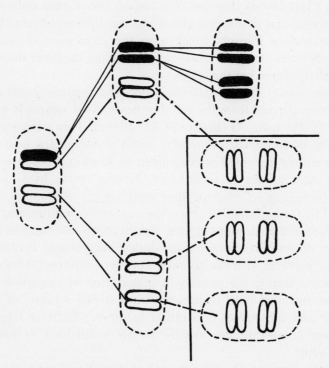

Text-fig. 3. Reductional division of the paired nuclear rods of the vegetative cell ensures rapid segregation of mutant characters.

DIVISION OF THE CELL

Granted the usual exceptions, animal cells divide by constriction of the relatively flexible cell membrane, and plant cells by the formation of a 'plate' which grows centrifugally to form a new relatively rigid cross-wall.

Bacteria are distinct from both, in that they divide by constriction, but may produce rigid cross-walls by this method (Pl. 1, figs. 1, 2, 3). The present writer's previous view that typical bacterium forms divide by constriction, but that the semi-permanent cross-walls of Gram-positive bacteria are secreted *in situ*, was disproved by the remarkable electron micrographs of thin sections of *Bacillus cereus* published by Chapman & Hillier (1953), which showed the constrictive ingrowth of these cross-walls also.

The alternative concept that the division of the bacterial cell, like that of the plant cell, progresses from the centre outwards is not entirely without its protagonists. Chance (1953) suggested that *Sarcina* divided by a 'cell plate formed in the nucleus and extended so as to intercept the walls'. But the technique employed in this case was the same as that of Webb & Clark (1954), described previously, and it is the opinion of the present writer that in this case also it was the differentiation of the stain from the surface inwards which gave the impression of incomplete junction between wall and cross-wall, by leaving the latter more or less incompletely stained at the edges.

The ingrowth of the cell wall is preceded, and apparently also secreted, by a septum derived from the cell membrane. This septum is markedly basophilic (Pl. 1, fig. 7) (Bisset, 1953b, 1955a). This secretory septum appears to be composed of protein, with a strong nucleic acid content, and it is readily disrupted or coagulated by fixation procedures. In the electron micrographs of sections of *Bacillus cereus* by Chapman & Hillier, previously referred to, these septa appear as granules, and it is assumed by the authors that this is their natural condition, and that the appearance of a continuous septum seen in photo-micrographs is due to the lower power of resolution of the optical microscope. It is at least as probable, however, that the granules were produced by the coagulation of the septa during the process of preparation of the specimen; the technique included both treatment with a strong solution of osmium tetroxide and subsequent desiccation *in vacuo*. Bacteria which have permanent cross-walls are usually further subdivided by such cytoplasmic septa.

In septate bacteria, the main growth of the cell wall takes place at the points of junction of these septa with the cell-wall proper (Bisset, 1953b,

1955*a*), and this conclusion has been independently verified by the re-markable phase-contrast studies of Tomcsik & Guex-Holzer (1954), which, since they are the subject of a communication by Professor Tomcsik in this Symposium, need not be further elaborated here.

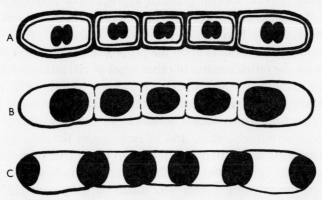

Text-fig. 4. Different granular effects produced by coagulation and shrinkage in multi-cellular bacteria. A, diagram of the morphology of an organism of the *Corynebacterium* or *Mycobacterium* type. B, shrinkage of cell contents centrally around the nucleus, as produced by some diagnostic techniques. C, coagulation of basophilic material around the cross-walls. This effect is produced on occasion by unsuitable cytological procedures.

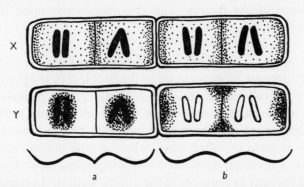

Text-fig. 5. Different effects produced by coagulation and shrinkage in large *Bacillus* types. X, diagram of natural morphology. The stippling represents basophilia of the cell envelopes and cytoplasm. Y, coagulation of the basophilia: (*a*) around the nucleus; (*b*) on the cross-walls. In the latter case the basophilia of the nuclear bodies themselves may be transferred to the cell envelopes.

In the case of unicellular bacteria, on separation after cell division, the portion of the secretory septum which underlies the new tip of the cell becomes the growing point; usually the main growth proceeds from one tip only, so that one of the daughter cells on division is effectively a bud, although approximately the same size as the parent cell (Bisset, 1951). Confirmation of this has now been obtained by cinematography (Malek,

Voskyova, Wolf & Fiala, 1954). The growing point is very often the most obvious structure in any bacterium stained with a simple aqueous dye, and its appearance has given rise to many misconceptions.

There is also reason to believe that the septa and growing points of bacteria may provide foci for granular aggregates of reagents (Weibull, 1953) or of nucleic acids derived from other parts of the cell (Bisset, 1954b) (Pl. 1, fig. 7; Text-figs. 4, 5).

These findings cast doubts upon the proposed identification of similar granules with the mitochondria of other types of cell advanced by Mudd (1954, and numerous other papers). However, Mudd (1955, personal communication) now recognizes that these bacterial granules lack the complex structure which recent advances in technical methods have revealed in true mitochondria, and he emphasizes the analogy of their staining reactions rather than continuing to claim true homology.

An exceptionally valuable contribution to the understanding of the function of the growing points was made by Bergersen (1953), who showed that in *Bacterium coli* growing in the presence of chloramphenicol, typical growing points appeared in the sides of the cell wall, and developed into branches growing from the tip in the manner postulated by Bisset (1951). Much of the evidence in the latter paper is based upon the behaviour of the flagella, and thus, implicitly, upon that of the blepharoplasts.

FLAGELLA

These structures are of importance to the problem of the peculiarities of division of the cell and the nucleus in bacteria. The blepharoplast has now been demonstrated with great clarity by Grace (1954), and its existence has at various times been indicated by other workers (Pl. 1, fig. 9). In protista of other types, where a true mitosis is found, the blepharoplast is closely associated with the nucleus; it divides independently and may act as centriole in the mitotic figures. In bacteria, where no such centriole exists (cf. Bisset, 1953a, for discussion of structures claimed to resemble centrioles) the blepharoplasts are remote from the nucleus and situated near the surface of the cell. They take no discernible part in the division of the nucleus and they do not even appear to be self-reproducing, but, in the case of polar flagellate bacteria at least, arise *de novo* at the opposite end of the cell, or even at the newly formed pole of a multicellular spirillum. The solitary example of an organism claimed by some authorities to be a bacterium, *Selenomonas*, wherein the blepharoplasts are self-reproducing, and closely associated with the nucleus, is of doubtful taxonomic status (Text-fig. 6).

The flagella themselves consist of single fibrils (Grace, 1954; Bisset, 1955a), but in some forms they are intermediate between these and the complex flagella of other protista.

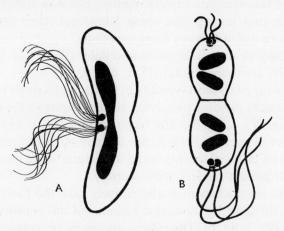

Text-fig. 6. The role of the blepharoplast in nuclear division. A, in *Selenomonas*, which is probably a protozoan, although claimed by some authorities to be a bacterium, the blepharoplast divides with the nucleus, with which it appears to have some connexion, and for which it may provide centrioles, in protozoan fashion. (I am indebted to Mr M. H. Jeynes for information concerning *Selenomonas*.) B, the characteristically bacterial condition is seen in *Pseudomonas*. The blepharoplasts of the newly arisen flagella (above) do not appear to be formed by fission of their predecessors (below), from which they are remote in position. They have no visible connexion with the nucleus, and cannot act as centrioles.

GONIDIA

The phenomenon of reproduction in bacteria by the release of tiny motile gonidia, resembling very small flagellate bacteria in all major respects (Plate 1, fig. 8), has been fully and repeatedly attested for so many years that it is remarkable to find it treated still as a theory of dubious authenticity, even in so well-known a case as that of *Azotobacter* (Jensen, 1954). The clearest examples of such gonidial reproduction are found in *Azotobacter*, *Rhizobium* and some spirilla (Bisset, 1955a), but it most certainly occurs also in a wide variety of other bacteria.

The processes whereby these tiny, but otherwise unexceptionable, bacteria are formed within a mother cell derived from the normal-sized phase of the life-cycle, are not known; but there is no reason to regard as surprising the occurrence in bacteria of a reproductive method which is found very commonly among other protista of the flagellate group.

GENERAL CHARACTERS OF CELLULAR ORGANIZATION

The consensus of evidence at present available is thus that bacteria form a division of the flagellate super-Kingdom, equal in status with plants and animals, and having, like these Kingdoms, their own points of resemblance to and difference from the others.

Bacteria may be unicellular or multicellular (Pl. 1, figs. 1–5).

The flagella are monofibrillar (Pl. 1, figs. 8, 9).

The nucleus appears most typically in the form of a single chromosome or a reductionally dividing pair, lying at right angles to the main axis of the bacterium (Pl. 1, fig. 5). The blepharoplast (Pl. 1, fig. 9) takes no apparent part in nuclear division, nor are any other of the mechanisms associated with classical mitosis found in bacteria, since the simple form of gene arrangement renders it unnecessary.

The vegetative nucleus may alternatively take the form of a longitudinal rod, dividing by transverse fission, and this is probably a polyploid phase (Pl. 1, fig. 6). The resting nucleus is vesicular.

Reproduction may be complex, by the production of motile gonidia, much smaller than normal bacteria but otherwise similar (Pl. 1, fig. 8), or by fission.

Cell division is by constrictive ingrowth of the wall, but leads to the formation, in multicellular species of bacteria, of permanent cross-walls (Pl. 1, figs. 1–3). The sites of division are marked by aggregates of basophilic material, both natural and artifact, to a much greater extent than in most other types of cell (Pl. 1, fig. 7).

Thus bacteria, while sharing many characters with other living cells, have their own peculiarities whereby they are distinguished. Their degree of cellular organization is neither greater nor less than that of other flagellate protista.

EPILOGUE: *APOLOGIA PRO LABORE MEO*

It is an axiom of science that nobody can presume to tell in advance whether any particular piece of information is of 'pure' or of 'applied' interest (the further epithet 'only' can be inserted before one or the other, according to taste). At the same time, the pursuit of knowledge for its own sake can never be justly regarded as entirely despicable. Nevertheless, the practical applications of the results of research in many branches of microbiology are so apparent that the bacterial cytologist is liable to be asked to explain the end and purpose of his own studies. Often enough the inquirer's interest in the question is genuine enough, but not everybody is satisfied with the real answer. To quote my betters: 'I like it!'

However, despite a firmly rooted disinclination to judge in advance the practical value of the results of his own researches, the present writer has found that an application which can claim to be at least semi-practical has been treading insistently upon his heels during a large part of the time which he has spent in this pursuit. A glance at the recently published Symposia of this Society will give a clear indication of its nature (Bisset & Grace, 1954; Bisset, 1955b). As in every other branch of biology, the most immediate and obvious application of morphology is in systematics, and it is where morphology has been worst neglected that systematics have proved least satisfactory, as in the obvious case of the autotrophic bacteria.

A piece of work immediately in hand provides an example of how systematics follow, more or less unsought, upon purely cytological researches. In the course of an investigation into the production of swarmers by *Rhizobium* (Bisset & Hale, 1951) it was noticed that this organism possessed certain cytological characters strongly suggestive of a relationship with *Bacillus*. Thus it came to be realized that the sporo-genous organisms found in root nodules of the less frequently studied species of legume were true *Rhizobium*, and had obvious affinities with *Bacillus polymyxa* (Bisset, 1952). An investigation of the production of swarmers by *Azotobacter* (Bisset & Hale, 1953b) showed that this process bore much too close a resemblance to that in *Rhizobium* to be the result of chance. And it was also apparent that the two species shared quite a number of other unusual cytological characters (Bisset, 1954c). This line of inquiry was followed in a further investigation in this laboratory (now in process of publication), which showed that the cell envelopes and 'cysts' of *Azotobacter*, like the comparable structures in *Rhizobium*, have a decidedly *Bacillus*-like character, despite the superficial differences.

This entire investigation leads to the rather startling conclusion that the two major types of aerobic nitrogen-fixers may well be quite closely related phylogenetically to the third, anaerobic group, among the clostridia.

Of more immediately apparent practical value is the knowledge that *Bacterium coli* and *Aerobacter* sp., usually regarded as morphologically similar, can be distinguished at sight by the shape of the resting cell (Bisset, 1950), and that the heterofermentative and homofermentative lactobacilli have an equally distinctive pattern in the cells of the vegetative bacillus (Davis, Bisset & Hale, 1955).

There exist, of course, other applications of bacterial cytology, especially to genetics and cell physiology. But the practitioners of these subjects, very justly contemptuous of those branches of science where the results cannot be applied to the solution of an equation, tend to resent being reminded of the possibility of aid from this source; not least if the cytologist shows any signs of having got there first with the same answer. Which does occasionally happen!

REFERENCES

BERGERSEN, F. J. (1953). Cytological changes induced in *Bacterium coli* by chloramphenicol. *J. gen. Microbiol.* **9**, 353.

BISSET, K. A. (1950). The differentiation of certain genera of *Bacteriaceae* by the morphology of the microcyst stage. *J. gen. Microbiol.* **4**, 413.

BISSET, K. A. (1951). The development of surface structures in dividing bacteria. *J. gen. Microbiol.* **5**, 155.

BISSET, K. A. (1952). Complete and reduced life-cycles in *Rhizobium. J. gen. Microbiol.* **7**, 233.

BISSET, K. A. (1953*a*). Do bacteria have mitotic spindles, fusion tubes and mitochondria? *J. gen. Microbiol.* **8**, 50.

BISSET, K. A. (1953*b*). Bacterial cell envelopes. *Bacterial Cytology, Symp. 6th Congr. Int. Microbiol., Rome.*

BISSET, K. A. (1954*a*). The cytology of *Micrococcus cryophilus. J. Bact.* **67**, 41.

BISSET, K. A. (1954*b*). The production of stainable granules by the adsorbtion of DNA upon bacterial cell envelopes. *Exp. Cell Res.* **7**, 232.

BISSET, K. A. (1954*c*). The cytology and reproductive elements of nitrogen-fixing bacteria. *Rapp. et Comm. 8th Int. Congr. Bot.* **21**, 34.

BISSET, K. A. (1955*a*). *The Cytology and Life-history of Bacteria,* 2nd ed. Edinburgh: Livingstone.

BISSET, K. A. (1955*b*). The value of cytological studies in elucidating natural relationships among bacteria. *J. gen. Microbiol.* **12**, 325.

BISSET, K. A. & GRACE, J. B. (1954). The nature and relationships of autotrophic bacteria. *Autotrophic Micro-organisms,* p. 28. Cambridge: University Press.

BISSET, K. A. & HALE, C. M. F. (1951). The production of swarmers in *Rhizobium* sp. *J. gen. Microbiol.* **5**, 592.

BISSET, K. A. & HALE, C. M. F. (1953*a*). Complex cellular structure in bacteria. *Exp. Cell Res.* **5**, 449.

BISSET, K. A. & HALE, C. M. F. (1953*b*). The cytology and life-cycle of *Azotobacter chroococcum. J. gen. Microbiol.* **8**, 442.

BRADFIELD, J. R. G. (1954). Electron microscopic observations on bacterial nuclei. *Nature, Lond.,* **173**, 184.

CHANCE, H. L. (1953). Cytokinesis in *Gaffkya tetragena. J. Bact.* **65**, 593.

CHAPMAN, G. B. & HILLIER, J. (1953). Electron microscopy of ultra-thin sections of bacteria. *J. Bact.* **66**, 362.

CLARK, J. B., GALYEN, L. I. & WEBB, R. B. (1953). The effect of organic solvents on the appearance of bacterial nuclei. *Stain Tech.* **28**, 313.

CLARK, J. B. & WEBB, R. B. (1954). Mitosis-like figures in *Corynebacterium pseudo-diphtheriticum. J. gen. Microbiol.* **11**, 394.

CLARK, J. B. & WEBB, R. B. (1955). A comparison of the crystal violet nuclear stain with other technics. *Stain Tech.* **30**, 73.

DAVIS, G. H. G., BISSET, K. A. & HALE, C. M. F. (1955). Correlation between morphological and physiological characters in the classification of members of the genus *Lactobacillus*. *J. gen. Microbiol.* **13**, 68.

DAWSON, I. M. & STERN, H. (1954). Structure in the bacterial cell-wall during cell division. *Biochim. biophys. Acta*, **13**, 31.

DeLAMATER, E. D. (1951). A new cytological basis for bacterial genetics. *Cold Spr. Harb. Symp. quant. Biol.* **16**, 381.

DeLAMATER, E. D. (1954). Cytology of bacteria. II. The bacterial nucleus. *Ann. Rev. Microbiol.* **8**, 23.

DeLAMATER, E. D. & WOODBURN, M. (1952). Evidence for the occurrence of mitosis in micrococci. *J. Bact.* **64**, 793.

DELAPORTE, B. (1954). État actuel de nos connaissances sur la cytologie bactérienne. *Rapp. et Comm. 8th Int. Congr. Bot.* **21**, 23.

FITZ-JAMES, P. C. (1954). The duplication of bacterial chromatin. *J. Bact.* **68**, 464.

GRACE, J. B. (1954). Some observations on the flagella and blepharoplasts of *Spirillum* and *Vibrio* spp. *J. gen. Microbiol.* **9**, 325.

HALE, C. M. F. (1954). Short note on the production of nuclear artifacts resembling mitotic figures in micro-organisms by treatment with organic solvents. *Exp. Cell Res.* **6**, 243.

JENSEN, H. L. (1954). The *Azotobacteriaceae*. *Bact. Rev.* **18**, 195.

KRIEG, A. (1954). Nachweis Kernäquivalenter Strukturen bei Bakterien *in vivo*. III. Mikrokokken. *Z. Hyg. InfektKr.* **139**, 61.

LÖHNIS, F. & SMITH, N. R. (1916). Life cycles of the bacteria. *J. agr. Res.* **6**, 675.

MALEK, I., VOSKYOVA, L., WOLF, A. & FIALA, J. (1954). Nerovnocennost bakterijnich bunek prideleni. *Ceskoslovenska Biol.* **3**, 135.

MUDD, S. (1954). Cytology of bacteria. II. The bacterial cell. *Ann. Rev. Microbiol.* **8**, 1.

NEWTON, B. A. (1955). A fluorescent derivative of polmyxin: its preparation and use in studying the site of action of the antibiotic. *J. gen. Microbiol.* **12**, 226.

ROBINOW, C. F. (1945). Addendum to *The Bacterial Cell*, by Dubos, R. J. Harvard University Press.

RYAN, F. J. & WAINWRIGHT, L. K. (1954). Nuclear segregation and the growth of clones of spontaneous mutants of bacteria. *J. gen. Microbiol.* **11**, 364.

STEMPEN, H. & HUTCHINSON, W. G. (1951). The formation and development of large bodies in *Proteus vulgaris* OX-19. *J. Bact.* **61**, 321.

TOMCSIK, J. & GUEX-HOLZER, S. (1954). Genese der komplexen Kapselstruktur. *Schweiz. Zeit. allg. Path. Bakt.* **17**, 221.

WEBB, R. B. & CLARK, J. B. (1954). Cell division in *Micrococcus pyogenes* var. *aureus*. *J. Bact.* **67**, 94.

WEIBULL, C. (1953). Observations on the staining of *Bacillus megaterium* with triphenyltetrazolium. *J. Bact.* **66**, 137.

WIGAND, R. & PETERS, D. (1954). Licht und elektronenoptische Untersuchungen über den Abbau gramnegativer Kokken mit Nucleasen und Proteasen. *Z. Naturf.* **96**, 586.

EXPLANATION OF PLATE
PLATE 1. Characteristics of bacterial structure

Fig. 1. Cell walls of *Bacillus* sp. showing one or two cells per organism. Tannic-acid-violet. × 3600.

Fig. 2. Cell walls of *Caryophanon latum*, showing numerous, disk-shaped cells separated by cross-walls. Hale's method. × 2400.

Figs. 3, 4. Cell walls and nuclei respectively of a coccus (*Micrococcus cryophilus*), each element of which consists of two, four or more cells. The great majority of coccal bacteria are multicellular. Cell walls by Hale's method; nuclei by trichloracetic acid and Giemsa. × 3200.

Fig. 5. The reductionally dividing, paired nuclei of bacteria are well seen in the giant bacteria of the herbivorous gut, *Oscillospira* sp. Nuclear structures by acid-thionin. × 1600.

Fig. 6. The nucleus in the form of a longitudinal rod, *Bacterium coli*. Acid-Giemsa. × 2400. (Reproduced from the *Journal of Hygiene*.)

Fig. 7. Basophilia of the cross-walls. *Bacillus megaterium* stained by iron-alum haematoxylin. The dark patches are cross-walls, the cell walls and nuclei are not seen. This type of reaction has been the cause of much confusion in bacterial cytology. × 2400.

Fig. 8. Swarmer of *Rhizobium* sp. Electron micrograph, gold-shadowed. × 13,000. (Reproduced from the *Journal of General Microbiology*.)

Fig. 9. Blepharoplast and monofibrillar flagellum in *Spirillum* sp. Electron micrograph. × 15,000. (By the courtesy of Miss Phyllis Pease.)

PLATE 1

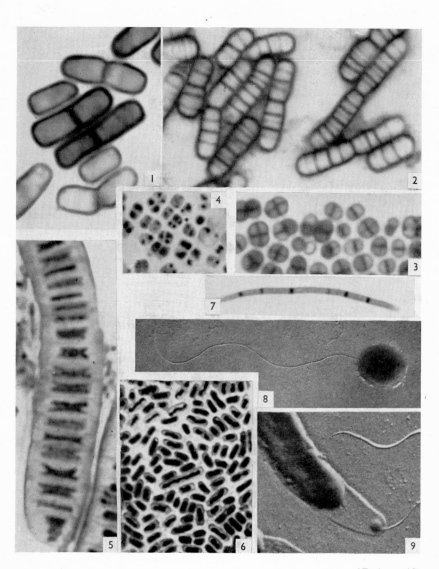

BACTERIAL FLAGELLA: MORPHOLOGY, CONSTITUTION AND INHERITANCE

B. A. D. STOCKER

Lister Institute of Preventive Medicine, London

Bacterial flagella have an unusual combination of characters in that anatomically they lie outside the cell wall, and like capsules and other extracellular material they may be removed without killing the cell; and yet they have a characteristic movement, which suggests that they are part of the living cell. The problem of whether or not bacterial motility results from flagellar movement was fully argued at an earlier symposium of this society (Miles & Pirie, 1949), and the discussion has continued since (Pijper, 1951, 1955; Weibull, 1951*b*; Koffler & Mallett, 1952; van Iterson, 1953; Kvittingen, 1955; etc.); it will therefore not be considered here. However, at some points the function of flagella cannot be ignored when considering their structure and inheritance, and at such points the argument is based on the premise that bacterial flagella are indeed locomotor organelles.

MORPHOLOGY OF BACTERIAL FLAGELLA

Modern instruments, such as the electron and phase-contrast microscopes, have in general strikingly confirmed the results obtained in the early days of bacteriology by the examination of stained films; most of what is now known about the morphology of flagella was already known for instance, to Migula (1897). Whether bacteria be examined *in vivo* by dark-ground or phase-contrast methods, or, after drying, in the optical or electron microscope, what is seen is a plane image of what in life is a three-dimensional structure. By all these methods bacterial flagella appear as unbranched sinuous filaments attached at one end to the bacterial body, the bends being approximately like a train of sine waves. As exceptions to this generalization we may note the electron micrographs of Bradfield & Cater (1952), where in organisms of the genera *Leptospira*, *Treponema* and *Cristispira* there are to be seen one or more filaments of about the size and shape of typical bacterial flagella, but which in the intact organism are wound spirally around the cylindrical or helical cell; in *Treponema duttoni* the fibrils appear to be enclosed within a sheath. It seems that these are spirochaetal flagella, differing from the usual bacterial kind by being attached to the body throughout their length, instead of at one end only.

An apparent exception to the statement that all flagella show in plan a sinuous form is the report of Pijper (1946, etc.) that organisms of various groups examined alive in broth by sunlight dark-ground micro-scopy show a fuzzy-looking straight 'tail', which becomes converted into a wavy structure or structures when the cell ceases to move, or momentarily at other times. However, it seems probable that a flagellar bundle performing very rapidly the kind of movement which can be seen occurring relatively slowly in *Proteus* filaments suspended in a viscous medium would appear both to the eye and to the camera as a wide, blurred, straight image.

The sinuous form of the flagella seen in plan has been generally taken to indicate that their shape is a cylindrical helix. Weibull (1950c) has confirmed this interpretation by phase-contrast microscopy of wet preparations of bundles or 'zöpfe' formed by the aggregation of detached flagella of *Proteus vulgaris*. By careful focusing he distinguished the upper surface from the lower and concluded that the helix was a left-handed or anti-clockwise one in all the strains examined.

The wave-length and amplitude of the projected wave form may be measured; in wet preparations (in which probably only aggregates of bacterial flagella can be seen) these distances give a direct measure of the pitch and diameter of the helix. Some distortion must occur in making dry preparations, and the exact relation of the wave-length and ampli-tude of the dry flagellum to the pitch and diameter of the helix is not certain; however, the discrepancy is likely to be small.

It has long been known that these measurements are approximately constant for any one bacterial strain, but vary between strains in a way that is correlated with other bacterial characters, so that flagellar wave-length is a character of some taxonomic value. Two groups of investi-gators, using different methods, have recently shown that a single strain may have flagella of either of two different wave-lengths, one wave-length being exactly or very nearly twice the other. Pijper & Abraham (1954), using sunlight dark-ground, showed that in live preparations of *Sarcina* sp., *Caryophanon latum* and *Salmonella typhi* flagella of two different wave-lengths might be seen; and in each of two *Sarcina* species the ratio of long to short wave-lengths was between $1.92/1$ and $1.97/1$. Leifson (1951), Leifson & Hugh (1953) and Leifson, Carhart & Fulton (1955), examining fixed, stained preparations, made comparable observa-tions in various *Salmonella* and *Proteus* species. Both groups of observers have photographed individual cells bearing flagella of both kinds.

Leifson and his collaborators have shown that the wave-length may be determined by both genetic and environmental factors: from a strain of *Salmonella wichita* they obtained two substrains with predominantly long and short wave-lengths, respectively; and in a particular strain of *Proteus mirabilis* they found that alteration of the pH of the suspension from about 7·2 to 6·2 changed the wave-length from long to short. Prior treatment with formaldehyde prevented alteration of wave-length on altering pH. Leifson and his colleagues (1955) published photomicrographs showing not only that a single bacterium may bear some flagella of long wave-length and some of short, but that a single flagellum may show a long wave-length in some segments, and a short in others, or even that long and short waves may alternate; the last phenomenon is reminiscent of the 'double wave form' of *Pseudomonas macroselmis* described and photographed by Migula (1897). They also describe certain aberrant flagella shapes in strains of *Proteus*, the Providence group, aeromonads and *Bacillus*. One, which they term 'semi-coiled', has waves with an amplitude considerably greater than the wave-length, and *in vivo* is presumably a helix with rather shallow turns. In another, which they term 'coiled', the flagella appear to be coiled up into circles; they are perhaps helical flagella with a pitch so shallow that on drying they collapse with the axis of the helix normal instead of parallel to the surface.

Astbury, Beighton & Weibull (1955) argue that the helical shape of detached flagella results from their breaking off and 'dying' in the very act of transmitting their wave motion, and remaining thereafter fixed in the same shape. However, it is also possible that the flagellum at rest is a helix, and that the wave motion results from added movement of some kind, conceivably from rotation of a fixed helix. Some strains of *Salmonella* have flagella which look normal after flagellar staining, and are antigenically normal, and yet the cells are entirely non-motile. If, as seems probable, the bacteria are non-motile because the flagella do not move, then their wave form cannot result from 'freezing' of a circular wave in 'molecular rigor mortis', as Astbury (1951) has termed it.

The electron microscope has confirmed the impression obtained from light microscopy, that flagella are filaments of very uniform diameter, which do not taper. An apparent exception is the terminal flagellum of bacteria such as *Spirillum undula*, which in stained preparations or in the dark-ground seems to taper; but in electron micrographs it appears that the individual flagella constituting the aggregated structure seen in the light microscope are all of uniform diameter, the variation in diameter of the aggregate arising, as Migula (1897) believed, from the varying lengths of its constituent strands.

LIBRARY
SIENA HEIGHTS COLLEGE
ADRIAN, MICHIGAN

The thickness of the filament varies somewhat from species to species. In *Proteus* it is about 12 mμ. Houwink & van Iterson (1950) noted an unusual organism which showed, in addition to peritrichous flagella, a polar flagellum slightly thicker than the others. Though in most electron micrographs flagella appear as simple filaments, evidence of organized structure is sometimes visible.   For instance, van Iterson (1953) has published electron micrographs of a strain of *Vibrio metchnikovii*, prepared by standing in distilled water in the refrigerator, which indicated that the rather thick polar flagellum of the strain consisted of a central filament, and a surrounding sheath which partly disintegrated during the process of preparation.   Robertis & Franchi (1951) in electron micrographs of a strain of *Bacillus brevis* which had been exposed to trypsin found indications of a central filament and a fragmented sheath; this suggested that the filament was resistant to trypsin and the sheath sensitive. The central filament, which was estimated to be 12–15 mμ in diameter, seemed to be a coiled structure, probably a tightly coiled double helix. There have been other reports of flagella apparently composed of subfibrils twisted together.   Starr & Williams (1952) found evidence that the flagella of a Gram-positive rod consisted of a left-handed triple helix, Labaw & Mosley (1954, 1955) found a right-handed double helix in the flagella of an unidentified organism, and a left-handed triple helix in those of a strain of *Brucella bronchiseptica*. Though on theoretical grounds (Weibull, 1951 *b*; Astbury *et al.* 1955) it is to be expected that each flagellum consists of a series of fibrils, most published electron micrographs reveal no such fine structure, which may, however, exist but be below the limits of resolution.   It is noteworthy that there is no evidence that bacterial flagella have the structure which seems to be universal in the cilia and flagella of both animals and higher plants, viz. nine peripheral fibrils with usually two fibrils of an apparently different composition in the central space.

BACTERIAL PSEUDO-FLAGELLA

The sinuous flagella are not the only kind of filamentous appendage recorded in bacteria. There are many reports (e.g. Houwink & van Iterson, 1950; Smith, 1954; Brinton, Buzzell & Lauffer, 1954) of filaments differing from flagella by the absence of wave form, and in their relative thinness and shortness; they may be arranged peritrichously or at one or both poles. They are seen in both flagellated and non-flagellated bacteria. There is no reason to suppose that they are concerned in locomotion; indeed, nothing is known about their function. The filaments recovered

by Weibull & Hedvall (1953) by differential centrifugation of disintegrated *Proteus* X 19 H, which were perhaps of this kind, did not break up
at a low pH, as flagella do, which suggests a different composition.

COMPOSITION OF FLAGELLA

It had long been supposed that the flagella of bacteria differed in their
chemical composition from the bodies. The studies of Weibull (Weibull
& Tiselius, 1945; Weibull, 1948, 1949 *a*, *b*, 1950 *a*, *b*, *c*, 1951 *a*, *c*, 1953 *a*)
have now provided a great deal of information about the chemistry of
purified flagella of *Proteus* and *Bacillus subtilis*. Weibull used flagella
detached from the bacterial body by vigorous shaking, and purified by
alternate high- and low-speed centrifugation. Craigie (1931) and others
had previously obtained suspensions of flagella by shaking followed by
centrifugation to remove the bacterial bodies; Gard (1944) applied this
method to *Salmonella paratyphi* B and pointed out the interesting combination of properties of the preparations thus obtained. They can be
shown by flagellar staining (Craigie, 1931) or electron microscopy
(Gard, 1944; Weibull, 1948) to contain filaments differing from the
flagella of the bacteria only by their shorter average length, presumably
a result of fragmentation. Yet the preparations are stable, viscous suspensions, showing a strong Tyndall cone and marked bi-refringence of
flow, and their content of flagella can be precipitated by high concentrations of ammonium sulphate (Craigie, 1931; Gard, 1944; Weibull,
1949 *a*) or by ethyl alcohol in an appropriate ionic medium (Uchida,
Sunakawa & Fukumi, 1952); they behave as approximately homogeneous solutions on ultra-centrifugation and electrophoresis (Gard,
1944; Weibull, 1950 *c*, etc.). That is to say, the stable suspension of
flagella behaves like a solution of a protein having long, thin molecules.

Flagella irreversibly disintegrate when exposed to a pH below 4·0 or
above 11·0, or on boiling. The material obtained by exposure to a low
pH is a protein, fairly homogeneous in the ultra-centrifuge, of molecular
weight about 41,000 and having very elongated molecules. The protein
composition of flagella, suspected by Migula (1897) and Boivin &
Mesrobeanu (1938), has been conclusively established by Weibull for the
flagella of *Proteus* and *Bacillus subtilis*. His best preparations contained
at least 98 % protein, no phosphorus, and only traces of carbohydrate
and fat, which were probably impurities. This protein, for which the
name 'flagellin' is proposed (Astbury *et al.* 1955) has a characteristic
amino-acid composition; it contains at least fourteen amino acids, but no
detectable histidine, tryptophane, hydroxyproline or cystine-cysteine.

X-ray diffraction studies on films composed of ordered arrays of dried flagella indicate that the protein composing them falls into the same class as keratin, myosin, epidermin and fibrinogen (Astbury & Weibull, 1949). Two sets of reflexions are seen, one attributed to polypeptide chains folded in the α-configuration, the others, called the cross-β-reflexions, being those given by proteins of the k-m-e-f group in the super-contracted configuration (Astbury et al. 1955); the latter is believed to be the configuration of actively contracted muscle. Astbury et al. (1955) argue that the active motion of the flagellum in vivo results from rhythmic interchanges of its polypeptide chains between the two configurations; and that the two sets of reflexions, indicating the simultaneous presence of two kinds of folding in the detached flagella, result from the preservation of the polypeptide chains in the configurations in which they were at the moment the flagella were detached from the bacterium.

IMMUNOLOGICAL EVIDENCE

The mass of evidence indicating that the H antigens of bacteria are associated with the flagella and the O antigens with the bodies need not be repeated here. The most conclusive is perhaps the finding that removal of flagella by shaking renders cells non-agglutinable by H antisera, and that purified flagella are agglutinated by H antisera but not by O antisera (Craigie, 1931). The material obtained when flagella are disintegrated by heat or by exposure to acid retains antigenic specificity; for though it can no longer be agglutinated it precipitates and fixes complement with, and inhibits the agglutinating action of, homologous sera, and in some cases evokes H antibody when injected into rabbits. Jenkins (1946) extracted the H antigen from bacteria with pyridine or dioxan; the extracted material, which was a protein, agglutinated with anti-H sera, and though flagella could not be seen in stained preparations it seems fairly certain that it consisted of flagella or fragments of flagella, since it could be concentrated on a candle filter.

When detached flagella have been injected into rabbits, they have generally stimulated the production of both H and O antibodies, even when the injected material contained a negligible number of bacterial bodies (Craigie, 1931), or contained less than 0·2% of carbohydrate (Gard, Heller & Weibull, 1955). In both these cases the presence of O antigen in the purified flagellar preparation was demonstrated by precipitation tests. The published data can perhaps be explained by assuming the presence of traces of O antigen as a contaminant, even in the material of Gard et al., which had been purified by salting-out and differential centrifugation, but one cannot exclude the possibility that the flagella contain O antigen as an integral component, though in very small amounts. The evidence that the H antigen is contained only in the flagella is also incomplete (Craigie, 1931).

Flagellar proteins from *Proteus* and *Bacillus subtilis* differ only slightly in their amino-acid composition (Weibull, 1949a). This suggests that the wide range of H antigens found in a single genus such as *Salmonella* are determined by differences in arrangement of amino acids, rather than by differences in amino-acid composition. Flagella of different antigenic type show some differences in chemical and physical properties. The agglutination of *Salmonella* cells at about pH 4·0 is due to agglutination of their flagella, for detached flagella are similarly agglutinated, whereas cells whose flagella have been removed by shaking are no longer agglutinable (Arkwright, 1914, 1931; Malek, 1938; Scholtens, 1938). Each of the *Salmonella* H antigens has a characteristic pH optimum for acid agglutination; for instance, pH 3·8 for antigens *b*, *k* and *r*, and pH 5·0 for antigen *g,o,q* (Ogonuki, 1940; see also Arkwright, 1931). These differences probably reflect differences in the isoelectric points of the flagellar proteins. *Salmonella* cells with H antigens of the Phase 1 (specific phase) series are agglutinated by concentrations of acridine dyes which do not agglutinate cells with Phase 2 (group phase) antigens; detached flagella behave similarly (Sertic & Boulgakov, 1936; Bernstein & Lederberg, 1955).

Nakaya, Uchida & Fukumi (1952) showed by agglutination tests on detached flagella of *Salmonella enteritidis* that the antigenic reactivities denoted by the symbols *g* and *m* assigned to the H antigen of this organism are both borne on each flagellum, for either anti-*g* or anti-*m* serum agglutinated all flagella. On *a priori* grounds I should anticipate that both reactivities are carried by every molecule of 'flagellin', but this does not seem to have been tested as yet. Gard *et al.* (1955), however, using the agar-gel diffusion test, demonstrated two independent antigens in preparations of flagella of a strain of *Proteus* X 19 H, both apparently flagellar antigens. One of these antigens was more heat-labile than the other; it was not detectable in some of their preparations, and in others it could be demonstrated only after the flagella had been boiled or exposed to acid. This makes it unlikely that the two antigens were derived respectively from cells of two different 'phases', such as occur in cultures of diphasic *Salmonella* species.

ARRANGEMENT OF FLAGELLA ON THE BACTERIAL CELL; AGGREGATION OF FLAGELLA

In nearly all rod-shaped flagellated species the flagella arise either at or near one or both poles, or are distributed over the rest of the surface, the poles being generally bare. Leifson *et al.* (1955) recently proposed a more detailed classification. However, there are reports of strains showing both peritrichous flagella and a polar flagellum or flagella, which may differ from the rest by a different wave form or thickness. A single culture of some *Aeromonas* or *Alkaligenes* strains may contain some individuals with a polar flagellum only, some with several lateral flagella and some with both a polar and lateral flagella (Leifson & Hugh, 1953); in some strains lateral flagella were produced in a young culture and polar flagella in the later stages. From some strains they isolated more or less stable variants with predominantly polar or peritrichous or mixed flagellation, respectively; in one such case there was evidence that the polar flagella contained an antigen absent from the lateral ones. These results indicate that in some groups flagellar arrangement is a character of but limited taxonomic value.

The number of flagella per bacterium is also variable. Species which in one environment produce cells with numerous lateral flagella may in other environments produce only non-flagellated cells; the presence of phenol or a raised temperature of incubation may have this effect. In some species with peritrichous flagellation some environments produce populations in which most cells have no flagella, and most of the minority with flagella have only one flagellum each (Griffin & Robbins, 1944). What has been termed 'degenerate peritrichous flagellation' (Conn & Wolfe, 1938) is perhaps of this type. In species with polar flagella the presence of flagella at both poles or at one only probably depends on whether the cell is about to divide, or has just divided. In species such as *Vibrio cholerae*, most cells have only a single flagellum at a pole; but a minority have two or three (Migula, 1897; Leifson, 1951).

In bacteria in which flagella are detectable *in vivo* in the light microscope, using dark-ground illumination or phase-contrast, the number seen is often much smaller than the number seen in stained preparations or by electron microscopy. This may be taken to indicate that the unstained individual flagellum does not scatter enough light to be seen, or photographed; and that *in vivo* the individual flagella aggregate into bundles with a greater light-scattering effect. Detached flagella also aggregate under certain conditions, but it is probable that different forces are here involved. Aggregation *in vivo* may occur spontaneously, in broth, etc., as in *Spirillum undula*, where the bunch of polar flagella function together, forming a single effective flagellum. In *Sphaerotilus natans* this bundle is large enough to be seen by phase-contrast microscopy (Stokes, 1954). In peritrichously flagellated organisms aggregation occurs, or occurs to an increased extent, when the suspending medium contains various macromolecular substances, such as methylcellulose, gum arabic or gelatin. Pijper (1946, 1947) attributes the effect of at least some of these agents on the visibility of flagella or 'tails' (aggregated flagella, on the view here presented) to their forming a deposit on the flagella, thus thickening them. However, it seems from the experiments of Neumann (1928) and of Kingma Boltjes (1948) that these materials not only make flagella (or flagellar bundles) visible in the darkground, but also diminish the number of separate flagella seen *in vivo* or in stained films of cells exposed to these substances while alive. This would be expected if they cause aggregation. The materials which have this effect would all increase viscosity, which for objects as small as bacteria or flagella provides virtually the only resistance to motion in liquid, the inertial forces being negligible (Taylor, 1951, 1952; Herbert, 1951). It has often been observed that when separate cells having each a propulsive flagellum, e.g. spermatozoa, lie side by side, their flagella come into apposition and move as one. This phenomenon has been observed in bacteria also (Neumann, 1928; Wei, 1936). Such apposition presumably results from mechanical forces only. The theoretical analysis of Taylor (1951) cannot be applied directly, since he dealt with a simplified model of sine waves travelling down adjacent sheets; but his results suggest that hydrodynamic forces may tend to keep together active flagella which chance to come into contact. Since the resistance to flagellar movement results only from the viscosity of the medium, any increase in viscosity would presumably enhance the tendency to aggregation. If this explanation is correct, aggregation of flagella caused by macromolecular substances depends on the active motility of the flagella.

Electron micrographs of flagellar bundles, whether produced *in vitro* by aggregation of loose flagella or *in vivo* by aggregation of the flagella of a motile bacterium, always show wavy filaments lying side by side over several wave-lengths, not filaments twisted round one another like the strands of a rope. This arrangement necessarily involves some distortion of the regular helical shape of the constituent flagella of a bundle; the alternative, rope-like, arrangement would permit the packing together of a number of helical fibres without distortion, but would require axial rotation of one flagellum in relation to another to separate them.

When purified preparations of flagella are treated with high concentrations of ammonium sulphate the flagella are thrown out of suspension and aggregate into bundles in which they lie side by side, retaining their helical shape; and when a suspension of flagella in distilled water is dried on a glass slide, a coherent film is obtained, which in the light microscope shows light and dark banding, corresponding approximately to the pitch of the helix (Weibull, 1950a). Electron micrographs of broken fragments of well-dried films show that they consist of wavy filaments lying side by side, such as would be expected to result from the distortion by flattening of bundles of helices. These regular aggregates were formed only from purified suspensions of flagella, cruder preparations giving only amorphous material. Yet it is well known that flagellar bundles are very frequently to be seen in stained preparations of bacteria grown in broth, or by dark-ground or phase-contrast microscopy of living *Proteus* swarmers; it may be that these bundles arise by the aggregation, through hydrodynamic forces, of the flagella while still motile, before detachment from the bacteria.

Flagella may be precipitated from purified suspensions by a number of different agents which precipitate proteins. In addition to ammonium sulphate and alcohol, mentioned above, phosphotungstic acid and mercury salts precipitate suspended flagella of *Bacillus subtilis* (Koffler & Mallett, 1952). Craigie (1931) found that ammonium sulphate caused floccular H-type aggregation of flagellated *Salmonella typhi*, whereas a non-flagellated suspension was aggregated into fine O-type granules only. In general detached flagella do not aggregate spontaneously in broth, etc. Henderson (1932) reported that suspensions of flagellated *Clostridium chauvoei* heated for 5 min. at 100° were stable, whereas the unheated cultures agglutinated spontaneously under all conditions tested; it is possible that the instability resulted from the presence of flagella with a spontaneous tendency to aggregate, but other explanations, e.g. the presence of some other heat-labile surface component, cannot be excluded.

When bacteria are grown on solid media very large flagellar bundles are sometimes formed; they may be much bigger than the bacteria themselves (Malvoz, 1902). It does not seem likely that such large bundles arise through flagellar motion; perhaps here also there has been spontaneous aggregation of flagella.

MECHANICAL PROPERTIES OF FLAGELLA

Very little is known about the mechanical properties of flagella; and arguments about the rigidity, etc., of such minute structures are to be viewed with suspicion when they are based on intuition or analogy with larger objects rather than on calculation. However, a few inferences may be made. Three hypotheses might be proposed as to the source of the energy required for the movement of the distal part of a flagellum or flagellar bundle. The mechanical energy might be locally generated, e.g. by a chemical reaction, or the energy might be mechanically transmitted from the base of the flagellum, as, for instance, by the rotation of a rigid helix, or the energy might be transmitted distally as momentum from the base, as occurs when a series of waves travel down a cord one end of which is moved rapidly from side to side. The last of these hypotheses seems to be excluded by calculation of the order of magnitude of the force of viscous resistance for a body of the size of a flagellum moving with the speed observed, and of the momentum of a segment of it. From these values one can calculate approximately the time required for the speed of a segment of flagellum to be reduced to zero. This calculation indicates that a segment of flagellum moving only through its own momentum would be brought to rest virtually instantaneously, in a distance far too short to account for the observed motion. However, since there is no good reason to doubt the first hypothesis (generation of mechanical energy distally) one cannot draw any conclusion as to the ability of the flagellum to sustain the transmission of mechanical energy.

Kvittingen (1955) observed that flagellar bundles, not attached to bacteria, were pushed aside, without being bent, when struck by motile *Proteus* filaments. His inference that the bundles are rigid is justified, though without calculating the order of magnitude of the forces involved one cannot tell whether or not the observations indicate the degree of rigidity denoted by the description 'rigid' when applied to larger objects. His inference that the bundles are light does not seem valid; the inertial resistance of the bundles, even if they were very heavy, would be quite negligible compared with the viscous resistance of the liquid medium.

The breaking-off of flagella from bacterial bodies, and their subsequent fragmentation, produced by vigorous shaking must result from stresses produced by viscous resistance when the suspending medium is undergoing rapid shearing motion. In the recorded experiments on removal of flagella by agitation the data are not of a kind which would permit even approximate calculation of the magnitude of this shearing velocity; if this were known it might be possible to calculate approximately the tension required to break a single flagellum.

In the course of experiments on the genetics of motility some phenomena relevant to this problem have been observed (Stocker, unpublished). One is that *Salmonella* cells taken up by micro-pipette and then expelled generally emerge still motile, even when the diameter of the orifice of the pipette is only 2 or 3μ. Another is that a cell may sometimes travel rapidly round and round a fixed point for many minutes, a kind of movement which can only be explained by assuming that a flagellum (or flagella) is tethering the cell to some fixed point. When motile cells are injected by micro-pipette into homologous anti-H serum, their translational movement ceases in a matter of seconds, but some of them move in the way just described, or spin round an axis passing through their body, or show a regularly repeated twitching motion. This kind of movement, which was noted by Arkwright (1927) and Pijper (1938), may continue for many minutes, or for hours. Occasionally a pair of cells, both actively motile, yet never separating by more than a short distance, have been seen; they are presumably cells with entangled flagella. From these observations one may infer that a flagellum, or perhaps a bundle of flagella, is strong enough to sustain a force of the magnitude required to propel a bacterium through the medium. This has been calculated as about 10^{-8} dyne (Angerer, 1919). From the tensile strength of silk it has been calculated that the breaking strength of a single polypeptide chain is at least 10^{-4} dyne (Goldacre, 1954), and a flagellum probably consists of several parallel polypeptide chains; the inability of a tethered cell to escape by breaking its flagellum is therefore not surprising.

The presence of the H antigen on bacteria to some extent impedes their agglutination by somatic antibodies, particularly if the cells have been exposed to formalin or phenol, or heated, say to 80° for half an hour. This inhibition is certainly due to the presence of flagella, as it disappears if the flagella are removed by shaking (Craigie, 1931). Presumably the flagella mechanically impede accidental contacts of the sensitized bacterial bodies, and one may perhaps conclude that formalin increases the rigidity of flagella.

INTERNAL STRUCTURES CONNECTED WITH FLAGELLA

The analysis of isolated flagella shows that they differ chemically both from the cell wall and from the protoplasm of the cell. Two kinds of observation give information about the site of origin of flagella.

Removal of the cell wall of *Bacillus megaterium* with lysozyme produces a spherical protoplast, which retains the flagella of the treated cell (Weibull, 1953 *b*). When certain marine bacteria are exposed to distilled water, the cell wall may peel off, leaving a cell body to which flagella remain attached (Johnson, Zworykin & Warren, 1943). One may conclude that the flagella have a point of attachment to some cell structure deeper than the rigid cell wall. Weibull found that the protoplasts were non-motile, despite the presence of flagella. This is surprising in view of the fact that the protoplasts displayed most of the metabolic activities of the intact cell. It is possible that their non-motility results not from non-motility of the flagella, but from the lack of a rigid cell wall for them to exert their thrust upon. Autolysed cells of various species commonly retain their flagella, from which one may infer that the flagella are in some way attached either to the rigid cell wall, or to some structure which remains attached to it when autolysis occurs.

Many published electron micrographs (e.g. van Iterson, 1953) show the presence in autolysed cells of electron-dense granules apparently situated at the point of origin of flagella. Such basal granules are sometimes seen in the relatively electron-transparent peripheral zone that presumably results from the retraction on drying of the contents of the cell. In some of the large *Spirilla* the polar group of very thin flagella appear to be connected with a single basal granule (Grace, 1954). Since such granules are not detectable in many electron micrographs it would as yet be premature to conclude that there is a specialized structure at the base of each flagellum in all bacterial species, though it seems possible that failure to detect it may result from difficulties of technique only. Until such basal granules can be regularly demonstrated it will be impossible to test whether or not the basal granules of bacterial flagella always arise by division of pre-existing granules, as in the case of the corresponding granules of ciliates.

It has sometimes been argued that the apparently co-ordinated activity of the numerous flagella of *Proteus*, for instance, requires the existence of some internal conducting structure. Fibres possibly having this function have been demonstrated in ciliates. However, no such 'primitive nervous system' has been seen in bacteria, and the argument for its necessary existence is fallacious. When swarming *Proteus* cells are examined by dark-ground microscopy after suspension in a viscous medium one observes long motile filaments each apparently propelled by several flagella (in reality flagellar bundles), all of which point backwards. It is argued above that hydrodynamic forces alone will account for the aggregation of separate active flagella into bundles. The apparent co-operation of the flagellar bundles remains to be accounted for. Let it be assumed that in a motile, but momentarily stationary, bacterium, the angle each flagellar bundle makes with the cell is determined by chance only; and let it be assumed that the force exerted by each bundle is of the kind which would be generated by its apparent motion, viz. a thrust along the axis of the helical bundle and a torque about the axis in the sense contrary to the sense of the helix (Taylor, 1952). The combined effect of the randomly directed thrusts will then at times have by chance a resultant component sufficient to move the bacterial body along a direction parallel to its long axis. When this occurs the viscosity of the medium will resist the flagellar bundles being carried forward, and will cause a couple tending to bend them backwards at their site of attachment to the cell. As a result of such bending backwards the thrusts of the bundles will now have a larger component acting in the direction of the original movement of the body, which will therefore continue at a greater speed, which in turn will produce increased angulation backwards and so on. Apparently co-ordinated activity will thus result.

SYNTHESIS OF FLAGELLA

If there is indeed a granule at the base of each flagellum, a number of functions might be attributed to it. Astbury *et al.* (1955) suggest that it may generate the signals which cause the rhythmic contractions of the polypeptide chains constituting the flagellum. It may be the source of the energy required for the motion of the flagellum. It also seems probable that it is concerned with the synthesis of the flagellum, which is presumably extruded as a filament through a perforation in the rigid cell wall.

Very little is known about the rate of synthesis of flagella and whether or not there is any appreciable wearing out of their distal ends. Some preliminary experiments (Stocker, unpublished) suggest that growth of flagella is fairly rapid. A young culture of motile *Salmonella paratyphi* B was treated in a 'blender', in which a small propeller revolved at 18,000 r.p.m. Three minutes exposure reduced the proportion of motile cells from more than 80% to less than 1% without significantly lowering the viable count; but the proportion of motile cells began to increase some minutes after the end of the treatment. In the presence of a bacteriostatic concentration of chloramphenicol there was no increase in the proportion of motile cells, which suggests that this agent, believed to specifically inhibit protein synthesis, inhibits also the synthesis of flagella. Untreated cells of the same strain incubated at 37° in the presence of a bacteriostatic concentration of chloramphenicol remained motile for many hours; this seems to indicate that there is no rapid wearing out or fraying away of existing flagella during bacterial movement in broth.

INHERITANCE OF FLAGELLAR CHARACTERS AND OF FLAGELLA

The genetics of flagellar characters in *Salmonella* have been investigated in some detail, and some studies have also been made in other genera. These studies show that flagellar characters are determined, like other characters, by the combined effects of the genes and the environment. Genes regulating flagellar characters, like other bacterial genes, behave as though arranged in an ordered array in some genetic organelle (or organelles), presumably analogous to the chromosomes of larger organisms. They undergo spontaneous mutations; they may be transferred or transduced from cell to cell by particles of temperate phage in *Salmonella* (Zinder & Lederberg, 1952; Stocker, Zinder & Lederberg, 1953; Lederberg & Edwards, 1953), and in *Escherichia coli* they undergo recombination as a result of some process of conjugation (Furness & Rowley, 1955).

Bacteria, like multi-cellular organisms, receive genes from cells of the previous generation; unlike multi-cellular organisms, they receive also a large fraction of the soma of their 'parent' cell, and it is of interest to consider the way in which such somatic structures as flagella are distributed at cell division.

We may first consider the position in the caulobacteria, a group of rod-shaped bacteria whose cells at one stage bear a stalk at one end, the stalk serving to attach them to some solid material. The stalked end of the cell may be termed the proximal end. These organisms typically bear a polar flagellum, and electron micrographs of one strain permit some inferences about the relation of the flagellum to cell division (Houwink, 1955). Free-swimming cells have no stalk, and bear a single flagellum at one pole. It is inferred that free swimming cells become attached by one pole to a solid substrate, and grow a stalk at the attached end. Stalked cells which are not dividing commonly have a single flagellum, arising from the attached end of the stalk, and it is inferred that the free-swimming cell becomes attached by its flagellum-bearing pole. Stalked cells which are dividing, as shown by a transverse constriction, bear a flagellum at their distal end, that is, at the end which will constitute one pole of a non-stalked free-living daughter cell. In this strain, and in a generally similar one reported by Bowers, Weaver, Grula &

Edwards (1954), it seems safe to infer from the electron micrographs that the flagellum and stalk of the parent cell form part of one daughter cell, whereas the other acquires a newly synthesized flagellum. In this organism then, cell division is asymmetric, as it is in many unicellular organisms, e.g. the yeasts, where one daughter cell, the bud, has a new cell wall, the other retaining the parental cell wall.

In most rod-shaped bacteria with polar flagellation there is no obvious difference between the two ends of the rod, other than the presence of a flagellum or flagella at one end only of many or most of the cells. However, there seems no reason to doubt that the flagella are distributed at cell division in the same way as in the caulobacteria, one cell receiving the original flagellum, or flagellar bundle, of the parent cell, while the other receives a newly synthesized one.

In bacteria with peritrichous flagellation the position is less clear. Stained preparations and electron micrographs show the presence of a proportion of cells with several flagella on one half of the cell, and none on the other. These appearances have been interpreted, for instance, by Bisset (1951), as cells in process of division into one cell which retains the cell wall and flagella of the parent cell, and one cell having a newly synthesized cell wall through which new flagella have not yet made their way. Since a motile bacterium generally divides into two motile daughter cells one must postulate that by the time division is completed the 'new' flagella are sufficiently developed to confer motility. However, this kind of interpretation has not been universally accepted (Migula, 1897). An alternative theory would be that the original flagella are divided about equally amongst the daughter cells at cell division. If it is assumed that the point of attachment of a flagellum is fixed in relation to the cell wall this requires the assumption that the cell wall grows by intercalation along its length, rather than by intercalation at a specialized growing end only (Bisset, 1951). The phenomenon of unilinear transmission of motility, described below, seems relevant to this question.

UNILINEAR TRANSMISSION OF MOTILITY

This phenomenon was discovered during experiments on the transduction of motility from motile to non-motile strains of *Salmonella*; but it later appeared that it occurs under other circumstances also, so that it will not be necessary to describe here the phenomena of complete and abortive transduction of motility (Stocker *et al.* 1953; Stocker, unpublished; Lederberg, personal communication). If a cell having a certain character divides to produce one cell without the character, and one cell with it; if the latter cell in turn produces only one daughter cell with the character; and if the process continues at subsequent divisions: then the character will at no time be manifested by more than one of the descendants of the original cell. The character will pass down but one line of the pedigree to but a single descendant in any generation, and it may therefore be said to be *unilinearly transmitted* (Stocker, unpublished).

The unilinear transmission of the character motility has been encountered in a number of non-motile *Salmonella* strains, occurring after a cell has apparently acquired a transitory ability to manufacture locomotor apparatus. Cells with this transitory ability may be produced by transduction; in some strains, however, they occur spontaneously with a low frequency. As the latter case is the less complex it will be described first. Some non-motile (because non-flagellated) *Salmonella* strains rarely or never mutate to produce stable motile variants; yet in broth cultures of some such strains one can detect the presence of a very small proportion of motile cells. My colleague, C. Quadling, has isolated such motile cells by micro-manipulation, and followed the behaviour, as to motility, of their progeny. Fig. 1 illustrates one such experiment, in which a motile cell was isolated from a culture of a *S. typhimurium* O strain, SW 545; in this strain, such motile cells occur in a proportion of about 10^{-5} to 10^{-6}. It will be seen that the motile cell isolated from the broth culture divided into two, of which one was non-motile, and produced non-motile progeny only, whereas the other was itself motile, and divided to produce eight progeny, of which two only were motile. The latter were in turn isolated; and each transmitted motility to but one of its descendants. Unilinear transmission through eight generations was demonstrated in one line, and through thirteen generations in the other. In other non-motile strains motile cells have been produced by abortive or incomplete transduction, using phage produced by lysis of cells of motile strains. Amongst the progeny of such cells unilinear transmission of motility through more than twenty generations (Stocker, unpublished) and through more than sixty generations (Lederberg, personal communication) has been demonstrated.

Homologous anti-flagellar serum arrests the movement of cells to which motility has been unilinearly transmitted; their motility is therefore attributed to the possession of one or more flagella. A cell to which motility has been unilinearly transmitted produces non-motile progeny indistinguishable from the cells of the parent strain, and like them non-flagellated. The observed transmission of motility down a single line of descent therefore represents a corresponding transmission of a flagellum or flagella, or of the ability to synthesize flagella. When the actual instant

3-2

of division is observed, a motile cell of the kind under discussion always produces one daughter cell which is non-motile from the moment of separation; this suggests that this daughter cell receives no flagella from its parent cell.

If this be so, two explanations may be proposed. If cell division in *Salmonella* is unequal, one cell receiving the original cell wall of the

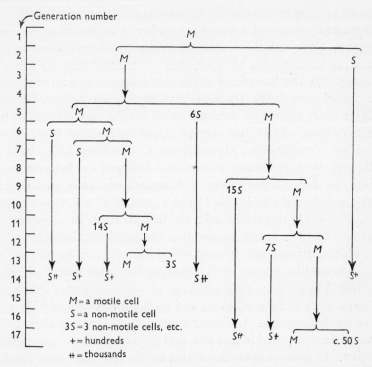

Fig. 1. Pedigree of progeny of a motile cell isolated by micro-manipulation from a culture of *S. typhimurium* O strain SW545. The slide with the droplet containing the isolated cell was incubated at room temperature, and examined at intervals; motile progeny cells were transferred to separate droplets as indicated. (Data of C. Quadling.)

parent cell together with the flagella which penetrate it, and the other receiving a newly synthesized cell wall, then a cell with flagella but without the ability to initiate new ones will transmit its cell wall and flagella, and consequent motility, to but one of its descendants. If, on the contrary, cell division is equal, each daughter cell receiving on the average half of the flagella of the parent cell, then a cell with several flagella but no ability to make new ones will produce after several generations descendants having either no flagella or but one each; and each of the latter will transmit its flagellum, and consequent motility, down one line of descent only. If the production of a flagellum is dependent on the presence of a basal granule, then in each case the unilinearly transmitted particles may well be flagellum-determining granules, rather than flagella as such.

Though the experimental results so far obtained do not permit an unequivocal decision between these hypotheses, some considerations favour the hypothesis of equal cell division and unilinear transmission of a flagellum, or flagellum-determining granule. The original cell in the pedigree shown in Fig. 1 produced two motile descendants, each of which transmitted motility unilinearly; in other experiments the number of such motile descendants has been as large as eight. On the hypothesis of equal cell division and unilinear transmission of flagella, a cell producing such a progeny is probably a cell with eight flagella; on the alternative hypothesis, of unequal cell division and unilinear transmission of a cell wall and the flagella which penetrate it, such a cell is one amongst whose progeny the ability to make flagella has persisted for a time, so that all its eight descendants of the third generation have this ability, which is then lost. Cells which give rise to several motile descendants appear to be more motile than cells which transmit motility to but one descendant, for the former but not the latter are able to travel through a semi-solid medium. This would be explained if the former cells had several flagella and the latter one only. In theory it should be possible to make a direct test as to whether cells motile by unilinear transmission have one flagellum each, as required by the hypothesis of equal cell division and unilinear transmission of a single flagellum. However, such cells can only be recognized with certainty in pedigree experiments, and technical difficulties impeding the examination of selected single cells by flagellar staining or electron microscopy have not so far been overcome.

REFERENCES

ANGERER, V. (1919). Über die Arbeitsleistung eigenbeweglicher Bakterien. *Arch. Hyg.* **88**, 139.

ARKWRIGHT, J. A. (1914). Experiments on the agglutination of watery extracts of *B. typhosus*. *J. Hyg., Camb.*, **14**, 261.

ARKWRIGHT, J. A. (1927). Microscopic evidence of the different manner of clumping of motile bacteria with somatic and flagellar agglutinins. *J. Path. Bact.* **30**, 566.

ARKWRIGHT, J. A. (1931). *A System of Bacteriology in Relation to Medicine*, vol. 6, chapter 12: Agglutination. Medical Research Council. London: H.M. Stationery Office.

ASTBURY, W. T. (1951). Some recent adventures among the proteins. *Pubbl. Staz. zool. Napoli*, **23**, Suppl. p. 1.

ASTBURY, W. T., BEIGHTON, E. & WEIBULL, C. (1955). The structure of bacterial flagella. In *Fibrous Proteins and their Biological Significance*. (*Symp. Soc. exp. Biol.* **9**, 282.) Cambridge University Press.

ASTBURY, W. T. & WEIBULL, C. (1949). X-ray diffraction study of the structure of bacterial flagella. *Nature, Lond.*, **163**, 280.

BERNSTEIN, A. & LEDERBERG, J. (1955). Agglutination of motile Salmonellas by acridines. *J. Bact.* **69**, 142.

BISSET, K. A. (1951). The development of the surface structures in dividing bacteria. *J. gen. Microbiol.* **5**, 155.

BOIVIN, A. & MESROBEANU, L. (1938). Sur la résistance à l'acide trichloracétique de l'antigène flagellaire (antigène H) du bacille typhique et sur la nature chimique possible de cet antigène. *C.R. Soc. Biol., Paris*, **129**, 136.

BOWERS, L. E., WEAVER, R. H., GRULA, E. A. & EDWARDS, O. F. (1954). Studies on a strain of Caulobacter from water. I. Isolation and identification as *Caulobacter vibrioides* Henrici and Johnson with emended description. *J. Bact.* **68**, 194.

BRADFIELD, J. R. G. & CATER, D. B. (1952). Electron-microscopic evidence on the structure of spirochaetes. *Nature, Lond.*, **169**, 944.

BRINTON, C. B., Jr., BUZZELL, A. & LAUFFER, M. A. (1954). Electrophoresis and phage susceptibility studies on a filament-producing variant of the *E. coli* B bacterium. *Biochim. biophys. Acta*, **15**, 533.

CONN, H. J. & WOLFE, G. E. (1938). The flagellation of bacteria. *Science*, **87**, 283.

CRAIGIE, J. (1931). Studies on the serological reactions of the flagella of *B. typhosus*. *J. Immunol.* **21**, 417.

FURNESS, G. & ROWLEY, D. (1955). Transfer of motility by *Escherichia coli* K12 to *E. coli* B. *J. gen. Microbiol.* **12**, v (abstract).

GARD, S. (1944). Preparation of bacterial flagella. *Ark. Kemi Min. Geol.* **19**A, no. 21.

GARD, S., HELLER, L. & WEIBULL, C. (1955). Immunological studies on purified flagella from *Proteus* X19. *Acta path. microbiol. scand.* **36**, 30.

GOLDACRE, R. J. (1954). Crystalline bacterial arrays and specific long-range forces. *Nature, Lond.*, **174**, 732.

GRACE, J. B. (1954). Some observations on the flagella and blepharoplasts of *Spirillum* and *Vibrio* spp. *J. gen. Microbiol.* **10**, 325.

GRIFFIN, A. M. & ROBBINS, M. L. (1944). The flagellation of *Listeria monocytogenes*. *J. Bact.* **48**, 114.

HENDERSON, D. W. (1932). Studies on *Clostridium chauvoei*. I. The analysis of the 'H' and 'O' antigens of *C. chauvoei*. *Brit. J. exp. Path.* **13**, 412.

HERBERT, D. (1951). Hydrodynamic aspects of bacterial locomotion. *J. gen. Microbiol.* **5**, xx (abstract).

HOUWINK, A. L. (1955). *Caulobacter*, its morphogenesis, taxonomy and parasitism. *Leeuwenhoek ned. Tijdschr.* **21**, 49.

HOUWINK, A. L. & VAN ITERSON, W. (1950). Electron microscopical observations on bacterial cytology. II. A study on flagellation. *Biochim. biophys. Acta*, **5**, 10.

JENKINS, C. E. (1946). The preparation of pure flagellar antigens from Salmonella. *Brit. J. exp. Path.* **27**, 121.

JOHNSON, F. H., ZWORYKIN, N. & WARREN, G. (1943). A study of luminous bacterial cells and cytolysates with the electron microscope. *J. Bact.* **46**, 167.

KINGMA BOLTJES, T. Y. (1948). Function and arrangement of bacterial flagella. *J. Path. Bact.* **60**, 275.

KOFFLER, H. & MALLETT, G. E. (1952). Sind Bakterien-Geisseln aktive Bewegungsorgane oder nur Fäden der Aussenschicht? *Zbl. Bakt.* Abt I, Orig., **158**, 357.

KVITTINGEN, J. (1955). Some observations on the nature and significance of bacterial flagella. *Acta path. microbiol. scand.* **37**, 89.

LABAW, L. W. & MOSLEY, V. M. (1954). Periodic structure in the flagella and cell walls of a bacterium. *Biochim. biophys. Acta*, **15**, 325.

LABAW, L. W. & MOSLEY, V. M. (1955). Periodic structure in the flagella of *Brucella bronchiseptica*. *Biochim. biophys. Acta*, **17**, 322.

LEDERBERG, J. & EDWARDS, P. R. (1953). Serotypic recombination in *Salmonella*. *J. Immunol.* **71**, 232.

LEIFSON, E. (1951). Staining, shape, and arrangement of bacterial flagella. *J. Bact.* **62**, 377.

LEIFSON, E., CARHART, S. R. & FULTON, M. (1955). Morphological characteristics of flagella of *Proteus* and related bacteria. *J. Bact.* **69**, 73.

LEIFSON, E. & HUGH, R. (1953). Variation in shape and arrangement of bacterial flagella. *J. Bact.* **65**, 263.

MALEK, I. (1938). Influence de l'antigène H d'*Eberthella typhi* sur la flocculation par les ions H. *C.R. Soc. Biol., Paris*, **129**, 795.

MALVOZ, E. (1902). Sur les cils composés. *Ann. Inst. Pasteur*, **16**, 686.

MIGULA, W. (1897). *System der Bakterien*. Jena: Fischer.

MILES, A. A. & PIRIE, N. W. (1949). (Edit.) *The Nature of the Bacterial Surface*. Oxford: Blackwell.

NAKAYA, R., UCHIDA, H. & FUKUMI, H. (1952). Studies on the antigenic patterns of bacterial flagella. *Jap. J. med. Sci. Biol.* **5**, 467.

NEUMANN, F. (1928). Die Sichtbarmachung von Bakteriengeisseln am lebenden Objekt im Dunkelfeld. II Mitteilung. *Zbl. Bakt.* Abt I, Orig., **109**, 143.

OGONUKI, H. (1940). Acid agglutination in Salmonella group. *Kitasato Arch.* **17**, 80.

PIJPER, A. (1938). Dark-ground studies of flagellar and somatic agglutination of *B. typhosus*. *J. Path. Bact.* **47**, 1.

PIJPER, A. (1946). Shape and motility of bacteria. *J. Path. Bact.* **58**, 325.

PIJPER, A. (1947). Methylcellulose and bacterial motility. *J. Bact.* **53**, 257.

PIJPER, A. (1951). Bacterial flagella. *Nature, Lond.*, **168**, 749.

PIJPER, A. (1955). Shape of bacterial flagella. *Nature, Lond.*, **175**, 214.

PIJPER, A. & ABRAHAM, G. (1954). Wavelengths of bacterial flagella. *J. gen. Microbiol.* **10**, 452.

ROBERTIS, E. DE & FRANCHI, C. M. (1951). Electron microscopic observation on the fine structure of bacterial flagella. *Exp. Cell Res.* **2**, 295.

SCHOLTENS, R. TH. (1938). The importance of receptor analysis for the study of physico-chemical properties of typhoid bacilli. *J. Hyg., Camb.*, **38**, 273.

SERTIC, V. & BOULGAKOV, N.-A. (1936). L'agglutination par la trypaflavine des *Salmonella* de structure antigénique flagellaire non-spécifique. *C.R. Soc. Biol., Paris*, **123**, 951.

SMITH, I. W. (1954). Flagellation and motility in *Aerobacter cloacae* and *Escherichia coli*. *Biochim. biophys. Acta*, **15**, 20.

STARR, M. P. & WILLIAMS, R. C. (1952). Helical fine structure of flagella of a motile diphtheroid. *J. Bact.* **63**, 701.

STOCKER, B. A. D., ZINDER, N. D. & LEDERBERG, J. (1953). Transduction of flagellar characters in *Salmonella*. *J. gen. Microbiol.* **9**, 410.

STOKES, J. L. (1954). Studies on the filamentous sheathed iron bacterium *Sphaerotilus natans*. *J. Bact.* **67**, 278.

TAYLOR, SIR G. (1951). Analysis of the swimming of microscopic organisms. *Proc. Roy. Soc.* A, **209**, 447.

TAYLOR, SIR G. (1952). The action of waving cylindrical tails in propelling microscopic organisms. *Proc. Roy. Soc.* A, **211**, 225.

UCHIDA, H., SUNAKAWA, S. & FUKUMI, H. (1952). Studies on the bacterial flagella. I. Methods of purification. *Jap. J. med. Sci. Biol.* **5**, 351.

VAN ITERSON, W. (1953). Some remarks on the present state of our knowledge of bacterial flagellation. *Bacterial Cytology, Symp. 6th Congr. Int. Microbiol.*, Rome, p. 24.

WEI, H. (1936). A study of bacterial flagella by dark-field illumination. *Chin. med. J.*, Suppl. 1, 135.

WEIBULL, C. (1948). Some chemical and physico-chemical properties of the flagella of *Proteus vulgaris*. *Biochim. biophys. Acta*, 2, 351.

WEIBULL, C. (1949a). Chemical and physico-chemical properties of the flagella of *Proteus vulgaris* and *Bacillus subtilis*. A comparison. *Biochim. biophys. Acta*, 3, 378.

WEIBULL, C. (1949b). Morphological studies on salt precipitated bacterial flagella. *Ark. Kemi*, 1, 21.

WEIBULL, C. (1950a). Ordered aggregation of salted out and dried bacterial flagella. *Ark. Kemi Min. Geol.* 1, 573.

WEIBULL, C. (1950b). Electrophoretic and titrimetric measurements on bacterial flagella. *Acta chem. scand.* 4, 260.

WEIBULL, C. (1950c). Investigations on bacterial flagella. *Acta chem. scand.* 4, 268.

WEIBULL, C. (1951a). Some analytical evidence for the purity of *Proteus* flagella protein. *Acta chem. scand.* 5, 529.

WEIBULL, C. (1951b). Movement of bacterial flagella. *Nature, Lond.*, 167, 511.

WEIBULL, C. (1951c). Bacterial flagella as fibrous macromolecules. *Disc. Faraday Soc.* 11, 195.

WEIBULL, C. (1953a). The free amino groups of the *Proteus* flagella protein. Quantitative determination of dinitrophenyl amino acids using paper chromatography. *Acta chem. scand.* 7, 335.

WEIBULL, C. (1953b). The isolation of protoplasts from *Bacillus megaterium* by controlled treatment with lysozyme. *J. Bact.* 66, 688.

WEIBULL, C. & HEDVALL, J. (1953). Some observations of fractions of disintegrated bacterial cells obtained by differential centrifugations. *Biochim. biophys. Acta*, 10, 35.

WEIBULL, C. & TISELIUS, A. (1945). Note on the acid hydrolysis of bacterial flagella. *Ark. Kemi Min. Geol.* 20 B, no. 3.

ZINDER, N. D. & LEDERBERG, J. (1952). Genetic exchange in *Salmonella*. *J. Bact.* 64, 679.

BACTERIAL CAPSULES AND THEIR RELATION TO THE CELL WALL

J. TOMCSIK

Institute of Hygiene and Bacteriology, University of Basel

When reviewing the literature, one can hardly suppress the feeling that disproportionately more effort has been spent upon the staining of the bacterial capsule than upon the elucidation of its nature. It has not always been realized that staining coupled with fixation and mordanting leads invariably to shrinkage owing to the high water content of the capsule. In consequence such preparations cannot give a reliable picture of its morphological nature in the native condition. Electron-microscopic examinations necessitating complete drying are even less well adapted to this purpose. Only wet preparations such as Indian-ink films can give approximately accurate information about the shape and size of the capsule. By employing antibodies as specific immunochemical indicators, however, wet films can be used to detect the chemical nature and complex structure of the capsule. The non-recognition of this circumstance led to a number of erroneous statements, and to a divergence in the nomenclature which in part still persists. The expression 'capsular swelling' reaction is still in general use, even when in the majority of cases no trace of swelling is detectable. The highly divergent views which have been expressed concerning the bacterial capsule may justify the author in his intention to discuss in the first part of this review certain elementary notions and also some observations in the earlier literature.

DEMONSTRATION AND DEFINITION OF THE BACTERIAL CAPSULE

The bacterial capsule is commonly defined as a microscopically demonstrable gelatinous or slimy layer covering the cell wall and having a definite external surface. This definition would be unambiguous if we could characterize precisely the external surfaces both of the cell wall and of the capsule, and if the capsule were nothing more than a homogeneous gelatinous or slimy layer. The exact definition of the cell-wall surface is not always easy, however, as will be pointed out later. Further difficulties arise in respect of individual interpretations of what is to be

understood by a definite external surface to the capsule. Some bacteriologists speak of envelopes instead of capsules if the external boundary
is not sharp or if it has a tendency to dissolution, especially when the
bacteria are suspended for a few hours in water. Others assume that on
the surface of the same micro-organism both capsule and envelope may
exist, the interior more compact layer corresponding to the capsule
and the external loose layer to the envelope. Finally, the bacterial
capsule cannot be regarded in every case merely as a homogeneous slimy
layer of a single colloidal substance. Indeed, in *Bacillus megaterium* it
has a definite structure (Tomcsik, 1951). Instead of searching for a fully
valid definition of the bacterial capsule one purpose of this review is to
describe the various aspects of its morphology, its chemical nature and
its relation to the cell wall, and to determine whether any essential difference between capsule, envelope and slime can be established.

The Indian-ink method for the demonstration of the bacterial capsule
was discovered by Burri (1909) and modified by Preisz (1911). It is the
wet-film Indian-ink method of Preisz which gives in a simple way the
most accurate information about the shape and the size of the capsule.
This opinion of the author is shared among others by Duguid (1951)
and Edwards & Fife (1952). An excellent description of the technique is
given by Duguid (1951). Fallacious interpretations of apparently very
voluminous capsules or of narrow capsules, in too thin or too thick
layers respectively, can be easily avoided. If attention is paid to this
detail, the size of the capsule can be correctly judged in wet Indian-ink
films, and such preparations can serve as a basis for observations
regarding swelling or shrinkage of the capsule caused by non-specific
agents or by specific antibodies. In wet Indian-ink preparations a
zone of diffraction about 0.2μ in width can be observed between the
bacterial body (protoplast) and the capsule. This zone is seldom mentioned, and when it has been, it has been interpreted in a different manner.
Toenniessen (1919) described it as ectoplasm, Etinger-Tulczynska (1933)
as a capsule and Duguid (1951) as a diffraction halo outlining the outer
surface of the bacterium.

Toenniessen, who was the first to isolate a capsular polysaccharide
from *Klebsiella*, used the names 'capsule', 'envelope', 'slime layer' and
'outer coat' ('Kapsel', 'Schleimhülle', 'Gallerthülle', 'Aussenhülle')
alternatively in his earlier papers (1912, 1914). Later (1919, 1920) he
differentiated ectoplasm and envelope but described both as synonymous
with the capsule. He regarded the ectoplasm as an integral component of
the living bacterial cell and the envelope (slime layer or *Gallerthülle*) as a
secretion product consisting of galactan. The terms employed by Etinger-

Tulczynska (1933) are even less comprehensible; they should, however, be mentioned, since her paper led to the general acceptance of the expression 'capsular swelling' reaction. Duguid (1951) pointed out clearly that Etinger-Tulczynska gave the name 'capsule' to the narrow light halo at the cell surface and the name 'slime layer' to the wide capsule outside. He emphasized that the narrow diffraction halo must not be mistaken for a narrow capsule. It is my opinion that the diffraction zone indicates the position of the cell wall, which is not directly visible in Indian-ink films even by the phase-contrast microscope.

In the earlier literature some authors, mainly studying stained preparations, assumed the existence of a capsular membrane at the external surface. Churchman & Emelianoff (1933) thought that the capsule might even be a sac, sometimes collapsed, sometimes swollen. The existence of

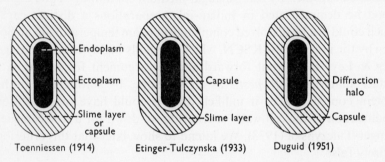

Text-fig. 1. Designation of the surface structures of capsulated bacteria.

a capsular membrane was never proved or even rendered plausible. Certainly the occasional staining of the capsular surface cannot be regarded as evidence for its existence. A peripheral capsular reaction visible under the microscope can be induced regularly by an appropriate concentration of the specific antibody, but at higher concentrations the same antibody reacts very rapidly with the interior of the capsule, indicating that the reacting substance at the surface and in the deeper layers is identical. Thus there is no foundation for any attempt to differentiate the capsule and envelope by seeking a distinct surface membrane.

Virulent strains of *Pneumococcus*, *Klebsiella* and *Bacillus anthracis* and most of those micro-organisms with similar surface structures are usually spoken of as capsulated bacteria. No agreement, however, could be attained in the description of the surface material of *Pasteurella pestis*. Rowland (1914) distinguished the capsulated varieties from those which produce envelopes. According to him the envelopes have no definite

limiting membrane; frequently a row of organisms is embedded in a
continuous mass of the substance. He could stain the capsule but not
the envelope of *P. pestis*. Schütze (1932) shares his opinion and points
out that the envelopes of plague bacilli suspended in saline dissolve
entirely at 60°. By culturing *P. pestis* in casein hydrolysate broth Seal
(1951) and Baker, Sommer, Foster, Meyer & Meyer (1947, 1952)
obtained the envelope substance mostly in a dissolved condition. On the
other hand, Sokhey (1940) is of the opinion that the capsule of *P. pestis*
is an integral part of the structure of the bacillus, and when grown on
solid media the periphery stains intensely, giving the impression of a
capsular membrane. According to Amies (1951) it is customary, though
probably incorrect, to describe the capsule and the envelope as separate
entities. He thinks that the envelope is no more than a particularly well-
developed capsule. By using an agar medium containing peptic digest of
blood he demonstrated in Indian-ink preparations a distinct capsule
which could not be dissolved completely at room temperature in an hour,
even by the use of 0·5 M-KSCN, which is usually highly effective. Engelsberg & Levy (1954) put forward another argument for regarding the
surface material of *P. pestis* as an envelope, by stating that its high
protein content makes it unlikely that it could have originated as a
modification of the cell wall—a criterion set down for a true capsule by
Etinger-Tulczynska (1933). We intend to show later that this criterion is
entirely false.

These data have been quoted to illustrate the type of arguments
brought forward to distinguish between capsule and envelope. But we
are unable to see any essential difference between the two.

Apart from the genetic characters of a given strain, it is primarily the
cultural conditions which determine whether the capsule is readily given
off in solution as a slime or whether it adheres as a compact mass to the
cell wall. It is the intermediate stage, where a sharply limited and
apparently intact surface is not shown, which might be described as an
envelope. Even if this term is preferred, it is apparent that no sharp
distinction can be drawn between the capsule and the envelope. Envelope,
slime layer and slime may often be observed as different stages in the dissolution of the capsule, wherein, at least so far as the serologically active
component is concerned, the same substance is usually involved.

The capsular substance is, as will appear later, frequently distinct from
those which form an integral part of the cell wall. Thus the question
arises whether any substance lying at the surface of the cell wall, but not
forming an integral part of it, should be regarded as a capsule even if it
cannot be detected by the microscope. The location and the properties of

the M protein of group A streptococci certainly justify this question. According to Lancefield (1943) the M protein can easily be removed from living cells by trypsin digestion without affecting the viability of the bacteria. Furthermore, it differs very sharply, both chemically and serologically, from the underlying cell wall which contains the group-specific polysaccharide and which cannot be thus removed. The existence of a microscopically invisible capsule on an apparently non-capsulated variety of a capsulated bacterium can thus be assumed, without departing too far from established ideas, if both strains can be agglutinated with the same capsular antibody. Burrows (1955) observed an identical resistance to phagocytosis by a capsulated, and by a virulent, non-capsulated, strain of *Pasteurella pestis*. He assumed the presence of an invisible but nevertheless effective degree of capsulation in the latter. It seems logical to assume the presence of a capsular layer, even if it is invisible, when the surface component, external to the cell wall, can be detected by a chemically defined antibody.

NON-SPECIFIC REACTIONS OF THE CAPSULE
Staining

The very large number of methods recommended up to date for the staining of the capsule awakens the suspicion that none of these produces satisfactory results. The shrinkage of the capsule during such procedures was emphasized by Toenniessen as long ago as 1912. He pointed out, in agreement with many previous authors, that the capsule of bacteria derived from the animal body ('tierische Kapsel') can be stained more easily and with great regularity and that it also shows less shrinkage. For a recent evaluation of a number of capsule-staining methods the careful work of Duguid (1951) should be consulted. According to him, of all the dry-film methods the most consistent results were obtained with the eosin serum method of Howie & Kirkpatrick (1934), which was next best after the wet-film Indian-ink method. It should, however, be mentioned that the method of Howie & Kirkpatrick is a 'relief staining' technique and that in the case of some bacteria (e.g. *Bacillus anthracis*) it leads to deformation of the capsule.

Duguid did not obtain uniformly successful results either for the capsule or for the slime by the staining methods of Klieneberger-Nobel (1948). Nevertheless, we consider that it is necessary to discuss briefly the theory of these methods, since they may indicate a difference between the non-specific reactions of the capsule and the slime layer. Klieneberger-Nobel stained the capsules of bacteria, previously fixed with

Bouin's solution, either by Giemsa or, after mordanting with tannic acid, by crystal-violet. The slime could be stained according to her last-mentioned method only when the bacteria were fixed with Chabaud solution. She concludes that the biochemical difference between capsule and slime is obvious, since the methods for the demonstration of capsules by fixation and staining are not applicable when slime only is present, or vice versa. This conclusion seems to be contradicted by previous observations that serologically identical glutamyl-polypeptide can be isolated from capsulated *Bacillus anthracis* and from a typically slime-producing culture of non-capsulated *B. subtilis*. There is, however, an essential immunological difference between these two bacteria. The capsulated strains of *B. anthracis* evoke a polypeptide antibody (Tomcsik & Szongott, 1933), the polypeptide-slime-containing *B. subtilis* culture does not (Ivanovics & Erdös, 1937). Thus it may be assumed that the native state of the polypeptide is different in these two organisms. It is possible that the capsular polypeptide of *B. anthracis* may form a protein complex, at least in the proximity of the cell wall, which is gradually dissociated by the dissolution of the capsule. The *subtilis* bacilli may produce the polypeptide in free form which is given off very easily as a slime, serologically a hapten. This assumption might explain the occasional differences in the staining reactions of the capsule and slime.

Novelli (1953) observed recently that alcian blue stains the bacterial capsule as well as the polysaccharide material separated from the bacteria, without any preliminary mordanting. McKinney (1953) confirmed this observation and regarded alcian blue as a useful stain for bacterial polysaccharides. Tomcsik & Grace (1955) used this dye for the elective demonstration of the bacterial cell wall of several Gram-positive micro-organisms.

Alcian blue is almost the only dye so far recorded which will stain the bacterial capsule without mordanting. Most of the other capsule-staining methods require the addition of proteins, and many of them of acids also. By an appropriate adjustment of the pH, after the addition of protein, very regular results can be ensured in staining the bacterial capsule with any of the basic aniline dyes or with the Gram stain (Tomcsik & Guex-Holzer, 1953). The underlying principle is discussed in the section upon the action of proteins on the bacterial capsule. By using this principle, however, the bacterial capsule can be demonstrated so clearly in the phase-contrast microscope in wet preparations that further staining, coupled with a disadvantageous fixation procedure, is superfluous.

Complex formation with proteins

A non-specific capsular reaction with proteins was first demonstrated with pneumococci. Löfström (1944) demonstrated the capsule of certain types of *Diplococcus pneumoniae* by adding acute-phase protein at neutral reaction in the presence of calcium ions. He described this reaction, analogous to that produced by specific antibodies, as 'capsular swelling'. The reacting protein is produced in the acute stage of bacterial infection and in some non-infectious diseases accompanied by disintegration of tissue. The nature of this reaction has not been fully cleared up. Furthermore, it is not known whether the capsule of any other bacterium reacts in a similar way with acute-phase proteins.

Jacox (1947) studied this reaction and discovered that several proteins and purified enzyme preparations render the capsule of *Diplococcus pneumoniae* visible when the pH is adjusted to 4. The addition of calcium was not necessary in this case; but curiously enough this reaction was inhibited by as low a concentration of sodium chloride as 0.02M. Jacox found no similar reaction with the capsules of *Klebsiella pneumoniae*, *Escherichia coli* and *Streptococcus haemolyticus*. The protein reaction at pH 4 seemed to be restricted to the pneumococci.

Tomcsik & Guex-Holzer (1954*a*) made an essentially different observation regarding the action of various proteins on the bacterial capsule. They studied the reaction of casein, various albumins and globulins, haemoglobin and lysozyme on the capsules of *Cryptococcus neoformans*, *Klebsiella pneumoniae*, *Streptococcus haemolyticus*, *Diplococcus pneumoniae*, *Bacillus anthracis* and several other members of the genus *Bacillus* at different pH. The capsules became visible in the phase-contrast microscope when any of these proteins and organisms were permitted to interact at a certain, usually very narrow, pH range, lying on the acid side of the isoelectric point of the proteins. The pH range at which the reaction occurs shifts with the isoelectric point of the protein used; it also depends, on the other hand, upon the capsular substance of the micro-organism. The absence of calcium or the presence of an isotonic concentration (0.145M) of sodium chloride do not inhibit the reaction. The isolated capsular substance usually behaves in a similar way to the entire capsule, giving a precipitation at the same pH range. The reaction is reversible; it disappears on changing the pH. According to the explanation of the authors, the non-specific capsular reaction is elicited through a salt-like combination of various proteins with the bacterial capsule, leading to a microscopic precipitation at a pH value on the alkaline side of the isoelectric point of the bacterial surface and on the acid side of the isoelectric point of the proteins.

The microscopically visible capsular reaction elicited at an isoelectric pH zone intermediate between those of the bacterial surface and of the proteins is certainly not a 'swelling' reaction. When any change in the size of the capsule is observed, in comparison with that in wet Indian-ink film, it is more often a shrinkage than a swelling.

There is an essential similarity between the non-specific and specific capsule reactions. The difference is that, while the non-specific reaction is induced by various proteins at an appropriate pH, the specific reaction is elicited, on the other hand, only by the homologous antibody and is independent of the pH.

SPECIFIC CAPSULAR REACTION: CHEMICAL NATURE OF THE CAPSULE

The action of antibodies on the bacterial capsule is generally referred to as Neufeld's capsular swelling reaction. In our opinion this designation is totally erroneous and it should be abandoned. The reaction was described first by Roger (1896) and it is not primarily a swelling reaction. We propose to designate it the specific capsular reaction.

Roger (1896) made a microscopic examination in wet films of the visible effect of a homologous immune serum on *Oidium albicans*. He discovered that in about 10 min. after the addition of the serum a hyaline-like surface structure appeared which he called a swelling of the cuticle ('gonflement de la cuticule'). Neufeld (1902) quoted Roger's observation and applied it to *Diplococcus pneumoniae*. He observed that immediately or a few minutes after the addition of immune serum 'the single cocci swell to twice or three times their original size'. He thought that the exterior layer of the bacterial cells was mostly involved in the swelling, but he did not recognize that before the addition of the immune serum an invisible capsule of the same size surrounded the bacterial cell. It was the demonstration of this structure which constituted the apparent swelling. In a much later work (Neufeld & Etinger-Tulczynska, 1931) the reaction is still referred to as a swelling of the 'bacterial bodies'. Etinger-Tulczynska (1933) first pointed out clearly that in the swelling of *D. pneumoniae* the capsule alone is involved, and she described a similar reaction produced by adding homologous antibodies to other capsulated micro-organisms such as *Klebsiella* and *Streptococcus*. Unfortunately, she believed the capsule to be represented by the interior layer, corresponding to the diffraction halo of Duguid (1951), and her microphotographs, figs. 4 and 7, which she quotes in her text (p. 776) for the demonstration of the capsular swelling, are incomprehensible, and probably misinterpreted by her. In this paper, which led to the general acceptance of the term capsular swelling reaction ('Quellungsreaktion'), she certainly did not demonstrate that the volume of the capsule after its reaction with antibody is greater than in a wet Indian-ink film of the untreated capsule.

We do not contest that a secondary swelling of the capsule may occur under certain circumstances, especially in the case of *Diplococcus pneumoniae*. Mudd, Heinmets & Anderson (1943) studied this reaction with the electron microscope, and noted a relative swelling in those preparations which contained, apart from the specific antibody, those components of fresh rabbit serum which are collectively known as complement. Johnson & Dennison (1944) also found, by using a centrifugal method, that the volume increase in the specific capsular reaction appears to be more than the aggregate volume of the antibody molecules adhering to the capsule. Thus a secondary hydration may take place as a result of the antigen-antibody combination. They consider, however, that the reaction is fundamentally a precipitin reaction.

It is questionable if the centrifugal method used by Johnson & Dennison has the same meaning in regard to the measurement of volume changes as the direct microscopic comparison of the size of the capsule in wet Indian-ink preparations and in antibody-containing films. Those who studied the specific capsular reaction on the basis of the last-mentioned criterion found no swelling. We did not observe any swelling by comparison with wet Indian-ink preparations when observing the capsular reaction of *Bacillus anthracis* after the addition of polypeptide antibody (Bodon & Tomcsik, 1934). Klieneberger-Nobel (1948) states clearly that in a number of tests in which immune serum was added to the homologous bacteria actual swelling of the capsule was never demonstrated. 'The capsules do not swell, though they solidify considerably by addition of immune serum.' According to her observations the immune serum reacts not only with the capsules but also with the surrounding slime. Duguid (1951) confirmed these observations with types I, II, III and XIX of pneumococci, with *Klebsiella* and with *Escherichia coli*. According to him the action of the antiserum is not to enlarge the capsule but merely to render visible the outlines of a capsule which is already large. Edwards & Fife (1952) describing a number of new *Klebsiella* types stated: 'In hundreds of observations of cells in parallel India-ink and serum preparations, swelling of the mass surrounding the cells has never been observed.' They noted a precipitation reaction occurring at the surface of the capsule or slime layer. Neill, Castillo, Smith & Kapros (1949) could not find a perceptible swelling of the capsule of *Cryptococcus neoformans*, though, as they state, 'swelling is a prominent visual feature in the capsular reactions of bacteria'.

It appears that the later findings cited here prove conclusively that the term 'capsular swelling reaction' was coined in consequence of an erroneous interpretation of the original observations. The combination of antibody with the capsular material leads within a very short time to precipitation, which renders the capsule visible, usually without changing its size and shape. This concept led us to use the specific capsular reaction for direct cytological studies in an investigation of structural elements in the capsule and as an indicator of the cellular localization of bacterial antigens.

The specific capsular reaction may be employed for diagnostic purposes, as was realized quite early. Schwab & Shaffer (1950) gave a list of micro-organisms for which the preparation of type-specific antisera suitable for the 'Quellung' test has been reported. These include *Diplococcus pneumoniae*, several groups of *Streptococcus*, *Neisseria meningitidis*, *Haemophilus influenzae*, *Klebsiella pneumoniae*, *Bacterium anitratum*, *Sporotrichum schenckii* and *Cryptococcus neoformans*. Among others, *Bacillus* and the *Pasteurella* group should be added to this list. Schwab & Shaffer (1950) succeeded in producing good immune sera for the specific capsular reaction with four injections of encapsulated organisms, given at weekly intervals.

Only a few of the recent observations upon the diagnostic application of the specific capsular reaction are mentioned in the following. Brooke (1951) used the 'swelling' test with rabbit immune serum to study the type distribution of 324 *Klebsiella* strains, and described twenty-seven new capsular types. By the same methods Edwards & Fife (1952) found eighteen, and Edmunds (1954) six, hitherto unknown *Klebsiella* types. Price & Kneeland (1954) observed a 'Quellung' reaction with the homologous serum in a mannitol- and coagulase-positive strain of *Staphylococcus aureus* after passage in the allantoic sac of chick embryos. Ewing, Edwards & Hucks (1952) described capsulated types of *Shigella boydii* with apparently thermolabile antigens. They demonstrated by both agglutination and 'Quellung' reactions that the capsular antigen of *S. boydii* 2 is related closely to that of *Klebsiella* type XXI. Malyoth & Bauer (1951) described envelopes ('Schleimkapsel') on mucoid variants of *Bacterium bifidum* which could be made visible in the phase-contrast microscope by reaction with immune serum. Norris, de Sipin, Zilliken, Harvey & György (1954) did not find in such variants a demonstrable true capsule, but only an extracellular mucoid substance. This substance is a highly polymerized polysaccharide, from which, upon hydrolysis, glucose, galactose, fucose and an unidentified pentose could be obtained.

Antibodies were not used in the earlier work designed to prove the capsular origin of the substances isolated from capsulated bacteria. Still, we have enough evidence today to be able to accept the substance isolated first by Toenniessen (1919, 1920) from capsulated *Klebsiella* as corresponding to the capsular material. Edwards & Fife (1952) comment on this early work as follows: 'Toenniessen was the first worker to draw attention to the serologic specificity of *Klebsiella* capsules and to demonstrate the carbohydrate nature of the capsular antigens.' This comment is erroneous; from a potassium hydroxide extract of capsulated *Klebsiella* Toenniessen isolated a polysaccharide which was identified as a galactan, but he did not suspect the serological activity of this substance. He states clearly (1914, p. 335) that 'no agglutinin is formed which reacts with the envelope. This can be explained, since the envelope consists probably of high molecular carbohydrates and not of proteins. In consequence, no agglutinin is produced which may react with the surface layer of these bacteria.' Toenniessen worked in a period when the serological reactivity of the polysaccharides had not yet been discovered, and when only proteins were held to be capable of such activity. Serologically active polysaccharides were first described in capsulated bacteria by Heidelberger & Avery (1923, 1924) and in non-capsulated microorganisms by Mueller & Tomcsik (1924). Heidelberger & Avery isolated a substance which they called the 'soluble specific substance' of the pneumococcus. Its identity with the capsular substance was proved later in a more direct way, by the use of the specific capsular reaction. Since capsular polysaccharides have been discussed in a number of reviews, among others in the first symposium of this Society, they can be omitted here.

For a long period it was thought that all bacterial capsules consisted of polysaccharides (Heidelberger, 1935), though earlier reports had already pointed out that this generalization did not apply to *Bacillus anthracis*. The main cytological and immunological evidence of the topographical localization of non-carbohydrate substances in the anthrax capsule is cited below.

In the extract of a capsulated *Bacillus anthracis* strain prepared according to Toenniessen, apart from a considerable portion of polysaccharides, 7–8 % w/w nitrogen was found. On the supposition that the extract derived from the capsule, it was designated glycoprotein (Kramár, 1922). When ten capsulated and ten non-capsulated strains were extracted by the same process, the N content of the extracts from capsulated bacteria averaged 6·8%; those from non-capsulated bacteria were below 2·5%. $CuSO_4$ precipitated a substance from the extract of capsulated bacteria only. After $CuSO_4$ precipitation a polysaccharide was isolated from the solution, containing 0·8% N, 0·1% P and no S. Its reducing activity after hydrolysis corresponded to a 60% glucose content (Tomcsik & Szongott, 1932). The substance isolated from the extracts of capsulated bacteria by $CuSO_4$ precipitation contained 10% N, it was free of P and S and gave no reduction after hydrolysis. It was described as a protein-like or P substance. Immune sera prepared in rabbits against non-capsulated anthrax bacilli precipitated only the polysaccharide; those prepared against capsulated bacilli precipitated both the polysaccharide and the polypeptide (Tomcsik & Szongott, 1933). The P-antibody agglutinated only the capsulated bacilli (Tomcsik & Bodon, 1934). The polysaccharide antibody did not render the capsule visible; the P-antibody gave a specific capsular reaction without eliciting any swelling (Bodon & Tomcsik, 1934). The P-substance was identified as D-glutamic acid polypeptide (Ivanovics & Bruckner, 1937).

Analysis of the major steps leading to the conclusion that the anthrax glutamyl-polypeptide is located in the capsule suggests that the occurrence of a particular substance in capsulated bacteria and its absence in non-capsulated bacteria is by itself strongly indicative of a capsular origin for the substance in question. Direct proof of the capsular localization of the polypeptide is given, however, by the agglutination reaction, and still more convincingly by the specific capsular reaction, provided that the polypeptide antibody is defined immunochemically and all other antibodies are eliminated by absorption. Until such reactions can be demonstrated with the polysaccharide antibody in the capsule of *Bacillus anthracis*, it is not justifiable to assume the presence of polysaccharides in the capsule of this micro-organism (Tomcsik, 1954).

The problem of the chemical nature of the capsular substance of *Pasteurella pestis* was somewhat similar to the case of *Bacillus anthracis*. Schütze (1932) found that the anti-envelope serum causes agglutination when it acts upon envelope-producing bacilli; anti-somatic serum does not act upon these bacilli unless the envelope is destroyed at 100°. From envelope-producing *P. pestis* after extraction with neutral salts Baker *et al.* (1947) isolated two water-soluble fractions: IA, a carbohydrate-protein complex, and IB, a carbohydrate-free protein. Both fractions were electrophoretically homogeneous and induced immunity in mice but not in guinea-pigs. The two fractions seemed to be immunologically identical, indicating that no antibody was formed against the polysaccharide portion of the fraction I A. They regard the carbohydrate-protein complex as the native form of the envelope substance, the protein fraction being formed by dissociation during extraction or after the death of the bacteria. Amies (1951) removed the capsules from the cells by the use of aqueous solvents such as potassium thiocyanate, and isolated a simple protein rather than a protein-polysaccharide complex; this he believed to be the capsular substance. Baker *et al.* (1952) found the protein moieties in their fractions I A and I B to be identical, but their attempts to separate the carbohydrate and protein portions of fraction I A were unsuccessful. Engelsberg & Levy (1954) assumed at least a partial identity between fraction I and the envelope on the following grounds: both of them are produced in larger amounts by virulent strains at 37° than by avirulent strains at lower temperatures. Further-more, antiserum prepared with fraction I specifically alters the envelope of virulent bacilli. An immune serum deprived of fraction I antibody by specific adsorption fails to form aggregates on the envelope.

It seems to be safe to assume on the basis of recent work that the capsule of *Pasteurella pestis* consists of a protein which may occur in part as a protein-polysaccharide complex. There is no indication, how-ever, that any capsular structure occurs corresponding to the separate morphological distribution of two different substances in capsulated *Bacillus megaterium*.

COMPLEX STRUCTURE OF THE BACTERIAL CAPSULE

By using immunochemically defined antibodies a complex capsular structure was disclosed in *Bacillus megaterium* by Tomcsik (1951) and studied in detail by Tomcsik & Guex-Holzer (1951, 1952, 1954b, c). In addition to three authentic strains of *B. megaterium*, another strain designated *Bacillus* M was mainly used in these studies. It was so called because it was originally obtained from a Pasteur vaccine of *B. anthracis* during studies on induced mutation. Its derivation from *B. anthracis* is, however, doubtful, and as was established later it resembles *B. mega-terium* in its cell structure, showing only a few differences in fermentation reactions. Ruth E. Gordon (personal communication) classified it as *B. megaterium*.

None of the four capsulated *Bacillus megaterium* strains produced antibodies in rabbits capable of reacting with glutamyl-polypeptide. All of them, however, gave a typical specific capsular reaction when tested with anthrax polypeptide antibody. In this respect this capsular sub-stance of *B. megaterium* behaves in a similar manner to the slime of

B. subtilis. Ivanovics & Erdös (1937) isolated from cultures of *B. subtilis* a glutamyl-polypeptide which reacted with anthrax polypeptide antibody, but the slimy culture of *subtilis* bacilli did not induce the production of a similar antibody. The capsular substance demonstrated with polypeptide antibody in *B. megaterium* showed an apparently homogeneous distribution, and at its interior surface the diffraction halo, corresponding to the cell wall, was clearly visible (Text-fig. 2A).

A surprising capsular structure was revealed a few seconds after the addition of the homologous antibody (Text-fig. 2B); it consisted of transverse septa, polar condensation and an indefinite striation. As could be observed in several hundred subcultures on Gladstone-Fildes agar medium the transverse septa appeared regularly at the point of division of the cells within the chain. They frequently appeared thicker at the periphery of the capsule, and their continuation up to the surface of the cell wall was seldom visible, probably owing to the incomplete penetration of the antibody. In the centrifuged sediment of a 3 hr. aerated Sauton culture very large capsules were formed in 3 days at room temperature. When the homologous antibody was added to these bacteria the capsular transverse septa were demonstrated as thick disks of uniform thickness, located probably in the direct continuation of the cross-walls of the chain (Text-fig. 2D). Transverse gaps, corresponding to the considerable thickness of the transverse septa, could be observed in the distribution of the polypeptide material when polypeptide antibody was added to the bacterial suspension (Text-fig. 2C). The rough striation of the polypeptide mass in the last-mentioned preparation probably indicates that in their distribution the two substances, revealed by two different antibodies, are complementary one to another. The usually homogeneous appearance of the polypeptide mass (Text-fig. 2A) might be explained by the assumption that if they are too thin, films of the second substance cannot be resolved in the phase-contrast microscope as visible gaps. The photomicrographs Pl. 1, figs. 1 and 2, show the two reactions given schematically in Text-fig. 2C and D.

The homologous antibody, revealing the highly characteristic capsular structure, reacts with a type-specific polysaccharide isolated from the capsulated bacteria. The method of its isolation and its relation to the cell-wall polysaccharide will be described in the last section. The homologous serum absorbed with this polysaccharide has no visible effect on any part of the capsular structure. Thus we conclude that the capsule of *Bacillus megaterium* consists of a polysaccharide framework, the spaces within which are occupied by a larger amount of glutamyl-polypeptide.

Our conclusion was contested by Ivanovics & Horvath (1952, 1953), who suggested that the framework is made up of glutamyl-polypeptide micellae firmly bound to the surface of the bacteria, the interseptal spaces being filled with a polysaccharide which might be considered to be an intercellular substance. We are unable to understand this conception. Ivanovics & Horvath did not demonstrate a framework in any way resembling that in Text-fig. 2B and D. They state, in conformity with

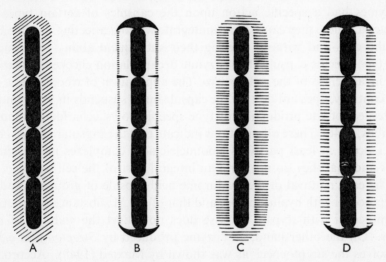

Text-fig. 2. Complex capsular structure of *Bacillus megaterium*. A, suspension from agar, with polypeptide antibody. B, suspension from agar, with homologous antibody. C, suspension from Sauton, sediment with polypeptide antibody. D, suspension from Sauton, sediment with homologous antibody.

our own observations, that the polypeptide antibody most frequently reveals a homogeneously distributed capsular material; they noticed, however, in a certain percentage of their observations, a narrow striation caused by the polypeptide antibody. The original publications should be consulted to realize the essential difference between the indistinct narrow polypeptide striation described by Ivanovics and Horvath within the capsule of one cell, and the transverse capsular polysaccharide septa located very regularly at the point of cell division within a chain demonstrated by Tomcsik & Guex-Holzer. Our further observations on enzyme-treated *Bacillus megaterium* make it quite clear that the poly-saccharide capsular framework is intimately related to the cell wall.

EFFECT OF ENZYMES ON THE BACTERIAL CAPSULE
AND ON THE CELL WALL

The most lucid information regarding the relation of the capsule to the bacterial cell is obtainable from the well-known enzymic studies of Dubos & Avery (1931; reviewed by Dubos, 1946) and of Sickles & Shaw (1950). These authors studied the effect of enzymes derived from soil micro-organisms on the capsules of *Diplococcus pneumoniae*. These enzymes had a specific action upon the capsules of certain types of bacteria. These they caused to disintegrate without affecting the viability of the cells and without altering their subsequent ability to produce the type-specific capsule. The enzymic decapsulation checked, however, the invasiveness of the cells *in vivo*. The application of ribonuclease, on the contrary, does not destroy the capsule but it suspends its antigenicity in respect of the production of type-specific polysaccharide antibodies (Dubos, 1946). These observations indicate that the capsular polysaccharides occur at least partly as ribonucleic-acid complexes in the intact cells and that they do not form an integral part of the cell wall.

The easy removal of the hyaluronic acid capsule of groups A and C streptococci with hyaluronidase and that of the M substance of group A streptococci with trypsin likewise does not affect the viability of the cells. On the other hand, an enzyme produced by *Streptomyces albus* dissolves the streptococci, as was shown by Maxted (1948). According to McCarty (1952) and Schmidt (1952) this enzyme acts on the streptococcal cell wall, depolymerizing its carbohydrate component.

It is to be inferred from these observations that the enzyme substrates in the capsules of pneumococci and streptococci differ from those in the cell wall of these micro-organisms. Other studies revealed, however, that in the case of *Bacillus megaterium* the same enzyme depolymerizes both the cell wall and certain elements of the capsular structure.

Tomcsik & Guex-Holzer (1952, 1954*b*, *c*) studied the cytological effect of lysozyme digestion on wet films of living capsulated *Bacillus* M with the phase-contrast microscope. A lysozyme concentration was selected at which the cell walls of a heavy bacterial suspension were totally dissolved in 30–60 min. at 20°. Appropriate dilutions of crystallized lysozyme or of egg-white gave an identical effect. Homologous serum was added to detect the action of lysozyme on the polysaccharide capsular structure. The bacteria formed chains, corresponding to the R type of cell division as defined by Bisset (1950). The first cellular change, visible in 3–5 min., manifested itself as a slight semilunar polar separation of the cytoplasm from the cross cell wall. At this stage the capsular transverse septa were rendered visible in their full length, from the capsular surface to the cell wall, indicating an increase in the permeability for the antibody. In about 10–15 min. a stage was reached in which the bulk of the capsular material was dissolved and only the most resistant structural elements, the transverse septa and the polar condensations, were visible (Text-fig. 3A). Simultaneously the cytoplasm assumed an ellipsoid shape and the cell walls as well as the cross-walls appeared very distinct. When the homologous antibody was either omitted or replaced by the anthrax glutamyl-polypeptide antibody the

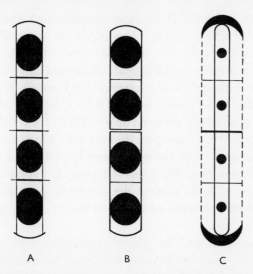

A   B   C

Text-fig. 3. Effect of lysozyme and trypsin digestion of *Bacillus* M. A, lysozyme 15 min. The polysaccharide antibody demonstrates the projecting transverse septa of the capsule, the polar condensation, the cell walls and cross-walls. B, lysozyme 25 min. The polysaccharide antibody shows only the cell walls and cross-walls. C, trypsin-treated bacteria. The polysaccharide antibody reveals all the corresponding capsular and cell-wall elements.

capsular transverse septa were invisible and the cross-walls and lateral cell walls could hardly be discerned. These antibody reactions were entitled, in consequence, specific capsular or specific cell-wall reactions. It could be clearly observed in microphotographs (Tomcsik & Guex-Holzer, 1952) that the capsular transverse septa are in direct continuation of the cross-walls. They project into the capsule and form an essential part of the capsular framework. After a few more minutes of lysozyme digestion the projecting transverse septa disappeared, whereas the cell walls and cross-walls still reacted very sharply with the homologous antibody. The cross-walls in certain places could be seen to be splitting, indicating the beginning of disarticulation within the chain

(Text-fig. 3B). At this stage of the lysozyme action the cytoplasm assumed a perfectly spherical shape which was retained even after the total dissolution of the cell wall.

The successive stages of the spherical transformation of the bacterial protoplasts appeared to be directly correlated with the progressive dilatation of the bacterial cell wall following the depolymerization of the cell wall polysaccharides by lysozyme. Mudd, Polevitzky, Anderson & Chambers (1941) predicted this phenomenon in the following words: 'The fact that most bacteria are not spheres, indicates that they possess rigidity of structure in some degree; otherwise the action of surface forces, relatively powerful at surfaces of such high curvature, would make the bacterial cells spherical.' Heating of the bacterial cells prevents the spherical transformation of the protoplasts, but the orderly sequence in the action of lysozyme on the capsular structure and on the dilatation and dissolution of the cell wall is unaffected (Tomcsik & Guex-Holzer, 1952). In our first experiments we used 0·85% NaCl. Under these circumstances the protoplasts survived only partially for 1–24 hr. even when kept at 4°. Weibull (1953) observed that the protoplasts can be preserved for one or more days when the experiment is performed with 0·1–0·2M buffered sucrose solution. We observed recently (Tomcsik, 1955) that Ringer's solution without sucrose preserves the protoplasts very well and permits the development of the same stages of lysozyme action as described above.

Bacillus megaterium and the special type *Bacillus* M are among the few Gram-positive micro-organisms which are exceptional in that they are amenable, without heating, to a certain degree of trypsin digestion (Tomcsik & Guex-Holzer, 1954*b,d*; Tomcsik & Grace, 1955). In the cells treated for 20 hr. with trypsin the protoplasts are reduced to a small body of unidentified nature, and the polysaccharide components of the capsule and of the cell wall can be rendered visible by the corresponding antibody (Text-fig. 3C).

Both experiments carried out with lysozyme and trypsin showed that the transverse septa of the capsular framework of *Bacillus megaterium* appear as direct outward projections of the cross-walls. It remained, however, to be proved that both structures are identical in respect of their origin and chemical composition.

THE RELATION OF THE CAPSULE TO THE CELL WALL

According to Bisset (1950) the new cell-wall material is secreted by a basophilic septum derived from the cell membrane which appears across the cell as the first sign of incipient division. The cross-walls form within the thickness of the septum which is thus split into two layers, lining the new cross-wall. We assume that a similar mechanism is involved in the production of those capsular components which are intimately related to the cell wall. In order to verify this assumption different stages of capsule production in *Bacillus* M were studied under the phase-contrast microscope, after the addition of the polysaccharide or the polypeptide antibody. The non-capsulated bacilli were obtained by growth in Gladstone-Fildes bouillon aerated for 5 hr. at 28°. The different stages of capsule production were observed by transferring the non-capsulated bacilli to Gladstone-Fildes agar medium which was examined after 1–5 hr. incubation at 28°. The portions of the bacterial surface most actively involved in the production of the capsular polysaccharide and polypeptide were deduced from appearances in a series of microphotographs (Tomcsik & Guex-Holzer, 1954c). Some of these findings are illustrated schematically in Text-fig. 4.

The outward growth of the cross-wall could be observed in the aerated bouillon culture in the absence of any other morphological sign of capsule formation. The thickened masses became visible only after the addition of the polysaccharide antibody and gave a bamboo-like appearance to the multicellular bacillus (Text-fig. 4A). A short time after the transfer of these cells to agar medium a further growth of the cross-walls corresponding to the capsular septa pushed the protuberances outward to the periphery of a narrow capsular layer. The parts of the cytoplasmic surface where, according to the schematic drawings of Bisset (1950), the active producing area was assumed to lie, were thus specially indicated. Bisset expressed the opinion (1953) that in septate bacilli the main growth of the cell wall takes place at the points of junction of cell wall and cross-wall. The same active area may well be responsible for the initiation of the outward growth of the cross-wall (Text-fig. 4A). In the second stage (Text-fig. 4B), however, it is possible that the whole cytoplasmic surface may be involved in this production, since a small amount of polysaccharide material could be detected with the corresponding antibody throughout the thin capsular layer. The first stage in the production of polypeptide material shows, on the other hand, irregular patches appearing on the surface of the cell wall except at the point of division.

These observations justify the assumption that the polysaccharide transverse septa form in the same way as the cross-walls, and that the part of the cytoplasmic surface which is involved in their formation does not produce any detectable amount of polypeptide. The contrary is true of capsulated *Bacillus anthracis* grown in undiluted inactivated horse serum. At the point of division more polypeptide is produced, giving a beaded appearance to the capsulated chain (Tomcsik, 1954).

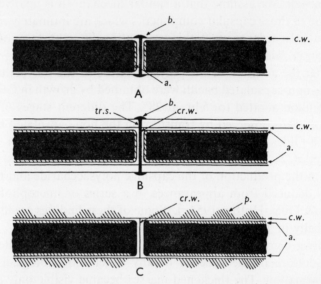

Text-fig. 4. Early stages in the development of the capsular structure in *Bacillus* M. A, aerated bouillon culture 5 hr. old; with polysaccharide antibody. B, agar culture 2 hr. old; with polysaccharide antibody. C, agar culture 2 hr. old; with polypeptide antibody. *a*, probable location of proteins of the cytoplasmic membrane active in the production of the polysaccharide and polypeptide moieties; *b*, protuberances of polysaccharide material; *c.w.* cell wall; *cr.w.* cross-wall; *p.* polypeptide; *tr.s.* transverse septa in the capsule.

The morphological relationship of the capsular framework of *Bacillus megaterium* to the cell wall was confirmed on an immuno-chemical basis. The capsular material could be extracted very simply by boiling an aqueous suspension of the bacteria. A similar method was used for the extraction of polysaccharides by Webb (1948) working with *Staphylococcus citreus* and by Aubert & Millet (1950) with capsulated *B.-megaterium*.

Guex-Holzer & Tomcsik (1955) extracted the capsulated *Bacillus* M in a bath of boiling water for 4 hr. During this procedure the capsules became progressively thinner but they could be detected, even after 4 hr. The polypeptide was separated from the extract by fractional precipitation with ethanol, and purified until, after acid hydrolysis, only D-glutamic acid could be detected by paper chromatography. A polysaccharide was obtained from the remaining extract and purified as described in outline below.

Impurities were precipitated with bovine plasma albumin fraction V at an appropriate pH; deproteinization was conducted according to Sevag; the residue was repeatedly dissolved in formamide in saturated urea and fractionally precipitated with ethanol until no change in the serological reactivity could be observed. Galactosamine, glucosamine and an unidentified amino sugar, but no free amino acids, could be detected in the acid hydrolysate by chromatographic analysis. The activity of the homologous immune serum, in eliciting the specific capsular and cell-wall reactions, disappeared completely after absorption with this polysaccharide.

The extraction of serologically active material from non-capsulated *Bacillus* M was more difficult. Alkalis, acids, sodium taurocholate, phenol, formamide and antiformin were tried without success. The cell wall of heated bacteria could, however, be brought into solution while retaining most of its serological reactivity, by a cautious disintegration with lysozyme; 5 mg. lysozyme was distributed evenly on the chilled suspension of 2 g. bacteria in a Mickle vibrator and the free lysozyme was removed by washing. The action of the bound lysozyme in a 35° water-bath was stopped immediately when the microscopic controls revealed the dissolution of the cell wall. The chilled extract was deproteinized by the method of Sevag, and fractionated by using the precipitation reaction with the homologous antibody as an indicator. Essentially the same major steps were used in the purification of the serologically active substance as for the capsular polysaccharide. After freeze-drying, a muco-protein of the following constitution was obtained: N 7·6%, P 4·7%, reducing substances after acid hydrolysis (calculated as glucose) 18%, acetyl *c*. 4%. Galactosamine, glucosamine, diaminopimelic acid, alanine and a small amount of glutamic acid could be identified in the hydrolysates by chromatographic analysis. Two other substances appearing as faint spots after spraying with ninhydrin could not be identified. A similar substance was also obtained from capsulated bacteria by lysozyme extraction after eliminating the capsular polypeptide. Both muco-proteins were precipitated by the homologous immune serum alone, at a dilution of 1×10^6. As in the case of the capsular polysaccharide they absorbed from this serum the antibody giving both the specific capsular and cell-wall reactions.

Since the capsular polysaccharide and the cell-wall muco-protein gave an identical serological reaction, it can be concluded that their serological specificity is dependent upon the configuration of the substance of simpler chemical composition, i.e. the polysaccharide. The composition of the muco-protein probably more closely resembles that of the specific substance as this occurs in the capsule and in the cell wall. Extraction with hot water apparently splits off the polysaccharide from more complex molecules within the cell structure. The specific polysaccharide can therefore be regarded as a common component of the more complex unknown substances which on the one hand compose the cell wall and on the other the peculiar capsular structure of *Bacillus* M. The D-glutamic acid polypeptide occurs in the capsule, but it does not take part in the composition of the cell wall.

The identity of the polysaccharides from the cell wall and from the capsule was also confirmed in a different way. Tomcsik & Guex-Holzer (1954*d*) immunized a group of rabbits with the cell-wall preparations obtained by trypsin digestion of non-capsulated *Bacillus* M, and another group with the cell-wall-free spherical protoplasts. The immune serum of the first group of rabbits gave a precipitation with the capsular polysaccharide and with the cell-wall muco-protein to the same titre; it gave both the specific capsular and cell-wall reaction, it agglutinated the cell-wall suspension but not the naked protoplasts. The immune serum against the protoplasts, on the other hand, agglutinated a suspension of these spherical elements, but contained no polysaccharide antibody and did not give the specific capsular and cell-wall reactions.

The identity or close similarity of the serologically active capsular substance with some integral material of the more complex cell wall is confined, according to our present knowledge, to *Bacillus megaterium*. We are not aware of any similar observations even for the related *B. anthracis*. Smith & Keppie (1955) stated at the last Symposium of this Society that polyglutamic acid almost certainly occurs in the capsule of *B. anthracis*, since non-capsulated strains do not produce it. According to them there is no evidence that the capsule of *B. anthracis* is composed entirely of polyglutamic acid; it appears that the polysaccharide forming part of the cell wall also projects into the capsule (Chu, 1953; Tomcsik, 1951). We do not fully agree with the concept of Smith & Keppie. It seems to us absolutely certain, on the basis of the evidence of the specific capsular reaction, that glutamyl-polypeptide occurs in the capsule of *B. anthracis*. We found, however, no observation in the report of Chu (1953) which indicated the existence of polysaccharide projections into the capsule. In our first observation (1951) it was clearly stated that *Bacillus* M, in which we recognized the polysaccharide capsular septa, was related to, but not identical with, *B. anthracis*. Even before its polypeptide nature was detected, we based our interpretation of the identity of the P substance with the capsule of *B. anthracis* on the observation that the specific capsular reaction of this bacillus can be elicited with the polypeptide and not with the polysaccharide antibody (Tomcsik & Szongott, 1933; Bodon & Tomcsik, 1934). We also showed recently (Tomcsik, 1954) that the anthrax polysaccharide antibody gives a specific cell wall but not a capsular reaction with virulent strains of capsulated *B. anthracis*. It was further demonstrated in photomicrographs that visible changes, resembling the capsular transverse septa of *B. megaterium*, appear in preparations of capsulated *B. anthracis* as late as 17 hr. after the addition of the polysaccharide antibody. We regard the instantaneous specific antibody reaction as a sensitive and reliable indicator of the disposition of capsular substances, but the late appearance of visible changes in the capsule points to a secondary phenomenon which is difficult to interpret. The antibody reacting with the cell wall might, after a period of time, increase its permeability, even for cytoplasmic substances partially disintegrated by autolytic enzymes.

In this review, only a part of the considerable body of experimental work carried out to clear up the nature of the bacterial capsule could be discussed. The extensive work done with the capsular substances of *Diplococcus pneumoniae, Streptococcus, Klebsiella, Bacillus anthracis* and *Pasteurella pestis* indicate with great probability that in contrast to *Bacillus megaterium* their capsular substances are not identical with those which form part of the cell wall proper. Toenniessen (1919) long since anticipated this tentative statement in saying: 'The bacterial capsule does not derive, as some authors believe, from the swelling of the ectoplasm but is a positive new chemical entity produced from the ectoplasm' (author's translation). If under the designation of ectoplasm Toenniessen not only included the cell wall but also the cytoplasmic membrane, his concept is supported by the present experimental evidence, in contrast to that of Etinger-Tulczynska (1933), who regarded the capsule as a modification of the bacterial cell wall. The chemical nature of the cell wall has only been studied intensively in recent years. There is, however, a paucity of experimental data concerning the majority of the pathogenic bacteria which might provide direct evidence to establish the relationship of the bacterial capsule to the deeper surface layers of the bacterial cell.

REFERENCES

AMIES, C. R. (1951). The envelope substance of *Pasteurella pestis*. *Brit. J. exp. Path.* **32**, 259.

AUBERT, J. P. & MILLET, J. (1950). Existence d'une capsule glucidique chez *Bacillus megatherium*. *Ann. Inst. Pasteur*, **79**, 468.

BAKER, E. E., SOMMER, H., FOSTER, L. E., MEYER, E. & MEYER, K. F. (1947). Antigenic structure of *Pasteurella pestis* and the isolation of a crystalline antigen. *Proc. Soc. exp. Biol., N.Y.*, **64**, 139.

BAKER, E. E., SOMMER, H., FOSTER, L. E., MEYER, E. & MEYER, K. F. (1952). Studies on immunization against plague. I. The isolation and characterisation of the soluble antigen of *Pasteurella pestis*. *J. Immunol.* **68**, 131.

BISSET, K. A. (1950). *The Cytology and Life-History of Bacteria*. Edinburgh: Livingstone.

BISSET, K. A. (1953). Bacterial cell envelopes. In *Bacterial Cytology, Symp. 6th Congr. int. Microbiol. Rome*, p. 9.

BODON, G. & TOMCSIK, J. (1934). Effect of specific antibody on the capsule of anthrax bacilli. *Proc. Soc. exp. Biol., N.Y.*, **32**, 122.

BROOKE, M. S. (1951). Further capsular antigens of *Klebsiella* strains. *Acta path. microbiol. scand.* **28**, 313.

BURRI, R. (1909). *Das Tuscheverfahren als einfaches Mittel zur Lösung einiger schwierigen Aufgaben der Bakterioskopie*. Jena: Fischer.

BURROWS, T. W. (1955). The basis of virulence for mice of *Pasteurella pestis*. In *Mechanisms of Microbial Pathogenicity*, ed. J. W. Howie, & A. J. O'Hea, Cambridge University Press.

CHU, H. P. (1953). Cytochemical structure of *Bacillus anthracis* with special reference to its cell-wall. *Proc. 6th Congr. int. Microbiol., Rome*, **1**, 179.

CHURCHMAN, J. W. & EMELIANOFF, N. V. (1933). A study of the bacterial capsule by new methods. *J. exp. Med.* **57**, 485.

DUBOS, R. J. (1946). *The Bacterial Cell*. Cambridge, Mass.: Harvard University Press.

DUBOS, R. J. & AVERY, O. T. (1931). Decomposition of the capsular polysaccharide of pneumococcus Type III by a bacterial enzyme. *J. exp. Med.* **54**, 51.

DUGUID, J. P. (1951). The demonstration of bacterial capsules and slime. *J. Path. Bact.* **63**, 673.

EDMUNDS, P. N. (1954). Further *Klebsiella* capsule types. *J. infect. Dis.* **94**, 65.

EDWARDS, P. R. & FIFE, M. A. (1952). Capsule types of *Klebsiella*. *J. infect. Dis.* **91**, 92.

ENGELSBERG, E. & LEVY, J. B. (1954). Studies on immunization against plague. VI. Growth of *Pasteurella pestis* and the production of the envelope and other soluble antigens in a casein hydrolyzate mineral glucose medium. *J. Bact.* **67**, 438.

ETINGER-TULCZYNSKA, R. (1933). Bakterienkapseln und Quellungsreaktion. *Z. Hyg. InfektKr.* **114**, 769.

EWING, W. H., EDWARDS, P. R. & HUCKS, M. C. (1952). Thermolabile antigens of *Shigella boydii* 2 cultures with special reference to an encapsulated culture. *Proc. Soc. exp. Biol., N.Y.*, **78**, 100.

GUEX-HOLZER, S. & TOMCSIK, J. (1956). Isolation and chemical nature of capsular and cell-wall haptens in a *Bacillus* sp. *J. gen. Microbiol.* (in the Press).

HEIDELBERGER, M. & AVERY, O. T. (1923). The soluble specific substance of pneumococcus. *J. exp. Med.* **38**, 73.

HEIDELBERGER, M. & AVERY, O. T. (1924). The soluble specific substance of pneumococcus (second paper). *J. exp. Med.* **40**, 301.

HEIDELBERGER, M. (1935). Immunochemistry. *Annu. Rev. Biochem.* **4**, 569.

HOWIE, J. W. & KIRKPATRICK, J. (1934). Observations on bacterial capsules as demonstrated by a simple method. *J. Path. Bact.* **39**, 165.

IVANOVICS, G. & BRUCKNER, V. (1937). Die chemische Struktur der Kapselsubstanz des Milzbrandbazillus und der serologisch identischen spezifischen Substanz des *Bacillus mesentericus. Z. ImmunForsch.* **90**, 304.

IVANOVICS, G. & ERDÖS, L. (1937). Ein Beitrag zum Wesen der Kapselsubstanz des Milzbrandbazillus. *Z. ImmunForsch.* **90**, 5.

IVANOVICS, G. & HORVATH, S. (1952). Die Struktur der Oberfläche des *Bakt. megatherium. Naturwissenschaften*, **39**, 455.

IVANOVICS, G. & HORVATH, S. (1953). The structure of the capsule of *B. megatherium. Acta Physiol. Hung.* **4**, 175.

JACOX, R. F. (1947). A new method for the production of non-specific capsular swelling of the pneumococcus. *Proc. Soc. exp. Biol., N.Y.*, **66**, 635.

JOHNSON, F. H. & DENNISON, W. L. (1944). The volume change accompanying the Quellung reaction of Pneumococci. *J. Immunol.* **48**, 317.

KLIENEBERGER-NOBEL, E. (1948). Capsules and mucoid envelopes of bacteria. *J. Hyg., Camb.*, **46**, 345.

KRAMÁR, E. (1922). Untersuchungen über die chemische Beschaffenheit der Kapselsubstanz einiger Kapselbakterien. *Zbl. Bakt.* Abt. I, Orig., **87**, 403.

LANCEFIELD, R. C. (1943). Studies on the antigenic composition of group A hemolytic streptococci. I. Effects of proteolytic enzymes on streptococcal cells. *J. exp. Med.* **78**, 465.

LÖFSTRÖM, G. (1944). Comparison between the reactions of acute phase serum with pneumococcus C-polysaccharide and with Pneumococcus type 27. *Brit. J. exp. Path.* **25**, 21.

MCCARTY, M. (1952). The lysis of group A hemolytic streptococci by extracellular enzymes of *Streptomyces albus. J. exp. Med.* **96**, 555 and 569.

MCKINNEY, R. E. (1953). Staining bacterial polysaccharides. *J. Bact.* **66**, 453.

MALYOTH, G. & BAUER, A. (1951). Die Darstellung der Schleimkapsel bei Mucoidstämmen des *Bac. bifidum* mittels Immunserum im Phasenkontrastmikroskop. *Z. Biol.* **104**, 404.

MAXTED, W. R. (1948). Preparation of streptococcal extracts for Lancefield grouping. *Lancet*, ii, 255.

MUDD, S., POLEVITZKY, K., ANDERSON, T. F. & CHAMBERS, L. A. (1941). Bacterial morphology as shown by the electron microscope. *J. Bact.* **42**, 251.

MUDD, S., HEINMETS, F. & ANDERSON, T. F. (1943). The pneumococcal capsular swelling reaction, studied with the aid of the electron microscope. *J. exp. Med.* **78**, 327.

MUELLER, H. & TOMCSIK, J. (1924). The chemical nature of residue antigen prepared from yeast. *J. exp. Med.* **40**, 343.

NEILL, J. M., CASTILLO, C. G., SMITH, R. H. & KAPROS, CH. E. (1949). Capsular reactions and soluble antigens of *Torula histolytica* and of *Sporotrichum Schenkii. J. exp. Med.* **89**, 93.

NEUFELD, F. (1902). Ueber die Agglutination der Pneumokokken und über die Theorien der Agglutination. *Z. Hyg. InfektKr.* **40**, 54.

NEUFELD, F. & ETINGER-TULCZYNSKA, R. (1931). Nasale Pneumokokkeninfektionen und Pneumokokkenkeimträger im Tierversuch. *Z. Hyg. InfektKr.* **112**, 492.

NORRIS, R. F., DE SIPIN, M., ZILLIKEN, F. W., HARVEY, TH. S., & GYÖRGY, P. (1954). Occurrence of mucoid variants of *Lactobacillus bifidus*. Demonstration of extracellular and intracellular polysaccharides. *J. Bact.* **67**, 159.

NOVELLI, A. (1953). New method of staining of bacterial capsules in films and sections. *Experientia*, **9**, 34.

PRICE, K. M. & KNEELAND, Y., JR. (1954). A mucoid form of *Micrococcus pyogenes* var. *aureus* which shows capsular swelling with specific immune serum. *J. Bact.* **67**, 472.

PREISZ, H. (1911). Studien über das Variieren und das Wesen der Abschwächung des Milzbrandbacillus. *Zbl. Bakt.* Abt. I, Orig., **58**, 510.

ROGER, H. (1896). Les infections non bactériennes. Recherches sur l'Oidio-Mycose. *Rev. gén. Sci.* **7**, 770.

ROWLAND, S. (1914). *J. Hyg.*, *Camb.*, Plague Supplement, **3**, 418.

SCHMIDT, W. C. (1952). Group A Streptococcus polysaccharide: Studies on its preparation, chemical composition and cellular localization after intravenous injection into mice. *J. exp. Med.* **95**, 105.

SCHÜTZE, H. (1932). Studies in *B. pestis* antigens: I. The antigens and immunity reactions of *B. pestis*. *Brit. J. exp. Path.* **13**, 284.

SCHWAB, M. P. & SHAFFER, M. F. (1950). Production of Quelling antisera in chickens. *Proc. Soc. exp. Biol.*, *N.Y.*, **74**, 726.

SEAL, S. C. (1951). Studies on the specific soluble protein of *Pasteurella pestis* and allied organisms. I. Isolation, fractionation and certain physical, chemical and serological properties. *J. Immunol.* **67**, 93.

SICKLES, G. M. & SHAW, M. (1950). Production of specific antisera for enzymes that decompose the carbohydrates of pneumococcus types III and VIII. *J. Immunol.* **64**, 21.

SMITH, H. & KEPPIE, J. (1955). Studies on the chemical basis of the pathogenicity of *Bacillus anthracis* using organisms grown *in vivo*. In *Mechanisms of microbial pathogenicity*, ed. J. W. Howie & A. J. O'Hea. Cambridge University Press.

SOKHEY, S. S. (1940). The capsule of the plague bacillus. *J. Path. Bact.* **51**, 97.

TOENNIESSEN, E. (1912). Untersuchungen über die Kapsel der pathogenen Bakterien. I. Die in Kulturen und im Tierkörper gebildete Kapsel: Darstellungsmethode. *Zbl. Bakt.* Abt. I, Orig., **65**, 23.

TOENNIESSEN, E. (1914). Ueber die Agglutination der Kapselbacillen. Untersuchungen über die Bedeutung der einzelnen Bestandteile der Bakterienzelle für die Agglutininerzeugung und für den Vorgang der Agglutination. *Zbl. Bakt.* Abt. I, Orig., **75**, 329.

TOENNIESSEN, E. (1919). Ueber die chemische Beschaffenheit der Bakterienhüllen und über die Gewinnung der Eiweisssubstanzen aus dem Inneren der Bakterienzelle. *Münch. med. Wschr.* **66**, 1412.

TOENNIESSEN, E. (1920). Untersuchungen über die Kapsel (Gummihülle) der pathogenen Bakterien. II. Die chemische Beschaffenheit der Kapsel und ihr dadurch bedingtes Verhalten gegenüber der Fixierung und Färbung. *Zbl. Bakt.* Abt. I, Orig., **85**, 225.

TOMCSIK, J. (1951). Complex structure of the bacterial capsule in the genus *Bacillus*. *Experientia*, **7**, 459.

TOMCSIK, J. (1954). Ueber die Oberflächenstrukturen des *Bacillus anthracis*. *Schweiz. Z. allg. Path. Bakt.* **17**, 457.

TOMCSIK, J. (1955). *Proc. Soc. exp. Biol.*, *N.Y.* **89**, 459.

TOMCSIK, J. & BODON, G. (1934). Agglutination of the encapsulated anthrax bacilli. *Proc. Soc. exp. Biol.*, *N.Y.*, **32**, 118.

TOMCSIK, J. & GRACE, J. B. (1955). The specific cell-wall reaction and staining of the bacterial cell-wall with Alcian blue. *J. gen. Microbiol.* **13**, 105.

TOMCSIK, J. & GUEX-HOLZER, S. (1951). Anthrax-Polypeptid und andere speziesspezifische Substanzen der Kapsel in der Bazillus-Gruppe. *Schweiz. Z. allg. Path. Bakt.* **14**, 515.

TOMCSIK, J. & GUEX-HOLZER, S. (1952). Aenderung der Struktur der Bakterienzelle im Verlauf der Lysozym-Einwirkung. *Schweiz. Z. allg. Path. Bakt.* **15**, 517.

PLATE 1

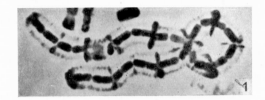

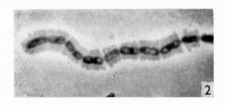

TOMCSIK, J. & GUEX-HOLZER, S. (1953). Ein neues Prinzip zur Färbung der Bakterienkapsel. *Schweiz. Z. allg. Path. Bakt.* **16**, 882.

TOMCSIK, J. & GUEX-HOLZER, S. (1954*a*). Demonstration of the bacterial capsule by means of a pH dependent, salt-like combination with proteins. *J. gen. Microbiol.* **10**, 97.

TOMCSIK, J. & GUEX-HOLZER, S. (1954*b*). A specific cell-wall reaction in *Bacillus* sp. *J. gen. Microbiol.* **10**, 317.

TOMCSIK, J. & GUEX-HOLZER, S. (1954*c*). Genese der komplexen Kapselstruktur. *Schweiz. Z. allg. Path. Bakt.* **17**, 221.

TOMCSIK, J. & GUEX-HOLZER, S. (1954*d*). Antikörperproduktion mit isolierter Bakterienzellwand und mit Protoplasten. *Experientia*, **10**, 484.

TOMCSIK, J. & SZONGOTT, H. (1932). Ueber die spezifischen Polysaccharide der Milzbrandbazillen. *Z. ImmunForsch.* **76**, 214.

TOMCSIK, J. & SZONGOTT, H. (1933). Ueber ein spezifisches Protein der Kapsel des Milzbrandbazillus. *Z. ImmunForsch.* **77**, 86.

WEBB, M. (1948). The action of lysozyme on heat-killed Gram-positive micro-organisms. *J. gen. Microbiol.* **2**, 260.

WEIBULL, C. (1953). The isolation of protoplasts from *Bacillus megaterium* by controlled treatment with lysozyme. *J. Bact.* **66**, 688.

EXPLANATION OF PLATE

Fig. 1. Originally non-capsulated *Bacillus* M from aerated Sauton culture; secondary capsule production in the centrifuged sediment at room temperature in 3 days. Polysaccharide antibody. Note the exceptionally thick transverse septa. Phase-contrast, × 2500.

Fig. 2. Bacteria as in fig. 1. Polypeptide antibody. The distribution of the secondarily produced polypeptide is not homogeneous. Gaps in place of the polysaccharide transverse septa. Phase-contrast, × 2500.

CAPSULE FORMATION AND GLUTAMYL POLYPEPTIDE SYNTHESIS BY *BACILLUS ANTHRACIS* AND *BACILLUS SUBTILIS*

C. B. THORNE

Camp Detrick, Frederick, Maryland

FACTORS AFFECTING POLYPEPTIDE PRODUCTION BY *BACILLUS ANTHRACIS*

Effect of CO_2

The stimulating effect of CO_2 or bicarbonate on capsule formation by *Bacillus anthracis* has been known for several years (Ivanovics, 1937; Sterne, 1937). Since most of the reports in the literature have been based on qualitative observations, we chose to do some quantitative studies in which the amount of glutamyl polypeptide was determined (Thorne, Gomez & Housewright, 1952; Thorne, Gomez, Blind & Housewright, 1953). The polypeptide was determined as the difference in the amount of glutamic acid present before and after acid hydrolysis. Typical results are shown in Table 1. For these studies a synthetic medium was used and the organisms were grown in Roux bottles containing 100 ml. of the agar medium. The results are reported as milligrams of soluble, bound glutamic acid present in the cell crop harvested from one Roux bottle. The virulent strain, 994, was grown in atmospheres of air, 25% N_2 in air, and 25% CO_2 in air on media adjusted to pH 6·5, 7·5 and 8·5. Little or no polypeptide was produced in the atmospheres of air or 25% N_2 at any of the pH levels tested. However, polypeptide was produced in the CO_2 atmosphere. The yield, which at pH 6·5 was very low, increased with rising pH to 21·3 mg. at pH 8·5. The nitrogen in this quantity of peptide represented over 7% of the total cell nitrogen. The increased yield at the higher pH is believed to be the result of greater CO_2 retention. Growth, as measured by the amount of total nitrogen, did not vary significantly at the three pH levels or in the three atmospheres.

Results of other experiments showed that while CO_2 is essential for polypeptide production by virulent strains, the avirulent, mucoid strains, M and HM, produce polypeptide in the absence of added bicarbonate or CO_2.

With respect to virulence and the CO_2 requirement for capsule formation (Sterne, 1937; Chu, 1952; Thorne *et al*. 1952) all strains of *Bacillus anthracis* that we have studied fall into one of three types. One type, which is the normal, virulent type, produces polypeptide when grown in the presence of bicarbonate or CO_2 but not when grown in air. A second type, which is avirulent, produces polypeptide when grown in air, and the addition of bicarbonate or CO_2 has little or no effect on the amount produced. A third type, which is also avirulent, does not produce polypeptide under any conditions of growth thus far tested.

Table 1. *Glutamyl polypeptide production by* Bacillus anthracis, *strain 994, in atmospheres of air,* N_2 *and* CO_2

pH of medium	Atmosphere	Growth as total nitrogen (mg.)	Peptide (soluble bound glutamic acid) (mg.)
6·5	Air	22·9	0
	25 % N_2 in air	22·6	0·8
	25 % CO_2 in air	26·3	1·4
7·5	Air	23·8	1·0
	25 % N_2 in air	23·2	0·3
	25 % CO_2 in air	24·3	9·2
8·5	Air	29·3	1·6
	25 % N_2 in air	24·7	1·9
	25 % CO_2 in air	28·3	21·3

Results are reported as milligrams of nitrogen and peptide present in the cell crop from one Roux bottle containing 100 ml. of agar medium.

These observations suggest a convenient method for determining whether a particular strain is potentially virulent. It has been our experience that cultures which produce mucoid colonies in air are avirulent; those that produce rough colonies in air and in CO_2 are avirulent; and those that produce rough colonies in air and smooth colonies in CO_2 are virulent. Our results of virulence tests with guinea-pigs have confirmed these observations. However, exceptions may occur and the method should probably be used only as a screening procedure until more cultures have been tested and the frequency of exceptions can be observed. Gladstone (1946) listed two strains that apparently produced capsules in CO_2 and were avirulent, and Sterne (1937) observed a variant which produced capsules in CO_2 but which apparently had lost its virulence for guinea-pigs. However, it was moderately virulent for mice.

The third type (rough in air and in CO_2) arises spontaneously from the virulent parent type and according to Chu (1952) the rate of mutation varies with different strains. On an agar plate inoculated with a virulent strain and incubated in CO_2, the colonies appear very mucoid, except that some of them have a rough outer edge. When transplants are made of the cells from the rough edge of a colony, they remain rough in both air and CO_2 and the organisms are avirulent. When transplants are made from the mucoid part of a colony they form rough colonies in air and mucoid colonies in CO_2 and the organisms are virulent.

Chu (1952) showed that the non-capsulated variant also occurs in cultures grown in the absence of serum or added bicarbonate or CO_2 and concluded that the dissociation is not induced by the presence of CO_2 or serum. He suggested that the presence of CO_2 or serum provides conditions favourable for capsule formation by those cells that are capable of doing so, which in consequence can be readily distinguished from the cells that are not able to produce capsules. He further suggested that the rapid outgrowth of the rough variants results from the fact that they grow in longer chains than capsulated cells and thus are able to grow beyond the mother colony into the medium where they have a better supply of nutrients.

Experiments in our laboratory indicate that CO_2 is selective for avirulent variants in liquid medium. Typical data are shown in Table 2. The organisms were grown with aeration in bottles containing a synthetic medium. The medium was a modification (Thorne *et al.* 1953) of that developed for *Bacillus anthracis* by Brewer, McCullough, Mills, Roessler, Herbst & Howe (1946). Various amounts of sodium bicarbonate were added and the bottles were aerated with a mixture of 30 % CO_2 in air. The organisms were counted by plating on agar containing bicarbonate and incubating in 50 % CO_2, so that the rough variants could be distinguished.

Less than 1 % of rough variants were present when bicarbonate was omitted or when a concentration of 0·2 % was added. But with higher concentrations of bicarbonate, 0·5 and 0·7 %, large numbers of the rough variants appeared, the higher percentage occurring with the higher concentration of bicarbonate. These data indicate that bicarbonate or some condition resulting from the presence of bicarbonate favours rough variants over the mucoid type. In a liquid culture both types of cells would have equal access to nutrients, and thus it is improbable that the availability of nutrients to the cells is a factor in causing the formation of rough variants. However, it may be that the capsule inhibits the diffusion of nutrients into the cell. Work on this problem is being continued in order to determine the nature of this selective action. One interesting observation is that the DL-erythro isomer of chloromycetin inhibits the formation of rough variants in CO_2 cultures.

The function of CO_2 or bicarbonate in polypeptide synthesis by the CO_2-requiring strains is not understood. In experiments with $^{14}CO_2$

in our laboratory large amounts of ^{14}C were incorporated into the α-carboxyl of the glutamic acid in the polypeptide. If CO_2 functioned only in the synthesis of glutamic acid, the addition of glutamic acid to the medium should relieve the requirement for CO_2. Although added glutamic acid did reduce the amount of $^{14}CO_2$ incorporated into polypeptide, CO_2 or bicarbonate was still necessary for polypeptide synthesis.

Table 2. *Effect of bicarbonate concentration on the occurrence of rough avirulent variants of* Bacillus anthracis, *M-36*

Age of culture (hr.)	NaHCO$_3$ added (%)	Organisms/ml.	Rough variant (%)
0	0	1.0×10^5	< 1.0
24	0	2.0×10^6	< 1.0
	0.2	2.4×10^7	< 1.0
	0.5	1.5×10^7	< 1.0
	0.7	6.8×10^6	53.3
48	0	6.4×10^7	< 1.0
	0.2	1.9×10^8	< 1.0
	0.5	1.4×10^8	2.0
	0.7	1.9×10^8	92.0
72	0	2.8×10^7	< 1.0
	0.2	2.8×10^7	< 1.0
	0.5	1.7×10^7	3.2
	0.7	1.9×10^7	93.6
96	0	2.1×10^7	< 1.0
	0.2	1.4×10^7	< 1.0
	0.5	5.2×10^6	46.4
	0.7	6.4×10^6	75.7

The organisms were grown in bottles of synthetic medium aerated with a mixture of 30 % CO_2 in air.

Effect of amino acids

The modified synthetic medium of Brewer (Thorne *et al.* 1953) contains seventeen amino acids. Only three of these are absolutely essential for growth of the virulent strains, 994 and M-36, and the capsulated avirulent strain M. They are leucine, valine and methionine. The organisms did not grow when any one of these was omitted from the medium. When each of the other amino acids was omitted, one at a time, there was little or no effect on growth. It was only when two or more were omitted that growth was reduced significantly. When each of the amino acids which were not required for growth was tested for effect on peptide synthesis, DL-isoleucine, DL-phenylalanine and L-glutamic acid were the only ones which affected peptide yields significantly.

Strains M-36 and 994 were tested in rubber-stoppered shaken flasks with bicarbonate added (Thorne *et al.* 1953), conditions which resulted in polypeptide formation. When isoleucine was omitted, there was poor utilization of glutamic acid and the peptide yield was low. When phenylalanine was omitted, free L-glutamic acid accumulated and there was little synthesis of peptide.

The results obtained when glutamic acid was omitted under these test conditions were variable. Although it was not essential for peptide production the addition of 50–100 μg./ml. resulted in earlier initiation of growth and more consistent results.

When strain M-36 was tested under more aerobic conditions, i.e. in bottles aerated with 30 % CO_2 in air, the results with isoleucine and glutamic acid were similar to those obtained in rubber-stoppered flasks. However, under these conditions the omission of phenylalanine did not affect the peptide yield.

Table 3. *Effect of isoleucine and phenylalanine on peptide production by strain M*

Amino-acid added		Peptide (soluble bound glutamic acid) (mg./ml.)
DL-phenylalanine (mg./ml.)	DL-isoleucine (mg./ml.)	
0·33	0	0·27
0·33	0·06	0·64
0·33	0·11	1·69
0·33	0·33	1·55
0·33	0·66	1·01
0·33	1·32	0·79
0	0·66	0
0·05	0·66	0·96
0·10	0·66	1·11
0·20	0·66	1·12
0·33	0·66	1·01

Organisms were grown in 500 ml. Erlenmeyer flasks containing 100 ml. of synthetic medium and incubated on a shaker for 70 hr.

Table 3 shows the effect of various concentrations of isoleucine and phenylalanine on peptide production by the avirulent strain, M, in cotton-plugged shaken flasks. The peptide yield was low when either amino acid was omitted, and the glutamic acid of the medium was not used.

The requirement of glutamic acid for peptide production was more pronounced for strain M than for the CO_2-requiring strains, 994 and M-36. D-Glutamic acid did not replace the L-isomer.

PEPTIDE PRODUCTION BY *BACILLUS SUBTILIS*

Some strains of other aerobic spore-formers produce glutamyl polypeptide similar to that produced by *Bacillus anthracis* (Ivanovics & Bruckner, 1937; Ivanovics & Erdos, 1937; Bovarnick, 1942). While the peptide of the latter organism is contained to a large extent in a capsule and is released into the medium upon autoclaving or upon ageing and autolysis of the cells (Thorne *et al.* 1953), that produced by *B. subtilis* occurs free in the medium.

Studies with growing cultures

Bovarnick (1942) studied the production of polypeptide by *Bacillus subtilis*. He used Sauton's medium and incubated the cultures without shaking. Yields of approximately 1·5 mg. of peptide per ml. were obtained. Thorne, Gomez, Noyes & Housewright (1954) investigated various factors affecting the production of peptide by *B. subtilis* in both static and shaken cultures. Yields of 2–3 mg./ml. were produced on modified Sauton's medium in static cultures. Highest yields, in excess of 15 mg./ml., were obtained when the organism was grown in shaken flasks on the following medium (values are in g./l.): glycerol, 80; citric acid, 12; L-glutamic acid, 20; NH_4Cl, 7·0; $MgSO_4$, 0·5; $FeCl_3.6H_2O$, 0·04; K_2HPO_4, 0·5; pH adjusted to 7·4 with NaOH.

During our studies on factors affecting peptide production by *B. subtilis* we observed that cultures which were maintained on nutrient agar slants gradually lost their ability to produce high yields of peptide. When such cultures were streaked on agar plates of Sauton's medium, two types of colonies were observed. One type was rough and the other was mucoid. Colonies which appeared most mucoid were selected and streaked on fresh agar to give isolated colonies. This process was repeated several times and the final isolate produced much higher peptide yields than the original culture. This procedure of isolation and selection of mucoid colonies was repeated with other cultures and similar results were obtained. As a result of these observations we adopted the practice of keeping reference stocks of spores on soil.

Peptide synthesis by cell-free preparations

In experiments on polypeptide production by growing cultures of *Bacillus subtilis*, Thorne *et al.* (1954) observed that after the peptide yield reached a maximum, it gradually decreased and the amount of free glutamic acid increased. This suggested the presence of an enzyme which hydrolysed the peptide to glutamic acid, and it was found that culture filtrates were active in hydrolysing peptide from both *B. subtilis* and *B. anthracis*. Active preparations were obtained by saturating culture filtrates with ammonium sulphate. The precipitate was dialysed and used as such or concentrated further by ammonium sulphate and isoelectric precipitation. We have observed recently that sonic extracts of *B. subtilis* also contain the enzyme, but culture filtrates yield more active preparations.

The same enzyme preparations that hydrolysed the polypeptide also catalysed the synthesis of glutamyl peptides by a transamidation reaction (Williams & Thorne, 1954a; Williams, Litwin & Thorne, 1955). The γ-glutamyl radical was transferred from glutamine to glutamic acid to form γ-glutamyl-glutamic acid. Table 4 compares the isomers of glutamine and glutamic acid as precursors of the dipeptide (Williams & Thorne, 1954a). Dipeptide was synthesized when either L- or D-glutamine was the only added substrate. D-Glutamic acid stimulated

Table 4. *Synthesis of glutamyl dipeptide from the isomers of glutamine and glutamic acid*

Optical isomers of substrate		Dipeptide formed (μM/ml.)
Glutamine	Glutamic acid	
L-	—	2·6
L-	D-	6·1
L-	L-	2·1
D-	—	3·3
D-	D-	3·4
D-	L-	0·5

Each tube contained 40 μM of glutamine, 30 μM of glutamic acid, 20 μM Tris buffer, and 0·12 mg. of protein in a total volume of 0·5 ml. The final pH was 8·8, and the tubes were incubated at 36·5° for 2 hr.

peptide synthesis from L-glutamine but had no effect on the synthesis from D-glutamine. L-Glutamic acid had little effect on the synthesis of dipeptide from L-glutamine, but it inhibited the reaction with D-glutamine. Thus both L- and D-glutamine acted as substrates for the enzyme, but the most active synthesis occurred when a combination of L-glutamine and D-glutamic acid was used. The optimum pH for the reaction between L-glutamine and D-glutamic acid was 8·8 and no added cofactors were required. No peptide was synthesized when either L- or D-glutamic acid was the only added substrate.

When reaction mixtures containing enzyme, L-glutamine and D-glutamic acid were allowed to incubate for several hours, other peptides of chain length greater than that of the dipeptide were synthesized. Chromatographic evidence was obtained for tri-, tetra- and penta-peptides and for even longer peptides that did not move on chromatograms.

In addition to the transamidation reaction just described, enzyme preparations also catalysed a transpeptidation reaction with γ-D-glutamyl-D-glutamic acid as the substrate (Williams & Thorne, 1954*b*). With appropriate substrate concentrations and short incubation periods, free glutamic acid and a tripeptide of glutamic acid were formed in equimolar quantities at equal rates. With lower substrate concentrations and longer incubation times, more glutamic acid than tripeptide was formed, indicating that hydrolysis of the peptide occurred under those conditions.

In experiments to determine whether peptide chains longer than three glutamic acid residues could be formed from the dipeptide as substrate, high concentrations of enzyme and substrate were incubated for several hours. Paper chromatograms of reaction mixtures revealed spots of higher peptides similar to those found in the experiments with L-glutamine and D-glutamic acid.

Thus it appears that the polypeptide produced by growing cultures of *Bacillus subtilis* may be synthesized by a combination of transamidation and transpeptidation reactions similar to those catalysed by the cell-free preparations. Such an enzyme system has not yet been demonstrated in cells or culture filtrates of *B. anthracis*.

SYNTHESIS OF D-GLUTAMIC ACID BY *BACILLUS ANTHRACIS* AND *B. SUBTILIS*

In attacking the problem of the mechanism of D-glutamyl polypeptide synthesis, one of the questions concerned the mechanism of synthesis of D-glutamic acid. This question was answered when Thorne, Gomez & Housewright (1955) showed that cell-free extracts of *Bacillus subtilis* catalysed a series of transamination reactions involving D-amino acids.

By ammonium sulphate fractionation and dialysis, transaminase preparations which were specific for D-amino acids were obtained from sonic extracts. With purified preparations, D-glutamic acid was synthesized by transamination between α-ketoglutaric acid and D-aspartic acid, D-alanine, D-methionine and D-serine. The L-isomers of aspartic acid, methionine and serine were inactive. Extracts contained an alanine racemase which converted both isomers to the DL-mixture. Since the racemase was present even in purified preparations, both L- and D-alanine appeared to be active in transaminating with α-ketoglutaric acid. However, the resulting glutamic acid was the D-isomer, indicating that only the D-isomer of alanine actually transaminated.

With the purified preparations, D-aspartic acid and D-glutamic acid transaminated with pyruvic acid to form alanine. The L-isomers were inactive. A balance was obtained between the reactants and products in the reaction between D-glutamic acid and pyruvic acid indicating that the reaction was a true transamination reaction.

Sonic extracts of *Bacillus anthracis* also catalysed transaminations of D-amino acids (Thorne & Molnar, 1955) and some of the reactions were different from those described for *B. subtilis*. Of the amino acids tested, the only D-isomer which transaminated with α-ketoglutaric acid to form D-glutamic acid was that of alanine. Several L-isomers, i.e. alanine, aspartic acid, histidine, isoleucine, leucine, methionine, phenylalanine and tryptophan, transaminated with α-ketoglutaric acid. On the other hand, the D-isomers of phenylalanine, glutamic acid, tryptophan, methionine, histidine, ethionine and leucine transaminated with pyruvic acid to form alanine. The only L-isomer that was found to transaminate with pyruvic acid was L-glutamic acid. Thus, with the exceptions of glutamic acid and alanine, only the L-isomers transaminated with α-ketoglutaric acid and only the D-isomers transaminated with pyruvic acid. One of the most active reactions catalysed by preparations from *B. anthracis* was that between D-phenylalanine and pyruvic acid to produce alanine and phenylpyruvic acid. A transaminase balance was obtained for this reaction indicating that it was a true transamination reaction.

This reaction is particularly interesting since earlier studies, as described above, indicate that phenylalanine is connected in some way with polypeptide synthesis by *Bacillus anthracis*. In those studies the L-isomer was active. It should be possible for the organism to convert one isomer of phenylalanine to a mixture of the D- and L-isomers by a series of reactions involving transamination and alanine racemization. Extracts of *B. anthracis*, like those of *B. subtilis*, catalysed the racemization of alanine. Thus the following reactions, all of which have been shown to occur in *B. anthracis* extracts, would result in the conversion of L-phenylalanine to a mixture of the two isomers:

(1) L-phenylalanine + α-ketoglutaric acid ⇌ phenylpyruvic acid + L-glutamic acid,

(2) L-glutamic acid + pyruvic acid ⇌ α-ketoglutaric acid + L-alanine,

(3) L-alanine → DL-alanine,

(4) D-alanine + phenylpyruvic acid ⇌ pyruvic acid + D-phenylalanine.

The optimum medium for production of glutamyl polypeptide by growing cultures of *Bacillus subtilis* contains a large amount of L-glutamic acid, but the glutamic acid of the polypeptide contains a large proportion of the D-isomer. Bovarnick (1942), studying peptide formation by *B. subtilis* and using isotopically labelled DL-glutamic acid, concluded that the glutamic acid molecule skeleton could be used by the organism as a substrate for the formation of peptide and that the reaction mechanism involved α-iminoglutaric acid or a derivative. Kogl, Emmelot & den Boer (1954) also used isotopically labelled D- and L-glutamic acids as substrates for polypeptide synthesis by *B. subtilis*. Their results indicated that both isomers were incorporated into the polypeptide as D-glutamic acid, and they postulated the presence of a glutamic acid racemase to explain their findings, i.e. the apparent conversion of L-glutamic acid to the D-isomer. Their preliminary attempts to demonstrate a glutamic acid racemase were unsuccessful. We have also made several unsuccessful attempts to demonstrate glutamic acid racemase in *B. subtilis* and *B. anthracis*. However, the finding of alanine racemase and D-amino acid transaminations in these organisms suggests that D-glutamic acid is probably synthesized by transamination and that a glutamic acid racemase is not necessarily involved. The following reactions, which have been demonstrated in extracts of *B. subtilis* and *B. anthracis* (Thorne *et al.* 1955; Thorne & Molnar, 1955) could result in the indirect conversion of L-glutamic acid to the D-isomer:

(1) L-glutamic acid + pyruvic acid $\rightleftharpoons$ α-ketoglutaric acid + L-alanine,

(2) L-alanine → DL-alanine,

(3) D-alanine + α-ketoglutaric acid $\rightleftharpoons$ pyruvic acid + D-glutamic acid.

STRUCTURE OF GLUTAMYL POLYPEPTIDE

Bricas & Fromageot (1953) reviewed the literature pertaining to the structure and properties of the glutamyl polypeptide of *Bacillus anthracis* and related organisms. Although there is no doubt that glutamic acid is the only amino acid released upon acid hydrolysis of the peptide, there are conflicting reports as to the configuration of the glutamic acid. Bruckner & Ivanovics (1937) and Ivanovics & Bruckner (1937) showed that D-glutamic acid was produced upon acid hydrolysis of polypeptide from *B. anthracis* and *B. mesentericus*. Bovarnick (1942) concluded that polypeptide from *B. subtilis* was composed solely of D-glutamic acid, but Watson, Cromartie, Bloom, Heckly, McGhee & Weissman (1947) found that only 85 % of the glutamic acid from polypeptide produced by *B. subtilis* was the D-isomer. The peptide preparations from *B. anthracis* studied by Hanby & Rydon (1946) contained only D-glutamic acid.

Results from our laboratory (Thorne *et al.* 1954) showed that different preparations of polypeptide produced by the same strain of *Bacillus subtilis* under different conditions varied in their content of D- and L-glutamic acid. The amount of D-glutamic acid in peptide samples varied from 20 to 80% of the total, depending on cultural conditions. Glutamic acid from peptide produced in static cultures usually contained 70–80% of the D-isomer, while that from peptide produced in shaken flasks usually contained 40–50%. This is in contrast to our results obtained with *B. anthracis*. We have not found any significant amount of L-glutamic acid in peptide preparations from this organism. Table 5 summarizes the analytical data on some of our peptide preparations from the two organisms.

Table 5. *Analysis of glutamyl polypeptide preparations*

| | | | | Glutamic acid | |
Prep. no.	Source	Form of peptide	Nitrogen (%)	Total (%)	L-isomer (% of total)
70–1	*B. subtilis*, 9945	Sodium salt	9·40	96·2	54·9
70–2	*B. subtilis*, 9945	Free acid	10·81	113·0	53·4
74	*B. anthracis*, M-36	Sodium salt	9·25	101·0	0·6
75	*B. anthracis*, M-36	Free acid	10·95	112·8	1·4
Theoretical values:					
Sodium salt $(C_5H_6O_3NNa)\infty$			9·27	97·4	—
Free acid $(C_5H_7O_3N)\infty$			10·85	113·9	—

Bovarnick (1942) concluded that the polypeptide of *Bacillus subtilis* was made up of D-glutamic acid residues connected in γ-peptide linkages. His conclusion was based on the observation that the polypeptide did not racemize in strongly alkaline solution at room temperature. Hanby & Rydon (1946) concluded that the polypeptide of *B. anthracis* was made up of α-peptide chains of 50–100 D-glutamic acid residues joined together by γ-peptide chains. This conclusion was based on the action of nitrous acid on peptides and also on the results of electrometric titrations.

Bruckner, Kovacs & Denes (1953) concluded that the polypeptides of *Bacillus anthracis* and *B. subtilis* were made up predominantly of γ-glutamyl links and that few, if any, α-glutamyl links were present. Their conclusions were based on the observation that in the acid hydrolysate of the polyamine derivative, prepared from the polypeptide by Curtius degradation of the polyhydrazide or by Hofmann degradation of the polyamide, β-formylpropionic acid appeared and no α,γ-diaminobutyric acid could be detected. In experiments with synthetic α-polyglutamic acid, α,γ-diaminobutyric acid was produced on acid hydrolysis of the degradation product.

Waley (1955) prepared synthetic poly(γ-L-glutamyl)-L-glutamic acid and compared its properties with those of polypeptides isolated from

Bacillus anthracis and *B. licheniformis*. He concluded that the naturally occurring peptides were also γ-linked.

Experiments in our laboratory with the polypeptide-hydrolysing enzyme from *Bacillus subtilis* show that it will hydrolyse synthetic γ-D-glutamyl-D-glutamic acid, γ-L-glutamyl-L-glutamic acid and α-L-glutamyl-L-glutamic acid. It does not hydrolyse α-D-glutamyl-D-glutamic acid. Since enzyme preparations hydrolyse the polypeptide of *B. anthracis* and since this polypeptide contains only D-glutamic acid, probably γ-links occur in the peptide. Experiments are now under way to determine whether the polypeptide can be hydrolysed completely by the enzyme. Complete hydrolysis to free glutamic acid would indicate that no α-links were present.

REFERENCES

BOVARNICK, M. (1942). The formation of extracellular D(−) glutamic acid polypeptide by *Bacillus subtilis*. *J. biol. Chem.* **145**, 415.

BREWER, C. R., McCULLOUGH, W. G., MILLS, R. C., ROESSLER, W. G., HERBST, E. J. & HOWE, A. F. (1946). Studies on the nutritional requirements of *Bacillus anthracis*. *Arch. Biochem.* **10**, 65.

BRICAS, E. & FROMAGEOT, C. (1953). *Advances in Protein Chemistry*, vol. **8**. New York: Academic Press.

BRUCKNER, V. & IVANOVICS, G. (1937). Über das natürliche Vorkommen und über eine einfache biologische Gewinnungsart der L(−)-Glutaminsäure. *Hoppe-Seyl. Z.* **247**, 281.

BRUCKNER, V., KOVACS, J. & DENES, G. (1953). Structure of poly-D-glutamic acid isolated from capsulated strains of *B. anthracis*. *Nature, Lond.*, **172**, 508.

CHU, H. P. (1952). Variation of *Bacillus anthracis* with special reference to the non-capsulated avirulent variant. *J. Hyg., Camb.*, **50**, 433.

GLADSTONE, G. P. (1946). Immunity to anthrax: protective antigen present in cell-free culture filtrates. *Brit. J. exp. Path.* **27**, 394.

HANBY, W. E. & RYDON, H. N. (1946). The capsular substance of *Bacillus anthracis*. *Biochem. J.* **40**, 297.

IVANOVICS, G. (1937). Unter welchen Bedingungen werden bei der Nährboden-züchtung der Milzbrandbazillen Kapseln gebildet? *Zbl. Bakt.* Abt. I, Orig., **138**, 449.

IVANOVICS, G. & BRUCKNER, V. (1937). Die chemische Struktur der Kapselsubstanz des Milzbrandbazillus und der serologisch identischen spezifischen Substanz des *Bacillus mesentericus*. *Z. ImmunForsch.* **90**, 304.

IVANOVICS, G. & ERDOS, L. (1937). Ein Beitrag zum Wesen der Kapselsubstanz des Milzbrandbazillus. *Z. ImmunForsch.* **90**, 5.

KOGL, F., EMMELOT, P. & DEN BOER, D. H. W. (1954). Über die Biosynthese der Poly-D-glutaminsäure von *Bacillus subtilis*. II. Die Umsetzung der L-Glutamin-säure in den D-Glutaminsäure-Baustein. *Liebigs Ann.* **589**, 15.

STERNE, M. (1937). Variation in *Bacillus anthracis*. *Onderstepoort J. vet. Sci.* **8**, 271.

THORNE, C. B., GOMEZ, C. G. & HOUSEWRIGHT, R. D. (1952). Synthesis of glutamic acid and glutamyl polypeptide by *Bacillus anthracis*. II. The effect of carbon dioxide on peptide production on solid media. *J. Bact.* **63**, 363.

THORNE, C. B., GOMEZ, C. G., BLIND, G. R. & HOUSEWRIGHT, R. D. (1953). Synthesis of glutamic acid and glutamyl polypeptide by *Bacillus anthracis*. III. Factors affecting peptide production in synthetic liquid media. *J. Bact.* **65**, 472.

THORNE, C. B., GOMEZ, C. G., NOYES, H. E. & HOUSEWRIGHT, R. D. (1954). Production of glutamyl polypeptide by *Bacillus subtilis. J. Bact.* **68**, 307.

THORNE, C. B., GOMEZ, C. G. & HOUSEWRIGHT, R. D. (1955). Transamination of D-amino acids by *Bacillus subtilis. J. Bact.* **69**, 357.

THORNE, C. B. & MOLNAR, D. M. (1955). D-Amino acid transaminations in *Bacillus anthracis. J. Bact.* **70**, 420.

WALEY, S. G. (1955). The structure of bacterial polyglutamic acid. *J. Chem. Soc.* p. 517.

WATSON, D. W., CROMARTIE, W. J., BLOOM, W. L., HECKLY, R. J., McGHEE, W. J. & WEISSMAN, N. (1947). Studies on infection with *Bacillus anthracis*. V. The isolation of an inflammatory factor from crude extracts of lesions of *B. anthracis* infection and its biological and chemical relationship to glutamyl polypeptide. *J. infect. Dis.* **80**, 121.

WILLIAMS, W. J. & THORNE, C. B. (1954*a*). Biosynthesis of glutamyl peptides from glutamine by a transfer reaction. *J. biol. Chem.* **210**, 203.

WILLIAMS, W. J. & THORNE, C. B. (1954*b*). Elongation of γ-D-glutamic acid peptide chains by a transfer reaction. *J. biol. Chem.* **211**, 631.

WILLIAMS, W. J., LITWIN, J. & THORNE, C. B. (1955). Further studies on the biosynthesis of γ-glutamyl peptides by transfer reactions. *J. biol. Chem.* **212**, 427.

BACTERIAL CELL WALLS

M. R. J. SALTON

Department of Biochemistry, University of Cambridge

INTRODUCTION

The discovery that some micro-organisms could synthesize their proto-plasm from simple constituents, such as mineral salts and carbon dioxide (Winogradsky, 1887), misled some microbiologists into believing that this apparent biochemical simplicity was synonymous with structural simplicity. However, cytological studies, investigations of staining reactions and plasmolysis experiments all pointed to the structural complexity of the minute bacterial cell. Cytologists are now in general agreement as to the main structural features of micro-organisms. Most bacteria possess a rigid cell wall of different properties from the enclosed cytoplasm, and in this respect they closely resemble cells of higher plants.

The existence of a well-defined cell wall in bacteria was suspected by Cohn (1875). He believed that the resistance of bacteria to dissolution by alkalis and acids was due not to the nature of the cell protoplasm, but to a 'membrane' similar in properties to that of fungus mycelium. From the early cytological investigations it became apparent that the surface layers of bacteria could be differentiated into capsules and slime layers and cell wall. By analogy with the structure of higher organisms it has been held that the bacterial cell possesses a membrane which may be differentiated from its external neighbour, the cell wall, and from the inner protoplasm (Fischer, 1895; Knaysi, 1938). However, until recently the proof for the existence of a structural entity, the cytoplasmic membrane, has been less satisfactory. More convincing evidence for the differentiation of the cytoplasmic membrane from the wall and inner protoplasm has been provided by the excellent cytological study of Robinow & Murray (1953) and the exciting isolation of protoplasts by Weibull (1953).

The relationship of the surface layers (capsule, cell wall and cytoplasmic membrane) to the morphological integrity of the bacterial cell has become amenable to direct investigation with specific enzyme systems. Thus it has been possible to remove the type III pneumococcus polysaccharide by enzymic digestion (Avery & Dubos, 1931) and the M-protein antigen from haemolytic streptococci by treatment with trypsin (Lancefield, 1943) without affecting the viability of the organisms. It is clear, then, that certain superficial layers may be removed enzymically without any radical structural alteration of the organism. The dissolution of the cell wall of the rod-shaped *Bacillus megaterium* by treatment with lysozyme in 0·2 M-sucrose in 0·03 M-phosphate (Weibull, 1953) is accompanied by a transformation to spherical protoplasts. This provided further evidence for the general belief that a rigid outer wall is the structural component which circumscribes the protoplast to the characteristic shape of the cell wall.

Although the earlier cytological investigations provided adequate evidence for the existence of a rigid cell-wall structure in most 'true bacteria', a precise definition of its thickness, general properties and chemical constitution presented certain difficulties. It was generally assumed that the material left after extraction of bacteria with alkali represented the resistant cell walls. Such residues did indeed possess the typical outline of the extracted cells (Vincenzi, 1887), but there was rarely sufficient evidence to suggest complete removal of intracellular components. The limits of resolution imposed by the light microscope presented the main difficulty—layers of alkali-resistant material or fine particles would have probably escaped detection, especially if there were no staining reactions for their differentiation from the wall. The main advances in the problem of isolating the cell wall as a single morphological entity, uncontaminated by cytoplasmic materials, had to await the development of the electron microscope with its enhanced powers of resolution.

ISOLATION OF BACTERIAL CELL WALLS

Early methods for the isolation of what were assumed to be the cell-wall structures were based on the extraction of organisms with alkali. As early as 1887 Vincenzi isolated the wall ('Hülle der Zellen') of *Bacillus subtilis* by extraction with 0·5 % NaOH and treatment with 'synthetic gastric juice'. From Vincenzi's description of the residues it is evident that they corresponded closely to cell-wall material, but it is difficult to assess the extent of degradation that may have resulted from this method of isolation. We now know that the residues of alkali-extracted cells differ markedly in appearance in the electron microscope from the walls isolated by other methods (Salton & Horne, 1951*b*) and that some degradation of walls may occur on treatment with NaOH (Salton, 1952*a*).

One of the obvious methods which could have avoided chemical alteration of the walls was, of course, the mechanical disintegration of microbial cells. Such methods are by no means recent, as Barnard & Hewlett in 1911 described a specially constructed apparatus in which bacteria and yeast were disintegrated. They showed concomitant loss of viability and staining; but, in the smears of disrupted yeast, the thick cell walls were clearly visible. The nature of the cell debris from the disintegrated bacteria was not apparent.

Electron microscopy of mechanically disintegrated bacteria

Mudd & Lackman (1941) and Mudd, Polevitzky, Anderson & Chambers (1941) were the first to examine disintegrated bacteria in the electron microscope. They showed that sonically disrupted streptococcal cells and cells of several *Bacillus* spp. lost much of their electron-dense protoplasmic material, and as a result, the rigid cell-wall structures were revealed.

As long ago as 1901, MacFadyen & Rowland used agitation with fine sand as a method of disintegrating the typhoid bacillus. Refinements of such techniques have been made by King & Alexander (1948), using minute glass beads of fairly uniform dimensions. Dawson (1949) showed that *Staphylococcus aureus* could be disintegrated by shaking with glass beads in the Mickle (1948) tissue disintegrator. By centrifugation of the broken cells at 8000 r.p.m., Dawson separated the heavier unbroken cells and cell walls from the cytoplasmic components. Examination of such preparations in the electron microscope revealed the separation of the rigid staphylococcal walls from intracellular cytoplasmic material.

In order to obtain isolated cell walls for chemical characterization, Salton & Horne (1951 b) used essentially the same method as that described by Dawson (1949) for the disintegration of *Streptococcus faecalis*, *Escherichia coli* and *Salmonella pullorum*. For the chemical analysis of the cell walls it was obviously necessary to reduce to a minimum the contamination of the wall preparations with unbroken bacteria and cytoplasmic constituents. By centrifuging first at 2000–3000 r.p.m. for 10–15 min. it was possible to sediment any intact bacteria and coarse debris passing through the sintered-glass filter used for removal of the glass beads. By differential centrifugation followed by careful washing of the walls with distilled water, homogeneous cell-wall preparations relatively free of electron-dense, cytoplasmic material could be obtained (Salton & Horne, 1951 b). With some of the Gram-negative bacteria the removal of contaminating cytoplasmic material from the walls was rather more difficult, but it could be achieved by carefully washing the cell-wall deposits with suitable buffers or with solutions of M-NaCl. Washing the crude cell-wall deposits with M-NaCl has been adopted in the routine preparation of cell walls of both Gram-positive and Gram-negative bacteria (Salton, 1952a, 1953a).

Although it is now well established that bacterial walls are not attacked by enzymes such as trypsin, ribonuclease and deoxyribonuclease, I have in general avoided the use of these enzymes for the 'cleaning up' of the cell wall preparations. The main arguments against their unrestricted use are that with enzymes such as trypsin, the wall preparations may be contaminated with insoluble plasteins and that crude enzymes may conceivably contain small amounts of wall-degrading enzymes. These disadvantages may be outweighed by the efficiency of removal of electron-dense cytoplasmic materials by enzymic treatment of walls of Gram-negative bacteria in particular.

In addition to methods using agitation with glass beads for the disintegration of bacteria, the walls of some organisms may be isolated equally well by using sonic and supersonic disruption. However, some organisms, in particular staphylococci, streptococci and *Micrococcus lysodeikticus*, could not be disintegrated sufficiently even by prolonged exposure in the Raytheon 9Kc magnetostriction oscillator. Many variations of mechanical rupture of cells may be used, and McCarty (1952b) isolated the walls of group A streptococci by grinding in a ball-mill. McCarty (1952b) found that much of the protein and nucleic acid remained in the insoluble residue but could be removed by trypsin and ribonuclease; after such treatment the wall residues were examined in the electron microscope and found to be relatively free of intracellular materials.

Other methods of isolation

Apart from the mechanical methods of disrupting bacteria for the isolation of walls, several other procedures have been developed. Weidel (1950, 1951) isolated the walls of *Escherichia coli* by autolysing cells under toluene and digesting with trypsin. The walls so isolated were still capable of adsorbing and inactivating bacteriophages. Although the uniformity of the wall material was confirmed by examination in the ultracentrifuge and by electrophoresis (Weidel, 1950), some trypsin-resistant residue could be seen in electron micrographs of the walls.

The observation that the walls of certain Gram-negative bacteria were ruptured when cell suspensions were squirted into distilled water at temperatures of 70–100° (Salton & Horne, 1951a) provided the basis for another method of isolating the walls. The disrupted walls could be separated from the coagulated protoplast by shaking and the walls isolated by differential centrifugation (Salton & Horne, 1951*b*). Owing to the small yields of cell-wall material and the probability that the heat treatment may have altered some of the cell-wall components, this method was considered less satisfactory than the mechanical disintegration procedure (Salton, 1953*a*).

Modification of the wall by isolation procedure

It is of course more difficult to decide whether the isolation procedures involving mechanical disintegration result in any chemical or biochemical modification of wall components. In general it appears that they do not; the wall material isolated by heat-treatment rupture, on the other hand, did show some evidence of chemical alteration (Salton, 1953*a*). However, with mechanically broken cells the presence of intracellular enzymes that may degrade some components of the walls seems a greater danger. In the intact organism such an enzyme may be kept away from its substrate by the organized nature of the cell, but on disintegration and release of the intracellular components the enzyme may be capable of manifesting its activity.

The isolated wall suspensions of some organisms remain stable for considerable periods of storage at *c.* 4° (Salton, 1952*b*). However, with incompletely washed cell-wall suspensions of *Staphylococcus aureus* substantial decreases in turbidity have been observed on storage with chloroform for up to 4 weeks at 4°, and it seems reasonable to suspect that the dissolution of the walls would be the result of contamination with a cell-wall degrading enzyme from the disintegrated staphylococci (Salton, unpublished observation). This suggestion is strengthened by the existence of the 'staphylolytique' systems established by Welsch & Salmon (1950).

Homogeneity of cell-wall preparations

The homogeneity or freedom of the isolated walls from contaminating materials is not easy to define quantitatively. Such a difficulty is inherent in any method of isolation involving mechanical disintegration and differential centrifugation. The basic criterion for homogeneity of the isolated walls is the absence of cytoplasmic contamination as determined by examination in the electron microscope. This is not an entirely satisfactory criterion and certainly not beyond criticism. However, despite these difficulties, by careful standardization of the disintegration in the Mickle (using an equal volume of beads and bacterial suspension containing 10–15 mg. dry-weight bacteria/ml.) and by washing cell-wall deposits with M-NaCl, it is possible to obtain cell-wall preparations free from electron-dense cytoplasmic particles, nucleic acid, intracellular pigments, etc.

The homogeneity of wall preparations isolated from *Micrococcus lysodeikticus* was determined by dissolving the walls with lysozyme and weighing the lysozyme-insoluble residues after sedimentation (10,000 r.p.m. for 30 min.). The lysozyme-insoluble residue accounted for only 0·8 % of the weight of the isolated wall preparation. Similar results were obtained with walls of *Sarcina lutea* and *Bacillus megaterium* (both lysozyme-sensitive), showing that contamination with insoluble material can be as low as 1 %. Although such determinations are likely to be underestimations, since any intact lysozyme-sensitive bacteria would be dissolved, they do give an approximation to the homogeneity that can be obtained.

Other criteria such as the amount of ash or contamination with known intracellular enzymes and nucleic acid could also be used. The ash values in general should correspond fairly well to the P contents (Salton, 1952a); high values would perhaps indicate contamination with glass fragments.

GENERAL PROPERTIES OF THE CELL WALL

Contribution of the wall to the weight of the bacterial cell

By direct isolation of the cell walls of *Staphylococcus aureus*, Cooper, Rowley & Dawson (1949) found that the walls accounted for 20 % of the dry weight of the organism. This value was confirmed by Mitchell & Moyle (1951). The cell walls of a number of Gram-positive organisms also contribute approximately 20 % to the dry weight of the bacteria and in some instances the wall of *Micrococcus lysodeikticus* may account for as much as 25–30 % of the dry bacterial substance (Salton, unpublished observations).

The insoluble cell-wall residues studied by Holdsworth (1952a) formed 45 % of the dry weight of the *Corynebacterium diphtheriae* cell. Fernell & King (1953) investigated the insoluble residues of a number of Gram-positive and Gram-negative bacteria, and the weights of insoluble fractions represented considerably higher fractions of the dry weights of the whole organisms. The insoluble residue of *Pseudomonas aeruginosa* accounted for 76–78 % of the dry weight of the whole organism. It seems doubtful whether these residues could have been solely cell-wall material.

The thinner walls of the Gram-negative organisms probably account for less than 20 % of the dry weight of the organism.

Thickness and rigidity

By measuring the length of the shadow cast by *Staphylococcus aureus* cell wall, Dawson (1949) estimated its thickness to be 15–20 mμ. Similar values have been obtained for the thickness of the walls of *Streptococcus faecalis*; electron micrographs of the walls of the Gram-negative bacteria *Escherichia coli* and *Salmonella pullorum* (Salton & Horne, 1951*b*), indicate that they are rather thinner, being of the order of 10–15 mμ. Birch-Andersen, Maaløe & Sjöstrand (1953), studying thin sections of *Escherichia coli*, reported a 'membrane' thickness of about 10 mμ. The thickness of the walls of *Mycobacterium tuberculosis* was approximately 23 mμ (Knaysi, Hillier & Fabricant, 1950).

Although the bacterial wall forms a continuous layer of fairly uniform thickness around the cell, there is some evidence from thin sections (Chapman & Hillier, 1953) and from examination of walls prepared for electron microscopy by freeze-drying (Salton & Williams, 1954) that the outer wall surface has a much rougher texture than that of the inner surface of the wall. Similar observations have been reported with walls of *Bacillus subtilis* (Yoshida, Fukuya, Kakutani, Tanaka, Tegawa & Hashimoto, 1954).

When cell-wall suspensions are dried in air on the supporting film for examination in the electron microscope, the walls appear as flat collapsed sacs. Such a collapsed appearance is undoubtedly due to the surface-tension forces exerted during the drying of the specimens for electron microscopy. Williams (1953) developed a freeze-drying method for the preservation of the structure of biological materials during preparation for electron microscopy, and when isolated bacterial walls were examined in this way the rigid nature of these structures was evident (Salton & Williams, 1954). Instead of showing a collapsed sac-like appearance, the walls of a number of rod-shaped bacteria were typically cylindrical. There is little doubt now that the walls of bacteria possess sufficient mechanical rigidity to confer on an organism its characteristic shape. The change from a typical rod shape to the spherical protoplast on dissolution of the wall of *Bacillus megaterium* by treatment with lysozyme in sucrose (Weibull, 1953) provided another manifestation of the rigid nature of the outer wall.

It is clear that the walls of some bacteria must be sufficiently rigid to maintain the structural integrity of the cell against high internal osmotic pressures. Mitchell & Moyle (1955) have estimated that intracellular constituents of *Staphylococcus aureus* exert osmotic pressures of 15–20 atmospheres. There are, however, many organisms that undergo osmotic lysis. Salton (unpublished observations) found that *Vibrio metchnikovii* was rapidly lysed on suspension in distilled water, and ultra-centrifugal analysis showed the liberation of the characteristic intracellular components with sedimentation constants of 45S, 29S and 5·2S; similar components were obtained by sonic disintegration or alumina grinding of other microorganisms (Schachman, Pardee & Stanier, 1952). Osmotic lysis of luminescent and halophilic organisms provides further instances of the susceptibility of the walls of some bacteria to osmotic damage. It seems that many of the organisms that exhibit this osmotic fragility belong to the Gram-negative group of bacteria. It is conceivable that this fragility may be correlated with the thinner nature of the walls of these organisms, different chemical constitution and the presence of a more complex wall structure containing spherical macromolecules.

Macromolecular structure in cell walls

Apart from showing the presence of bands and equatorial rings corresponding to the zones of cellular division and cross-wall formation (Dawson & Stern, 1954), the walls of many organisms have given no evidence of the presence of a fine structure. The presence of micromolecular components in a bacterial wall was first shown in the beautiful electron micrographs of the wall of a *Spirillum* sp. investigated by Houwink (1953). He found that the wall of this organism was composed of at least two layers, and where the inner layer had come off spherical macromolecules with a diameter of 120–140 A. and arranged in a hexagonal pattern were revealed.

Spherical macromolecules of about 100 A. diameter (also showing hexagonal packing) have been detected in the cell wall of *Rhodospirillum rubrum* (Salton & Williams, 1954). As shown in Pl. 1, fig. 1, the macromolecules are visible in the isolated wall and they show through the outer wall surface. The wall of *R. rubrum* is also composed of at least two layers as illustrated in the wall fragments in Pl. 1, fig. 2. With the wall of this organism it is rather more difficult to decide whether the macromolecular layer is inside or outside.

The presence of macromolecular components in *Spirillum serpens* wall (Houwink, 1953) has been confirmed by Horne (personal communication) and the spheres have a diameter of about 50 A. with a spacing of 80 A. between the centres of the macromolecules.

A different type of microstructure has been observed in the wall of an unidentified Gram-positive organism by Labaw & Mosley (1954). The spherical macromolecules, of about 115 A. diameter, were arranged in a regular rectangular fashion in the wall of this organism.

So far Houwink (1953) and Salton & Williams (1954) have been unable to confirm Knaysi's suggestion (1951) of the presence of fine structure in the walls of vegetative cells of *Bacillus* spp. The homogeneous appearance of the cell-wall structure of *B. megaterium* is illustrated in Pl. 1, fig. 3 and also Pl. 2, figs. 4 and 5, which show in addition the attachment of bacteriophages.

Some properties of cell-wall suspensions

The isolated walls form milky white, somewhat opalescent suspensions, differing markedly in appearance from the opaque suspensions of intact bacteria. With the exception of the walls of *Rhodospirillum rubrum*, the isolated walls of pigmented organisms, e.g. *Sarcina lutea, Micrococcus lysodeikticus* and *Staphylococcus aureus*, are completely devoid of pigments; the pigments are found in the small particles and 'soluble cytoplasmic' fractions.

Absorption spectra of isolated walls of many Gram-positive bacteria show a smooth scattering curve without any evidence of characteristic peaks at ultraviolet wave-lengths. Thus the walls of Gram-positive organisms can be readily differentiated from the cytoplasmic components possessing a characteristic absorption maximum at 260 mμ. The ultraviolet absorption spectra of walls (curve 2) and cytoplasm (curve 1) are shown in Text-fig. 1. Owing to the presence of aromatic amino acids in the walls of Gram-negative bacteria (Salton, 1953*a*) a characteristic 'hump' at wave-lengths of *c*. 270–280 mμ is detectable (Salton & Horne, 1951*b*).

CHEMICAL CONSTITUTION

Vincenzi (1887) was one of the early investigators to attempt the chemical characterization of a bacterial cell wall. He found that the 'wall' of *Bacillus subtilis* contained 5–11 % nitrogen, and apart from concluding that it was not composed of cellulose he was unable to give any indication of its general composition. Various claims have been made for the presence of cellulose, hemicellulose or chitin in the bacterial wall. Many of the tests were performed on residues isolated from alkali-treated cells, and as already pointed out (Salton & Horne, 1951*b*) such residues do not necessarily correspond to undegraded isolated walls.

With the development of suitable procedures for isolating cell walls and establishing their homogeneity by examination in the electron microscope, the methods of analytical chemistry and biochemistry could then be applied to the elucidation of the chemical constitution of the walls.

Weidel (1950, 1951) concluded that the cell wall of *Escherichia coli* was of lipo-protein nature. Mitchell & Moyle (1951) found that the cell 'envelope' of *Staphylococcus aureus* was composed of a glycero-phospho-protein complex. The cell wall of *Streptococcus faecalis* differed from the other organisms in that it was of a mucopolysaccharide

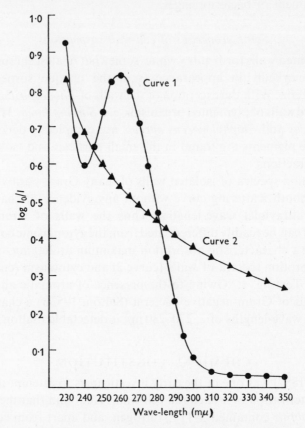

Text-fig. 1. U.V.L. absorption spectra of fractions from *Str. faecalis*. Curve 1: 'cytoplasmic' fraction (arbitrary concentration); Curve 2: cell wall suspension—200 μg. dry weight cell wall/ml.

nature, containing hexosamine, rhamnose, glucose and galactose in addition to a number of amino acids (Salton, 1952a). The cell wall of *Corynebacterium diphtheriae* investigated by Holdsworth (1952a, b) contained both protein and carbohydrate components, thus also falling into the general class of substances known as muco complexes (Kent & Whitehouse, 1955). These studies showed that bacterial walls possessed highly individualistic chemical characteristics. Subsequent investigations of the composition of the walls of other organisms have abundantly confirmed this impression, but some interesting similarities within different genera and within the Gram-positive and Gram-negative groups of bacteria have emerged.

Some differences between the cell wall constitution of Gram-positive and Gram-negative bacteria

Studies of the chemical composition of cell walls of Gram-positive and Gram-negative bacteria (Salton, 1952c, 1953a) have revealed two major differences:

(1) (a) the walls of the Gram-positive organisms contain a limited range of amino acids; the absence of aromatic and S-containing amino acids, and of proline, histidine and arginine, is a conspicuous characteristic.

(b) The walls of the Gram-negative bacteria, on the other hand, contain a similar range of amino acids to that found in most common proteins, including aromatic and S-containing amino acids, arginine and proline.

(2) The lipid contents of the walls of Gram-negative bacteria are generally greater than those of the Gram-positive organisms.

The results of several independent investigations of cell-wall composition (McCarty, 1952b; Newton, 1956) further substantiated these differences, and the collected data showing these characteristics are presented in Table 1.

Table 1. *Some characteristics of the amino-acid constituents and lipid contents of cell walls*

Organism	Amino-acid characteristics	No. of known amino acids identified by chromatography	'Total lipid' content (% dry weight cell wall)
Gram-positive:			
Strep. faecalis (4)*		9	2·3
Strep. pyogenes (4)	Absence of aromatic and	9	—
M. lysodeikticus (4)	certain S-containing	4	1·2
S. lutea (4)	amino acids; arginine	5	1·1
Staph. aureus (2)	and proline generally	12	4·4
B. subtilis (4)	not detected	10†	2·6
B. megaterium (4)		10†	—
C. diphtheriae (1)		10†	—
Gram-negative:			
Esch. coli (4)	Presence of aromatic and	17†	22
Salm. pullorum (4)	S-containing amino	16†	19
Ps. aeruginosa (3)	acids, arginine and	16†	11
R. rubrum (4)	proline	16†	21·7

* Data from: (1) Cummins & Harris (1954); (2) Mitchell & Moyle (1951); (3) Newton (1956); (4) Salton (1952a, 1953a, 1954; unpublished observations).
† Diaminopimelic acid found in these cell walls.

Amino-acid constitution

On a question of terminology it seems doubtful that we should use the term 'protein' for the description of the main nitrogen-containing components of the walls of Gram-positive bacteria. The amino-acid composition of these walls differs in some essential characteristics from the amino-acid constitution of a large number of proteins (Tristram, 1953). Phenylalanine and arginine, both regarded as 'essential amino acids' of proteins (Tristram, 1953), are not found in the walls of the Gram-positive organisms. Perhaps a more accurate and less misleading way of describing these constituents would be to describe them as containing 'amino acid' or as peptide components. From an inspection of the amino-acid composition of the walls of Gram-negative organism it is clear that their main nitrogen-containing components may be appropriately described as 'proteins'.

Although the total amounts of wall components containing amino acid (or 'protein') may vary from one organism to another, most of the walls so far investigated probably contain relatively large proportions of alanine and glutamic acid. Snell (personal communication) found that alanine may account for a high proportion (about 40 %) of the total nitrogen of the wall of *Streptococcus faecalis* and that both D- and L-alanine are present in the walls of *Lactobacillus casei* and *Streptococcus faecalis*. It will also be of interest to determine whether bacterial walls contain both D and L forms of glutamic acid. The *Staphylococcus aureus* cell wall studied by Mitchell & Moyle (1951) appears to differ from the walls of other organisms in that it contains a large amount of glycine in addition to alanine and glutamic acid.

Another characteristic amino-acid constituent of certain cell walls is diaminopimelic acid, first isolated by Work (1951) from *Corynebacterium diphtheriae*. Diaminopimelic acid was subsequently found in the wall of *C. diphtheriae* (Holdsworth, 1952 *a*, *b*) and its presence in the walls of a number of bacteria has now been established (Salton, 1953 *a*; Cummins & Harris, 1954, 1955). It will be of interest to see how closely its presence in cell walls will follow its distribution in other groups of micro-organisms (Work & Dewey, 1953). It is not yet clear whether diamino-pimelic acid is confined to the cell-wall components or whether it is also present in intracellular proteins.

So far the nature of the peptide components of wall complexes has not been investigated. With the cell wall of *Streptococcus faecalis* difficulty was experienced in breaking down the wall complex into polysaccharide moieties and those containing amino acid (Salton, 1952 *a*). However,

Holdsworth (1952*a*, *b*) successfully extracted the polysaccharide from *Corynebacterium diphtheriae* cell wall with boiling saturated picric acid, the peptide being left as an insoluble picrate. Both hexosamine and diaminopimelic acid were found in the peptide fraction. It is perhaps of some significance that the spore peptides studied by Strange & Powell (1954) also contained hexosamine, and it seems likely that such peptides may be common components of bacterial structures.

Polysaccharide and hexosamine constituents

Polysaccharide components have been detected in the isolated walls of both Gram-positive and Gram-negative bacteria (Salton, 1953*a*). As with the peptide and protein constituents, the actual amounts vary from one organism to another. Mitchell & Moyle (1951) could detect only small quantities of reducing substances in the staphylococcal wall.

The amounts of polysaccharide may be determined as reducing substances after acid hydrolysis and the sugar components identified by paper chromatography. In addition to reducing sugars, the cell walls of a number of bacteria also contain substantial amounts of amino sugar. Determinations of reducing substances and hexosamine and the identified reducing substances of the walls of various bacteria are summarized in Table 2. In general, the walls of Gram-negative bacteria contain less hexosamine than do those of most Gram-positive bacteria (the staphylococcal wall again differs in this respect). However, the amounts of polysaccharide and the nature of the sugar components show no striking differences as did the lipid and amino-acid compositions.

The significance of the polysaccharide components of the cell walls of Gram-negative bacteria deserves some special comment. There is insufficient information as yet to enable us to decide whether they represent structural units of the wall or whether they are merely components of superficial layers physically attached to the cell wall. It is conceivable that the polysaccharides may be part of the complex somatic 'O' antigens and not in chemical combination with the rigid cell-wall structure. The similarity of the monosaccharide constituents identified in the cell-wall preparation of *Salmonella pullorum* (Salton, 1953*a*) to the sugar components of the isolated somatic 'O' antigens of related species (Davies, 1955) adds some support to this suspicion. It seems likely that layers of the surface antigenic components of Gram-negative bacteria may be retained by the walls during isolation, in much the same way as the M protein adheres to the wall during disintegration of group A streptococci (Salton, 1953*a*). The most obvious way of deciding whether the polysaccharide components of the isolated walls of Gram-negative bacteria are integral components of the rigid wall structure would be to study their fate following extraction with diethylene glycol under the conditions used by Morgan (1937).

Table 2. *Reducing substances, hexosamine contents and sugar components of cell walls*

| | | Percentage dry weight cell wall | | |
| | | Reducing substances* (as glucose) | Hexos-amine* | Sugar components identified by chromatography |
Organism				
Gram-positive:				
Strep. faecalis	(5)†	61	22	rhamnose, galactose, glucose
Strep. pyogenes	(2)	55–62	18–22	rhamnose
M. lysodeikticus	(5)	45	16	glucose
S. lutea	(5)	46·5	16	glucose
Staph. aureus	(3)	0·5	*c.* 1	—
B. subtilis	(5)	34	8·5	glucose
B. megaterium	(5)	45–48	18	glucose
C. diphtheriae	(1)	25	—	galactose, mannose, arabinose
Gram-negative:				
Esch. coli	(5)	16	3	galactose, glucose
Salm. pullorum	(5)	46	4·8	galactose, glucose, mannose, rhamnose
Ps. aeruginosa	(4)	16·9, 16·8	2·1, 2·7	—
R. rubrum	(5)	23	2	—

* Reducing substances and hexosamine determinations performed after hydrolysis (usually 2N-HCl or H_2SO_4 for 2 hr. at 100°).

† Data from: (1) Holdsworth (1952a, b); (2) McCarty (1952b); (3) Mitchell & Moyle (1951); (4) data for two strains, Newton (1956); (5) Salton (1952a, 1953a, 1954, unpublished observations).

The only detailed investigation of a polysaccharide component known to have been derived from the cell wall is that of Holdsworth (1952b). The isolated oligosaccharide contains 2 molecules of D-galactose, 1 of D-mannose and 3 of D-arabinose and possesses a molecular weight of the order of 1000.

Although the earlier suggestions that certain bacterial walls may be composed of chitin now seem unlikely, the presence of considerable amounts of hexosamine in some cell walls has been established (McCarty, 1952b; Salton, 1952a). The hexosomine is probably present in the wall as N-acetylhexosamine, but there is no evidence to suggest that it exists as a polymer of the chitin type. The Elson & Morgan hexosamine reactions of hydrolysed walls do not appear to be due solely to glucosamine. Following the discovery of an unidentified amino sugar in the hexosamine-containing spore peptides (Strange & Powell, 1954), Cummins & Harris (1955) found a similar substance in the cell walls of other bacteria. The latter investigators have also indicated the presence of galactosamine in certain bacterial walls.

It seems likely that the role of the hexosamines in the muco-complex cell walls may be to provide the linkages between the polysaccharide and peptide moieties of the cell-wall substances.

Lipid components

The lipid constituents of the cell walls can only be defined by the methods of extraction, and on the basis of 'ether-extractable lipid' the cell walls of Gram-positive bacteria contain negligible amounts (Salton, 1952a; 1953a). The walls of Gram-negative organisms may contain as much as 8% 'ether-extractable lipid'. Extraction with ether after submitting the wall preparations to more drastic treatment (hydrolysis with 6N-HCl for 2 hr. at 100°) showed 'total lipid' contents as high as 22% for Gram-negative walls; only small amounts (1–2·5%) were found in the walls of Gram-positive organisms. It seems conceivable that the high lipid content of the Gram-negative walls could be accounted for on the basis of the lipid behaving as a 'cementing' substance for a mosaic of protein macromolecules, such as those seen in certain *Spirillum* species. As pointed out previously, the small quantities of lipid in the walls of Gram-positive bacteria may result from the strong binding of lipid during the isolation procedures.

There is no information about the chemical nature of the cell-wall lipids.

ACTION OF ENZYMES ON CELL WALLS

The bacteriolytic properties of various tissue extracts, secretions and microbial culture filtrates have long been known, and the action of such enzymes in terms of cellular structure has been reviewed by Salton (1955a). The rapid clearing of a bacterial suspension by enzyme preparations would indicate a radical alteration of the surface components of the cells. This appears to be a justifiable conclusion for the lysis of living bacteria, but as emphasized by Salton (1953b) the dissolution of heat-killed bacteria (especially Gram-negative organisms) by proteolytic enzymes does not necessarily imply a direct action upon the walls. Damage to the walls during the heat treatment will make the coagulated protoplast more accessible to the proteolytic enzyme. The isolated walls are not attacked by enzymes such as trypsin. There are, however, several bacteriolytic enzymes that have been shown to act directly on the cell walls.

Lysozyme

Fleming (1922) gave the name lysozyme to the powerful bacteriolytic agent found in secretions and tissues. Since Fleming's observations on the rapid lysis of *Micrococcus lysodeikticus* by lysozyme the lytic properties of this enzyme have been investigated in some detail. The relative ease with which egg-white lysozyme may be crystallized (Alderton, Ward & Fevold, 1945) has greatly facilitated our present understanding of its action on the bacterial cell.

Early studies of the action of lysozyme on sensitive bacteria indicated that the enzyme hydrolysed a mucoid substance of the 'membrane' (Meyer, Palmer, Thompson & Khorazo, 1936). Epstein & Chain (1940) suggested that the polysaccharide component attacked by lysozyme was present in the intact organism in an insoluble form and that such a component was essential for the maintenance of the morphological integrity of certain sensitive bacteria. Boasson (1938), on the other hand, believed that the cell wall of *Micrococcus lysodeikticus* was not destroyed by lysozyme but that it became more permeable to the cellular contents.

Turbidimetric determination of the lysozyme sensitivity of walls

The direct action of lysozyme on the isolated cell walls of *Micrococcus lysodeikticus* was established by observing the dissolution of the turbid cell-wall suspensions on incubation with crystalline lysozyme from egg-white (Salton, 1952b). The dissolution of the walls was accompanied by a 97% loss in turbidity and examination of the residual material in the electron microscope showed that only a few resistant walls and debris were left. It was concluded that the wall of *M. lysodeikticus* represented the 'native substrate' of lysozyme. In a similar way, the isolated walls of *Bacillus megaterium* and *Sarcina lutea* have been shown to be completely digested by lysozyme (Salton, 1953b, 1954).

By combined phase-contrast microscopy and immunological reactions Tomcsik & Guex-Holzer (1952) concluded that lysozyme acted specifically on the wall of a *Bacillus* sp. Welshimer (1953), using crushed bacterial preparations of *B. megaterium*, observed the dissolution of the wall fragments on treatment with lysozyme.

Inability to observe any turbidity change on treatment of intact bacteria with lysozyme does not necessarily mean that the organism is ysozyme-resistant. It is obvious that surface components may prevent the penetration of lysozyme to the underlying structures. Such an effect might be especially pronounced where the wall was covered with a layer of material possessing negatively charged groups—the basic lysozyme may form a strong complex with such components.

One of the most sensitive and certain methods of determining whether bacterial walls are degraded by lysozyme is to follow turbidimetrically the interaction of isolated cell walls with lysozyme. Differences in sensi-

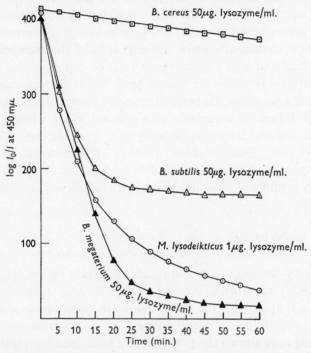

Text-fig. 2. Dissolution of bacterial cell walls by crystalline lysozyme at 37° and pH 6·0. Optical densities of c. 0·4 (log I_0/I at 450 mμ) correspond to 1·0–1·5 mg. dry weight cell wall/ml.

tivity to lysozyme may be demonstrated by determining the rates and extent of dissolution of the walls as shown in Text-fig. 2. For the degradation of the walls of *Bacillus* spp. much higher concentrations of lysozyme are required. Such differences may be due to the frequency and location of the linkages attacked by lysozyme differing in the walls of different organisms.

Although *Bacillus cereus* wall is relatively resistant to digestion with lysozyme (Text-fig. 2), continued incubation of walls for 10 hr. at 37° with 50 μg. crystalline egg-white lysozyme/ml. resulted in a maximum turbidity decrease of 58%. The extent of dissolution of *B. subtilis* cell walls is virtually the same—57% (Salton, 1955a). Thus the walls of these two organisms differ from those of B. megaterium in that they are not completely digested by lysozyme, and examination of residues after maximum lysis suggests the presence of residual wall-like structures in B. subtilis and B. cereus. These observations offer some experimental confirmation of the suggestion made by Epstein & Chain (1940) that the component attacked by lysozyme may not be the sole structural element in some organisms. On the basis of the chemical analysis of the wall of B. subtilis such a finding was anticipated (Salton, 1953a). It seems very likely that a lysozyme-sensitive component may be a common structural unit of the cell walls of the members of the genus Bacillus, and that an analogous relationship may also hold for similar components within the related sarcina and micrococcus groups.

No turbidity reduction has been observed on incubation of the isolated walls of the following organisms with crystalline egg-white lysozyme: Clostridium welchii, Streptococcus pyogenes, S. agalactiae, S. faecalis, Escherichia coli, Rhodospirillum rubrum, Pseudomonas aeruginosa (Salton, unpublished observations). It is evident that these walls do not contain any significant amounts of lysozyme-sensitive components.

Some characteristics of the isolated walls of lysozyme-sensitive bacteria and the action of lysozyme thereon

Superficially the most outstanding characteristic of the cell walls of Micrococcus lysodeikticus, Sarcina lutea, Bacillus megaterium and B. subtilis is that glucose and hexosamine are common constituents of all four. In addition to glucosamine, recent observations (Salton, unpublished) have shown the presence of a substance corresponding to the unknown amino sugar described by Strange & Powell (1954). Whether it is solely the presence of these components that confers lysozyme-sensitivity upon an organism cannot be said with certainty at the present time. At least the mucopolysaccharide or muco-complex nature of the 'native' lysozyme substrate has now been well established.

On lysozyme digestion of the soluble mucopolysaccharide isolated from Micrococcus lysodeikticus, the action of the enzyme was accompanied by a liberation of reducing substances (Meyer et al. 1936; Meyer & Hahnel, 1946; Epstein & Chain, 1940). Both Epstein & Chain (1940) and Meyer & Hahnel (1946) reported the liberation of N-acetylhexosamine, and in addition Epstein & Chain (1940) indicated that a substance giving the reactions of a ketohexose was also liberated. Apart from these investigations there have been no other indications of the types of molecular fragments resulting from the degradation of the muco-polysaccharide substrates by lysozyme.

With the availability of the methods for the isolation of the cell walls it seemed worth while reinvestigating the action of lysozyme on the insoluble cell-wall substrates. Salton (1954, unpublished observations) examined lysozyme-digested walls of *Micrococcus lysodeikticus*, *Sarcina lutea* and *Bacillus megaterium* in the ultra-centrifuge and found that the major components of all three digests possess molecular weights of the order of 10,000–20,000. Fragments of smaller molecular weight were also apparent and their presence has been confirmed by other techniques. The heterogeneity of the molecular fragments has been established by dialysis experiments and by electrophoresis of the non-dialysable material. In the non-dialysable fraction of lysozyme-digested *Micrococcus lysodeikticus* cell wall, there were at least three different electrophoretic components, and similar non-dialysable fractions from digests of *Sarcina lutea* and *Bacillus megaterium* were also electrophoretically complex. Some of the properties of cell wall digests are summarized in Table 3.

Table 3. *Some properties of lysozyme-digested cell walls*

Cell wall digests of	Ultracentrifugal analysis S_{20}	% non-dialysable material (48 hr. at 4°)	% reducing substances liberated (expressed as glucose)
M. lysodeikticus	1·15*	66	10–11
S. lutea	1·27	86	3·4–5·3
B. megaterium	1·50	71	6·7

* Solvent 0·1 M-phosphate buffer, pH 6·2.

Conditions of digestion: 15 mg. cell wall/ml.; 50 μg. crystalline egg-white lysozyme/ml.; 0·1 M-ammonium acetate, pH 6·3; digestion for 24 hr. at 37°.

As may have been expected from earlier investigations, reducing substances are liberated on digestion of the walls by lysozyme, and the digests give positive Morgan & Elson (1934) reactions for acetylhexosamine. Although the colour complexes formed under the conditions of the modified Morgan & Elson reaction (Aminoff, Morgan & Watkins, 1952) give absorption spectra identical to that of *N*-acetylglucosamine, no free acetylglucosamine could be detected by paper chromatographic examination of the wall digests (Salton, 1954). Glucose, the other reducing sugar common to all three cell walls, could not be detected as free glucose either by paper chromatography or by incubation with glucose-oxidase. None of the amino-acids found in the wall hydrolysates was liberated by the action of lysozyme.

Examination of the dialysable material from the wall digests by paper chromatography indicates that the major small fragment is a substance with a *Rf* close to that of acetylglucosamine when run in phenol-NH$_3$. This component can be detected on paper by spraying with aniline phthalate, ammoniacal silver nitrate and with the acetylhexosamine reagents—with the latter a yellow spot is obtained instead of the characteristic purple of *N*-acetylglucosamine. Separation of this fragment in the dialysable fraction from *Micrococcus lysodeikticus* digests has been achieved by placing multiple spots on Whatman paper no. 3 and irrigating with phenol-NH$_3$. The position of the fragment has been located by spraying strips, and the material eluted from adjacent strips gives on hydrolysis with 2N-HCl for 1 hr. a strong reaction for hexosamine. Chromatography after hydrolysis with 6N-HCl has shown the presence of glucosamine and a substance of somewhat similar properties to the unidentified amino sugar found in the spore peptides by Strange & Powell (1954). The determination of the exact nature of this small fragment liberated by lysozyme must await further investigation.

It is now clear that the walls of lysozyme-sensitive organisms such as *Micrococcus lysodeikticus*, *Sarcina lutea* and *Bacillus megaterium* are broken down into a complex mixture of fragments with different molecular weights and electrophoretic properties. It appears reasonable to suggest that the small fragment split off by lysozyme may form the link between the components containing amino acid and the polysaccharide portion of the cell-wall complex. The final elucidation of the nature of the heterogeneous collection of fragments resulting from lysozyme degradation of the walls should throw much light on the molecular anatomy of at least some bacterial cell walls.

Other enzymes degrading the cell wall

Maxted (1948) reported that the group-specific substances could be liberated from certain streptococci by treatment with the extracellular enzymes produced by *Streptomyces albus*. It seemed likely that such enzymes may possess a direct action on streptococcal walls, and experimental verification of this was provided by McCarty (1952b) and Salton (1952c; 1953a).

McCarty (1952a, b) has investigated the production, fractionation and action of the *Streptomyces albus* enzyme. It is of some significance that the purified enzyme fractions active against the streptococcal walls were devoid of activity for *Micrococcus lysodeikticus* (McCarty, 1952b). That the enzyme may have a substrate specificity differing from that of lysozyme was further substantiated from the analysis of the cell wall of the group A streptococcus (McCarty, 1952b). Rhamnose and hexosamine appear to be the two reducing substances common to streptococcal walls (McCarty, 1952b; Salton, 1952a, 1953a). The wall of *Streptococcus faecalis* contains, in addition, glucose and galactose (Salton, 1952a).

From the investigation of the action of the 'streptolytic' enzyme on group A streptococcal walls McCarty (1952b) concluded that the nondialysable products were heterogeneous. Some of the cell-wall glucosamine was dialysable after enzymic digestion, but the dialysable glucosamine was not free glucosamine nor was it made up entirely of acetylglucosamine. Thus the properties of these cell-wall digests are rather reminiscent of those of the lysozyme-digested walls.

That *Streptomyces* species other than *S. albus* produce enzymes active against streptococcal walls has been demonstrated (Salton, 1955b). Enzymes degrading the cell wall may be detected by incorporation of isolated walls into washed agar, and a number of actinomycetes have been found to be active producers of enzymes degrading the walls of *Streptococcus faecalis* and *S. agalactiae* (Salton, 1955b).

INTERACTION OF BACTERIOPHAGES WITH CELL WALLS

With the isolated cell walls of *Escherichia coli* B, Weidel (1951) found that specific adsorption of T_2, T_4 and T_6 bacteriophages occurred. This established the morphological location of the specific receptor substances for these phages. More recently, the receptor for phage T_5 has been isolated from *E. coli* B walls as a spherical particle, and the interaction of the receptor-sphere and phage has been elegantly demonstrated by electron microscopy (Weidel & Kellenberger, 1955). They concluded that the 'sphere' is probably deeply embedded in the intact cell wall. The nature of the receptor substance had been previously investigated and found to be a lipo-glycoproteid containing 34% lipid and 10.5% reducing substances (Weidel, Koch & Bobosch, 1954).

Hotchin, Dawson & Elford (1952) studied the interaction of staphylococcus K bacteriophage with the isolated 'cell membranes or shells' of the host *Staphylococcus aureus*. Adsorption of phage on the cell walls was established by direct examination in the electron microscope and by inactivation of the phages by the walls. The percentage of phage adsorbed was found to be proportional to the concentration of both phage and 'membranes', but was more dependent on the latter.

Salton & Stent (unpublished observations) also found adsorption and inactivation of the C phage of *Bacillus megaterium* when suspended with the isolated walls of this organism. Pl. 2, figs. 4 and 5, show the attachment of phage particles to the isolated walls of *B. megaterium*. In subsequent experiments (Salton, unpublished observations) it was found that on digestion with lysozyme the walls completely lost their ability to inactivate the bacteriophages; this is illustrated by comparison

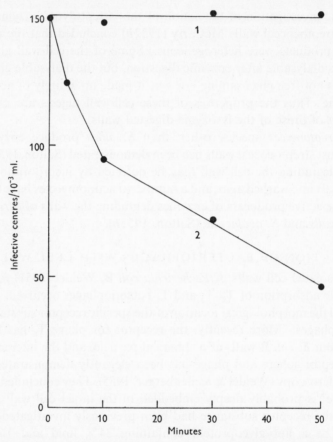

Text-fig. 3. Interaction of *B. megaterium* phage C with isolated cell walls of *B. megaterium*. Curve 1 shows inactivation of phage on incubation with cell walls (150 μg. dry weight/ml) suspended in 5% peptone at 37°; in curve 2 the bacteriophage titre is unchanged when the cell walls have been pre-digested with lysozyme.

of curves 1 and 2 in Text-fig. 3. Although the cell walls of *B. megaterium* and *Micrococcus lysodeikticus* are both attacked by lysozyme, the walls of the latter organism showed no inactivation of the *B. megaterium* phage C. The location of the specific receptor in the wall of *B. megaterium* was further confirmed by the inability of the bacteriophage to interact with protoplasts (Weibull, 1953).

IMMUNOLOGICAL PROPERTIES

As yet there is little information about the immunological properties of bacterial cell walls, and it is evident that investigations in this field would greatly clarify our knowledge of the immunological architecture of micro-organisms.

From the investigations of McCarty (1952a, b) and Salton (1952c, 1953a) it is evident that the group specific substance of *Streptococcus pyogenes* is located in the cell wall. Furthermore, specific slide agglutination of stable cell-wall suspensions of group B and D streptococci by their homologous antisera has been observed, and the interaction of group D walls and group D antiserum gives a typical complement-fixing reaction (Salton, unpublished observations).

The only systematic study of the immunological reactions of a bacterial cell wall is that of Cummins (1954). Two antigens were found in the walls of a *mitis* strain of *Corynebacterium diphtheriae*—a superficial specific protein and a deeper group antigen probably of polysaccharide nature. The surface protein antigen was relatively heat-labile and the group antigen in the wall was heat-stable, but rapidly attacked by periodate. The group antigen was found in all cultural varieties of *Corynebacterium diphtheriae* and was also present in one strain of *C. ovis*.

FUNCTION AND BIOCHEMICAL PROPERTIES
OF THE BACTERIAL WALL

It has often been asserted that the cell wall is a 'dead, inert structure'. I think our present state of knowledge of the relationship between cellular structure and function is insufficient either to confirm or to deny the validity of such a description. To settle the question by testing isolated walls for the presence or absence of enzymes seems an inelegant approach to the problem; such attempts would prove to be as contentious as the efforts to determine the enzymic activities of certain viruses.

A more profitable means of investigating the possible contribution of the cell wall to various cellular functions and biochemical processes has now become apparent by the recent isolation of the bacterial protoplast (Weibull, 1953). Thus instead of examining isolated walls for enzymic activities, it would seem better to determine the biochemical reactions which remain unimpaired or relatively so, in the absence of the outer wall structure. McQuillen (1955) has shown that the cell wall may be dispensed with, without drastically impairing the ability of the organized protoplast to synthesize protein and nucleic acid.

Although the wall of *Bacillus megaterium* is essential for the specific phage infection mechanism, it is evident that once the virus DNA has entered the cell, the wall may be removed without seriously affecting the subsequent synthesis and maturation of bacteriophages (Salton & McQuillen, 1955). Similarly, the protoplast can support the processes involved in the production of a complex biological entity such as the bacterial spore (Salton, 1955c).

The extension of protoplast studies to other groups of organisms, facilitated by the development of suitable wall-degrading enzyme systems, should enable us to decide whether the wall merely provides the cell with a rigid, protective framework or whether it is essential for the maintenance of certain biochemical processes.

GROWTH OF THE CELL WALL

Although there have been a number of cytological investigations of the appearance of the cell surfaces at the time of division, we have no precise knowledge of the location and manner of synthesis of the bacterial cell wall. The most obvious manifestation of the development and growth of the wall is shown by the thickened appearance of cross-bands, septa, etc. These have been demonstrated by many cytologists, and more recently the thickened equatorial bands have been shown in electron micrographs of isolated walls (Dawson & Stern, 1954). By combined phase-contrast microscopy and immunological methods, Tomcsik & Guex-Holzer (1954) have established that the specific cell wall reaction is greater at the point of cross-wall formation. Dawson & Stern (1954) concluded that, at least in some bacteria, the transverse cell wall septum originates in and grows centripetally from the cell wall, a conclusion also reached by previous investigators (see Robinow, 1945). In certain bacteria, cell-wall septum formation and cell-wall constriction ('splitting' or 'delamination'—Robinow, 1945) may be dissociable processes (Robinow, 1945; Dawson & Stern, 1954).

The superb ultra-thin sections of *Bacillus cereus* presented in the study by Chapman & Hillier (1953) show the presence of peripheral bodies that appear to be associated with the development of the cross wall. These peripheral bodies move inwards with the inner edge of the centripetally growing wall. Such observations, together with the apparent inability of the isolated protoplast of *B. megaterium* to revert to the rod-shaped cell by synthesis of a new cell wall, have led me to suggest that the cell wall-synthesizing mechanism may be located in the peripheral bodies and that these bodies may not be enclosed by the protoplast membrane. It is conceivable that the peripheral bodies may have rather tenuous connexions with the protoplast and that they may become detached during the dissolution of the wall by lysozyme. This need not imply that the protoplast would be incapable of synthesizing certain characteristic wall components that may resemble the relatively low molecular weight materials resulting from the digestion of walls with lysozyme. The possibility that the peripheral bodies possess the specific mechanisms for polymerization of low molecular weight components into the insoluble cell-wall structure appears worthy of experimental consideration. I realize of course that the apparent inability of the isolated protoplasts of *B. megaterium* to form a new wall may be due to less subtle considerations such as the continued presence of the basic lysozyme at cell-wall synthesizing sites at or near the protoplast membrane.

Robinow (1945) has suggested that in some bacteria the division of the cytoplasm, completed by the formation of a transverse plasma membrane or cell boundary, may be followed by septum formation; in other organisms transverse cell-wall development may occur well in advance of the division of the whole bacterium. The possibility that the protoplasts of some bacteria may undergo a process of division independent of cross-wall formation has now been strengthened by the excellent experiments performed by McQuillen (unpublished obsertations) with the isolated protoplasts of *Bacillus megaterium*.

DISCUSSION

The development of suitable methods for the isolation of bacterial cell walls freed from intracellular protoplasmic constituents has enabled us to study their microstructure and physical and chemical properties, and has facilitated our understanding of the possible contribution of the cell wall to certain biochemical processes and cellular functions.

There seems little doubt that the wall provides the bacterial cell with a rigid outer structure, thereby protecting the more delicate protoplast from damage due to unfavourable environmental conditions. Although the wall may not be essential for the continued existence of the bacterial cell (e.g. protoplasts can produce viable spores capable of germinating and giving rise to normal colonies—Salton, 1955 c) it is probably of considerable survival value to the cell. Owing to the capacity of soil microorganisms such as the actinomycetes and myxobacteria to produce cell-wall-degrading enzymes (Salton, 1955 b) it seems likely that bacterial protoplasts may not only be present but may persist under natural conditions. However, as the protoplast requires rather restricted osmotic conditions for its stability (Weibull, 1953), it is clear that the organisms with cell walls may survive a greater range of natural environments. The production of cell-wall-degrading enzymes under natural conditions has one other fascinating implication: such enzymes may facilitate the release of cellular DNA which may in turn be capable of bringing about transformations of either intact growing organisms or protoplasts in the surrounding environment. It seems possible that the prerequisite conditions for transformations under natural conditions in the soil or in a suitable aquatic environment may exist, and that the frequency of such transformations may be as great as mutational changes.

The investigations of the chemical constitution of the bacterial cell wall have shown that many different classes of substances can provide the micro-organisms with rigid cell-wall structures. Some of the cell walls, particularly those composed of muco-complexes, possess such distinctive chemical features that they may be characterized more readily than other cellular components such as proteins, nucleic acids, lipids, etc. In many respects some of the muco-complex walls of Gram-positive bacteria resemble the blood-group substances (Salton, 1952a), and it is tempting to entertain the possibility that they may also share the genetic implications of such constituents. There is already some indication that the composition of the walls of some groups of organisms may be sufficiently characteristic to act as an extremely useful guide in the taxonomy of bacteria (Cummins & Harris, 1955). As one more interested in the natural relationships within the microbial world, it seems to me that the identification of the nature of cell-wall components may provide a more hopeful means of establishing transitions in naturally related groups of micro-organisms. This may not only assist our understanding of the phylogenetic relationships of bacteria at a chemical level, but also reveal some fascinating details of the evolution of the bacterial cell wall.

Although the chemical analysis of the cell walls has given an indication of the types of substances to be expected in the walls, it only provides us with a crude picture of their molecular structure. There are, however, two elegant means of studying the macromolecular and molecular components of cell walls—by isolation and characterization of specific bacteriophage receptors in the walls, and by investigating the nature of the fragments of enzymically digested cell walls. The excellent investigations of the nature and location of the *Escherichia coli* B receptors for the T-series phages by Weidel and co-workers have shown how a detailed knowledge of specific cell-wall components may be gained. Studies of the constitution of the various fragments resulting from digestions of walls with enzymes such as lysozyme should tell us a great deal about the molecular constitution of the walls of certain organisms.

Our interest in the molecular and macromolecular components of the bacterial cell wall is not merely confined to their arrangement in the cell-wall structure. A knowledge of these molecular 'bits and pieces' should enable us to recognize the types of components being synthesized by the cell for the formation of the insoluble cell wall. As a single morphological entity of the bacterial cell, the wall accounts for approximately 20% of the dry weight of the organism and therefore represents the major structural component. It is thus inevitable that our interest in the structure of the cell wall is rapidly leading us to focus our attention on the enzyme systems involved in the biosynthesis of one of the main morphological entities of the bacterial cell.

I should like to thank Mr R. W. Horne and Dr R. C. Williams for taking electron micrographs of the preparations.

REFERENCES

ALDERTON, G., WARD, B. H. & FEVOLD, H. L. (1945). Isolation of lysozyme from egg white. *J. biol. Chem.* **157**, 43.

AMINOFF, D., MORGAN, W. T. J. & WATKINS, W. M. (1952). Studies in immunochemistry. 11. The action of dilute alkali on the *N*-acetylhexosamines and the specific blood-group mucoids. *Biochem. J.* **51**, 379.

AVERY, O. T. & DUBOS, R. (1931). The protective action of a specific enzyme against type III pneumococcus infection in mice. *J. exp. Med.* **54**, 73.

BARNARD, I. E. & HEWLETT, R. T. (1911). On a method of disintegrating bacteria and other organic cells. *Proc. Roy. Soc.* B, **84**, 57.

BIRCH-ANDERSEN, A., MAALØE, O. & SJÖSTRAND, F. S. (1953). High-resolution electron micrographs of sections of *Escherichia coli*. *Biochim. biophys. Acta*, **12**, 395.

BOASSON, E. H. (1938). On the bacteriolysis by lysozyme. *J. Immunol.* **34**, 281.

CHAPMAN, G. B. & HILLIER, J. (1953). Electron microscopy of ultra-thin sections of bacteria. I. Cellular division in *Bacillus cereus*. *J. Bact.* **66**, 362.

COHN, F. (1875). Untersuchungen über Bacterien. *Beitr. Biol. Pfl.* **1**, Heft 2, 127.

COOPER, P. D., ROWLEY, D. & DAWSON, I. M. (1949). Location of radioactive penicillin in *Staphylococcus aureus* after contact with the drug. *Nature, Lond.*, **164**, 842.

CUMMINS, C. S. (1954). Some observations on the nature of the antigens in the cell wall of *Corynebacterium diphtheriae*. *Brit. J. exp. Path.* **35**, 166.

CUMMINS, C. S. & HARRIS, H. (1954). Carbohydrate and amino acid constituents of the cell walls of *Corynebacterium diphtheriae*. *Biochem. J.* **57**, xxxii.

CUMMINS, C. S. & HARRIS, H. (1955). Differences in cell-wall composition among Gram-positive cocci and bacilli. *J. gen. Microbiol.* **13**, iii.

DAVIES, D. A. L. (1955). The specific polysaccharides of some Gram-negative bacteria. *Biochem. J.* **59**, 696.

DAWSON, I. M. (1949). *The Nature of the Bacterial Surface*, ed. A. A. Miles & N. W. Pirie. Oxford: Blackwell.

DAWSON, I. M. & STERN, H. (1954). Structure of the bacterial cell-wall during cell division. *Biochim. biophys. Acta*, **13**, 31.

EPSTEIN, L. A. & CHAIN, E. (1940). Some observations on the preparation and properties of the substrate of lysozyme. *Brit. J. exp. Path.* **21**, 339.

FERNELL, W. R. & KING, H. K. (1953). The chemical composition of the soluble and insoluble fractions of the bacterial cell. *Biochem. J.* **55**, 758.

FISCHER, A. (1895). Untersuchungen über Bakterien. *Jb wiss. Bot.* **27**, 1.

FLEMING, A. (1922). On a remarkable bacteriolytic element found in tissues and secretions. *Proc. Roy. Soc.* B, **93**, 306.

HOLDSWORTH, E. S. (1952a). The nature of the cell-wall of *Corynebacterium diphtheriae. Biochim. biophys. Acta*, **8**, 110.

HOLDSWORTH, E. S. (1952b). The nature of the cell wall of *Corynebacterium diphtheriae.* Isolation of an oligosaccharide. *Biochim. biophys. Acta*, **9**, 19.

HOTCHIN, J. E., DAWSON, I. M. & ELFORD, W. J. (1952). The use of empty bacterial membranes in the study of the adsorption of *Staphylococcus* K phage upon its host. *Brit. J. exp. Path.* **33**, 177.

HOUWINK, A. L. (1953). A macromolecular mono-layer in the cell wall of *Spirillum* spec. *Biochim. biophys. Acta*, **10**, 360.

KENT, P. W. & WHITEHOUSE, M. W. (1955). *Biochemistry of the Aminosugars.* London: Butterworth.

KING, H. K. & ALEXANDER, H. (1948). The mechanical destruction of bacteria. *J. gen. Microbiol.* **2**, 315.

KNAYSI, G. (1938). Cytology of bacteria. *Bot. Rev.* **4**, 83.

KNAYSI, G. (1951). *Elements of Bacterial Cytology*, 2nd ed. Ithaca, N.Y.: Comstock.

KNAYSI, G., HILLIER, J. & FABRICANT, C. (1950). The cytology of an avian strain of *Mycobacterium tuberculosis* studied with the electron and light microscopes. *J. Bact.* **60**, 423.

LABAW, W. & MOSLEY, V. M. (1954). Periodic structure in the flagella and cell walls of a bacterium. *Biochim. biophys. Acta*, **15**, 325.

LANCEFIELD, R. C. (1943). Studies on the antigenic composition of group A hemolytic streptococci. I. Effects of proteolytic enzymes on streptococcal cells. *J. exp. Med.* **78**, 465.

MAXTED, W. R. (1948). Preparation of streptococcal extracts for Lancefield grouping. *Lancet*, ii, 255.

McCARTY, M. (1952a). The lysis of group A hemolytic streptococci by extracellular enzymes of *Streptomyces albus.* I. Production and fractionation of the lytic enzymes. *J. exp. Med.* **96**, 555.

McCARTY, M. (1952b). The lysis of group A hemolytic streptococci by extracellular enzymes of *Streptomyces albus.* II. Nature of the cellular substrate attacked by the lytic enzymes. *J. exp. Med.* **96**, 569.

MACFADYEN, A. & ROWLAND, S. (1901). Upon the intracellular constituents of the typhoid bacillus. *Zbl. Bakt.* Abt. I, **30**, 48.

McQUILLEN, K. (1955). Bacterial protoplasts. I. Protein and nucleic acid metabolism in protoplasts of *Bacillus megaterium. Biochim. biophys. Acta*, **17**, 382.

MEYER, K., PALMER, J. W., THOMPSON, R. & KHORAZO, D. (1936). On the mechanism of lysozyme action. *J. biol. Chem.* **113**, 479.

MEYER, K. & HAHNEL, E. (1946). Estimation of lysozyme by a viscosimetric method. *J. biol. Chem.* **163**, 723.

MICKLE, H. (1948). Tissue disintegration. *J.R. micr. Soc.* **68**, 10.

MITCHELL, P. & MOYLE, J. (1951). The glycerophospho-protein complex envelope of *Micrococcus pyogenes. J. gen. Microbiol.* **5**, 981.

MITCHELL, P. & MOYLE, J. (1955). Permeability of the osmotic barrier of *Staphylococcus aureus* to some salts, amino-acids and non-electrolytes. (In the Press.)

MORGAN, W. T. J. (1937). Studies in immuno-chemistry. II. The isolation and properties of a specific antigenic substance from *B. dysenteriae* (Shiga). *Biochem. J.* **31**, 2003.

MORGAN, W. T. J. & ELSON, L. A. (1934). A colorimetric method for the determination of *N*-acetylglucosamine and *N*-acetylchondrosamine. *Biochem. J.* **28**, 988.

MUDD, S. & LACKMAN, D. B. (1941). Bacterial morphology as shown by the electron microscope. I. Structural differentiation within the streptococcal cell. *J. Bact.* **41**, 415.

MUDD, S., POLEVITZKY, K., ANDERSON, T. F. & CHAMBERS, L. A. (1941). Bacterial morphology as shown by the electron microscope. II. The bacterial cell-wall in the Genus Bacillus. *J. Bact.* **42**, 251.

NEWTON, B. A. (1956). The Polymyxins: their properties and mode of action. *Bact. Rev.* (In the Press.)

ROBINOW, C. F. (1945). Addendum to *The Bacterial Cell*, by R. J. Dubos. Cambridge, Mass.: Harvard University Press.

ROBINOW, C. F. & MURRAY, R. G. E. (1953). The differentiation of cell wall, cytoplasmic membrane and cytoplasm of Gram positive bacteria by selective staining. *Exp. Cell Res.* **4**, 390.

SALTON, M. R. J. (1952a). Studies of the bacterial cell wall. III. Preliminary investigation of the chemical constitution of the cell wall of *Streptococcus faecalis*. *Biochim. biophys. Acta*, **8**, 510.

SALTON, M. R. J. (1952b). Cell wall of *Micrococcus lysodeikticus* as the substrate of lysozyme. *Nature, Lond.*, **170**, 746.

SALTON, M. R. J. (1952c). The nature of the cell walls of some Gram-positive and Gram-negative bacteria. *Biochim. biophys. Acta*, **9**, 334.

SALTON, M. R. J. (1953a). Studies of the bacterial cell wall. IV. The composition of the cell walls of some Gram-positive and Gram-negative bacteria. *Biochim. biophys. Acta*, **10**, 512.

SALTON, M. R. J. (1953b). Cell structure and enzymic lysis of bacteria. *J. gen. Microbiol.* **9**, 512.

SALTON, M. R. J. (1954). The action of lysozyme on the cell walls of certain bacteria. *J. gen. Microbiol.* **11**, ix.

SALTON, M. R. J. (1955a). Cellular structure and enzymic bacteriolysis. *Proc. 3rd Congr. int. Biochem.*, Brussels.

SALTON, M. R. J. (1955b). Isolation of *Streptomyces* spp. capable of decomposing preparations of cell walls from various micro-organisms and a comparison of their lytic activities with those of certain actinomycetes and myxobacteria. *J. gen. Microbiol.* **12**, 25.

SALTON, M. R. J. (1955c). The formation of spores in protoplasts of *Bacillus megaterium*. *J. gen. Microbiol.* **13**, iv.

SALTON, M. R. J. & HORNE, R. W. (1951a). Studies of the bacterial cell wall. I. Electron microscopical observations on heated bacteria. *Biochim. biophys. Acta*, **7**, 19.

SALTON, M. R. J. & HORNE, R. W. (1951b). Studies of the bacterial cell wall. II. Methods of preparation and some properties of cell walls. *Biochim. biophys. Acta*, **7**, 177.

SALTON, M. R. J. & McQUILLEN, K. (1955). Bacterial protoplasts. II. Bacteriophage multiplication in protoplasts of sensitive and lysogenic strains of *Bacillus megaterium*. *Biochim. biophys. Acta*, **17**, 465.

SALTON, M. R. J. & WILLIAMS, R. C. (1954). Electron microscopy of the cell walls of *Bacillus megaterium* and *Rhodospirillum rubrum*. *Biochim. biophys. Acta*, **14**, 455.

SCHACHMAN, H. K., PARDEE, A. B. & STANIER, R. Y. (1952). Studies on the macromolecular organization of microbial cells. *Arch. Biochem. Biophys.* **38**, 245.

STRANGE, R. E. & POWELL, J. F. (1954). Hexosamine-containing peptides in spores of *Bacillus subtilis*, *B. megaterium* and *B. cereus*. *Biochem. J.* **58**, 80.

TOMCSIK, J. & GUEX-HOLZER, S. (1952). Änderung der Struktur der Bakterienzelle im Verlauf der Lysozym-Einwirkung. *Schweiz. Z. Path.* **15**, 518.

TOMCSIK, J. & GUEX-HOLZER, S. (1954). A specific cell-wall reaction in *Bacillus* sp. *J. gen. Microbiol.* **10**, 317.

TRISTRAM, G. R. (1953). Amino acid composition of proteins in *The Proteins*, vol. **1**, part A, p. 181, New York: Academic Press.

VINCENZI, L. (1887). Ueber die chemischen Bestandtheile der Spaltpilze. *Hoppe-Seyl. Z.* **11**, 181.

WEIBULL, C. (1953). The isolation of protoplasts from *Bacillus megaterium* by controlled treatment with lysozyme. *J. Bact.* **66**, 688.

WEIDEL, W. (1950). In *Viruses*, ed. M. Delbrück, Pasadena. California Institute of Technology.

WEIDEL, W. (1951). Über die Zellmembrane von *Escherichia coli* B. I. Präparierung der Membranen. Analytische daten. Morphologie. Verhalten der Membranen gegenüber den Bakteriophagen der T-serie. *Z. Naturf.* **6b**, 251.

WEIDEL, W., KOCH, G. & BOBOSCH, K. (1954). Über die Rezeptorsubstanz für den Phagen T$_5$. *Z. Naturf.* **9b**, 573.

WEIDEL, W. & KELLENBERGER, E. (1955). The *E. coli* B receptor for the phage T$_5$. II. Electron microscopic studies. *Biochim. biophys. Acta*, **17**, 1.

WELSCH, M. & SALMON, J. (1950). Quelques aspects de la Staphylolyse. *Ann. Inst. Pasteur*, **79**, 802.

WELSHIMER, H. J. (1953). The action of lysozyme on the cell wall and capsule of *Bacillus megaterium*. *J. Bact.* **66**, 112.

WILLIAMS, R. C. (1953). A method of freeze-drying for electron microscopy. *Exp. Cell Res.* **4**, 188.

WINOGRADSKY, S. (1887). Ueber Schwefelbacterien. *Bot. Z.* **45**, 489.

WORK, E. (1951). The isolation of $\alpha\epsilon$-diaminopimelic acid from *Corynebacterium diphtheriae* and *Mycobacterium tuberculosis*. *Biochem. J.* **49**, 17.

WORK, E. & DEWEY, D. L. (1953). The distribution of $\alpha\epsilon$-diaminopimelic acid among various micro-organisms. *J. gen. Microbiol.* **9**, 394.

YOSHIDA, N., FUKUYA, I., KAKUTANI, I., TANAKA, S., TEGAWA, J. & HASHIMOTO, T. (1954). Studies on the bacterial cell wall. I. Electron staining of the cell wall of *B. subtilis* by phosphotungstic acid. *Tokushima J. exp. Med.* **1**, 8.

EXPLANATION OF PLATES

PLATE 1

Fig. 1. Cell wall of *Rhodospirillum rubrum* prepared for electron microscopy by freeze-drying. × 50,000.

Fig. 2. Cell wall fragments of *Rhodospirillum rubrum* showing double layers. × 27,000.

Fig. 3. Cell wall of *Bacillus megaterium*. × 35,000.

PLATE 2

Fig. 4. Cell walls of *Bacillus megaterium* showing many adsorbed phage tails. × 14,000.

Fig. 5. Cell walls of *Bacillus megaterium* showing several adsorbed phage particles. × 18,500.

PLATE 1

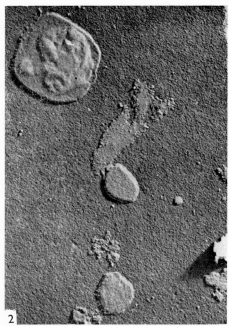

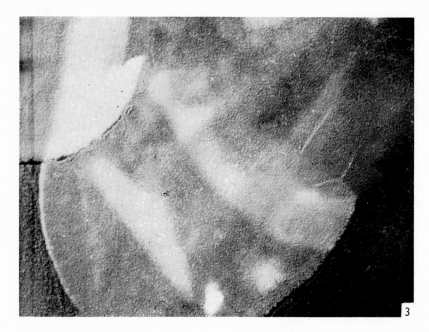

PLATE 2

4

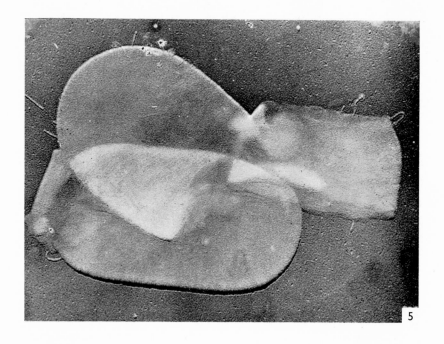

5

BACTERIAL PROTOPLASTS; THEIR FORMATION AND CHARACTERISTICS

C. WEIBULL

Biokemiska Institutionen, Uppsala Universitet, Uppsala, Sweden

The protoplasm of most bacteria is enclosed in a rigid envelope, usually called the cell wall. The maintenance of a constant cell form other than spherical is due to this envelope. When the cell wall is damaged the protoplasm as a rule disintegrates. Under certain conditions, however, the organization of the protoplasm may remain essentially unchanged even after a complete removal of the wall. The resulting structural unit has been named a protoplast (Weibull, 1953a) or a gymnoplast (Stähelin, 1954). In the present paper the former term will provisionally be used.

A considerable amount of research concerning bacterial protoplasts is currently going on in various laboratories. Therefore the present account of what is known about these bodies makes no pretence to comprehensiveness, although an effort has been made to keep track of recent developments. It is hoped, however, that this report, together with other contributions to this Symposium, will shed some new light on the properties of the protoplasts and, indirectly, on the structure and functioning of the intact bacterial cell.

FORMATION OF PROTOPLASTS. A HISTORICAL SURVEY

Like other cells, many bacteria can be plasmolysed when placed in a hypertonic medium. The protoplasm can be shown to shrink away from the cell wall under these conditions. In many cases very concentrated salt solutions have to be used. Sometimes no plasmolysis at all can be effected. Even if plasmolysis occurs the protoplasm is not entirely detached from the surrounding cell wall and no free protoplasts in the sense given above are obtained. The literature concerning plasmolysis of bacterial cells has been reviewed by Knaysi (1951).

The term plasmoptysis was coined by A. Fischer in 1900 (Fischer, 1900). When plasmoptysis, as defined by Fischer, takes place, the protoplasm is ejected from the cell and is thus separated from the cell wall. Fischer reported the occurrence of this phenomenon in several species, e.g. *Bacillus anthracis* and *Vibrio proteus*. The ejected protoplasm was found to assume the form of a sphere. Fischer's work was criticized by other scientists, and in a later paper he admitted that two similar but not identical phenomena could be observed when cells of *V. proteus* were submitted to unfavourable living conditions. Either a general, reversible swelling of the cell body occurred, or a true, irreversible plasmoptysis. In the latter case the empty cell wall adhered to the ejected spherical protoplast as a kind of stalk. In his later paper Fischer (1906) also reported the occurrence of empty cell walls entirely separated from the protoplasm. Considering Garbowski's work (Garbowski, 1907), however, it is doubtful whether a complete separation of the cell wall and protoplasm occurs when *Vibrio* cells undergo plasmoptysis. In other respects Garbowski confirmed most of Fischer's observations and probably Fischer really observed a true plasmoptysis, i.e. ejection of the bacterial protoplasm.

Garbowski investigated plasmoptysis in other species as well, e.g. *Spirillum*, and showed that in this case the ejected protoplasm does not assume a spherical shape but gives rise to irregular masses. This was confirmed by Raichel (1928).

Stapp & Zycha (1931) showed plasmoptysis of *Bacillus mycoides* in a rather clear-cut way when cells were grown in broth containing 0·5-M-magnesium sulphate. Highly refractile spherical vesicles were formed at many places along the thread-like cells. At the same time the refractility of these cells greatly diminished. Finally, the vesicles were released from the remains of the cells which shrank together and disappeared. The vesicles could be stained and contained lipid granules. No further growth or division of the protoplasmic vesicles was observed.

Stähelin has recently (Stähelin, 1953) published pictures of *Bacillus anthracis* cells obtained by phase-contrast microscopy. The pictures show in a very convincing manner the occurrence of true plasmoptysis in this bacterium. The plasmoptysis thus observed took place when the cells were suspended in salt solutions of various kinds. The pictures show that the protoplasts finally separate from the cell wall which remains as an empty cylindrical tube.

The factors causing plasmoptysis remain obscure. Fischer assumed that plasmoptysis represents a weapon for the bacteria in the struggle for life. This is probably not correct, since the free protoplasts have not been observed to reproduce and as a whole seem to represent a rather delicate kind of structure. Plasmoptysis cannot be explained as a purely osmotic phenomenon. Stähelin (1953) points out that both toxic and growth-promoting substances may favour plasmoptysis.

In 1935 Klieneberger-Nobel (Klieneberger, 1935) showed that a growth which did not contain bacillary forms but was composed of soft cytoplasmic elements, globules and minute granules could be separated from a *Streptobacillus moniliformis* culture. The new type of growth was designated by the letter L. It was later shown that the L form is a growth phase of *S. moniliformis*. Similar growth phases composed of soft elements forming microcolonies have since 1935 been demonstrated in several bacterial genera, e.g. *Bacteroides, Proteus, Salmonella, Haemophilus, Clostridium* and *Bacillus*. In order to obtain L forms of these bacteria, however, the cells have to be subjected to an unusual or unfavourable environment. Penicillin prevents the normal growth but induces the formation of the so-called large bodies which form the first stages of the L growth. Complete reviews of the properties of the L forms have recently been given by Dienes & Weinberger (1951), Klieneberger-Nobel (1951) and Tulasne (1951, 1953). I only wish to point out that the transformation of normal growth into L forms via large bodies has been reported to occur in connexion with typical plasmoptysis phenomena. Dienes (1946) describes the first stages of the transformation of normal *Proteus* bacilli into L forms as follows: 'the mechanism by which the large bodies are produced can be most clearly observed in tap water. They are produced by a process which has long been known as 'plasmoptysis'. The contents of the filaments ooze out and remain attached to the filaments as small droplets. A droplet may increase rapidly in size and may develop within 1 or 2 minutes into a full-sized round body. Meanwhile the filament shrivels. It is apparent that most of the content of the filaments flows out to produce a large body.' Tulasne (1951) and Höpken & Bartmann (1955), using the phase-contrast microscope, describe the process similarly, Stempen & Hutchinson (1951), on the other hand, do not interpret the enlargement as a purely physical process (plasmoptysis) but assume that the phenomenon is due primarily to actual growth. Probably a typical plasmoptysis is not a condition precedent for the formation of large bodies and hence these structures may still contain cell-wall material. Tulasne (1951) reports the presence of O antigens in the L form of *Proteus*.

From what has been said above, it should be evident that a separation of the protoplasm from the cell wall may be effected without the disintegration of either structure at the moment of separation. Protoplasts may, however, also be prepared by an actual dissolution of the cell wall under controlled conditions. This has been achieved by using the bacteriolytic agent lysozyme, shown by Salton (1952) to dissolve isolated walls of *Micrococcus lysodeikticus*. The procedure seems to be eminently suited for the preparation of protoplasts of bacteria that are sensitive to lysozyme under physiological conditions, e.g. *Micrococcus, Sarcina* and *Bacillus* spp.

The formation of bacterial protoplasts by means of lysozyme treatment was first demonstrated by Tomcsik & Guex-Holzer (1952). They investigated in detail the action of this enzyme on a bacterium, *Bacillus* M, according to the authors closely related to *B. megaterium*. By adding to the bacterial suspension an antiserum reacting specifically with the polysaccharide present in the capsular structure of *Bacillus* M, a morphological differentiation between protoplasm and cell wall could be observed in the phase-contrast microscope. When lysozyme was added a swelling of the cells was noticed, and at the same time the protoplasm was partly detached from the cell wall. The wall soon dissolved completely and the bacterial protoplasm remained as a spherical body suspended in the medium. Soon, however, the protoplasts changed into empty membranes which then disintegrated still further. The experiments of Tomcsik & Guex-Holzer were performed in physiological saline.

The present author investigated, independently, the action of lysozyme on *Bacillus megaterium* cells *in vivo* (Weibull, 1953a). It was observed that spherical protoplasmic bodies were formed when the cell walls were rapidly dissolved by a fairly high concentration of lysozyme. It was furthermore found that the protoplasts could be stabilized if kept semi-anaerobically in 0·1–0·2 M-sucrose or 7·5% polyethylene glycol. Analyses of the medium showed that at least the greater part of the cell wall was dissolved without any ultraviolet-absorbing constituents leaving the protoplasm. The complete dissolution of the wall has since been demonstrated morphologically (Weibull, 1955a).

The action of lysozyme on a luminescent bacterium, *Achromobacterium fischeri*, has been investigated by Warren & Durso (1952). The fact that the cell rods were transformed into spheroidal or spindle-shaped bodies makes it probable that even in this case a partial dissolution of the cell wall occurred. Luminescence was not inhibited by the concentrations of lysozyme employed.

Protoplasts of *Bacillus subtilis*, *Staphylococcus aureus*, *Sarcina lutea* and *Micrococcus lysodeikticus* have also been prepared by controlled treatment of the cells with lysozyme (Wiame, Storck & Vanderwinckel, 1955; Mitchell, personal communication).

A recovery of part of the cell structure probably occurred also in the experiments of Lester (1953) and Beljanski (1954). In these experiments cells of *Micrococcus lysodeikticus* were treated with lysozyme in sucrose solutions.

PREPARATIVE TECHNIQUES: STABILITY
OF PROTOPLASTS

I. *Preparation without lysozyme*

As previously mentioned Stähelin (1953, 1954) obtained protoplasts from cells of *Bacillus anthracis* by plasmoptysis. The author mentions that the cell wall of the strain used (A_1) was probably unusually weak. The best results were obtained when the bacteria were grown on CCY-agar (Gladstone & Fildes, 1940) containing an excess of yeast extract but no glutamine and no glycerophosphate. After 20 hr. growth at 37° the cells were suspended in Ringer's solution (0·9% NaCl, 0·03%KCl and 0·026% anhydrous $CaCl_2$). In this medium 80–95% of the cells were transformed into protoplasts. The stability of the protoplasts and the factors influencing it are not explicitly stated. Various plasmolysis experiments have, however, been reported (Stähelin, 1954).

II. *Preparation of protoplasts by controlled treatment with lysozyme*

Bacillus megaterium. The dissolution of the cell wall has in most cases been effected by a fairly high concentration of lysozyme, 0·01–0·05%. Since the protoplasts are most stable under anaerobic conditions, the lysis is preferably carried out in narrow test-tubes using dense bacterial suspensions (5–50 mg. bacterial dry weight/ml.) if a complete recovery of the protoplasts is desired.

When no stabilizing agent is present the protoplasts are destroyed almost immediately after their formation. As stabilizer sucrose or polyethylene glycol (average molecular weight 4000) has most often been used. The concentrations of these solutes have been 0·1–0·2 M and 7·5%, respectively, and the protoplasts have remained stable for at least 24 hr. The protoplasts may be precipitated by centrifugation without disintegration, but resuspended particles are markedly less stable. Other efficient stabilizers are 0·3 M-glucose and 0·15 M-raffinose, melibiose or trehalose. Cellobiose (0·15 M) and erythritol (0·3 M) do not confer any stability. Some stability is obtained in a medium containing 0·15 M-sodium chloride.

Even if a stabilizer is present the protoplasts disintegrate more or less rapidly when a suspension of them is shaken in air.

The cultural conditions seem to influence the stability properties of *Bacillus megaterium* protoplasts under aerobic conditions. The data given above refer to cells grown for 6–12 hr. in 2% 'Difco' peptone at 30° with a maximal depth of liquid of 25 mm. Aeration was effected by placing the culture flasks on a rotary shaker working at about 100 r.p.m.

When the speed of the shaker is about 400 r.p.m. the cells are smaller and the corresponding protoplasts show a higher degree of stability (Storck, personal communication).

The stability of the protoplasts is also improved when the cells are grown on a synthetic medium containing glucose as carbon source (McQuillen, 1955a). The protoplasts from such cells are stable even when aerated in a gentle way.

Bacillus M. The original experiments of Tomcsik & Guex-Holzer (1952) were performed using Ringer's solution as suspending medium. Evidently some stabilization is effected by this solution, since protoplasts can be observed several hours after the dissolution of the cell walls. Much better stability is obtained in 0·3 M-sucrose (Tomcsik & Guex-Holzer, 1954).

Bacillus subtilis. The properties of protoplasts obtained from this bacterium have been described by Wiame, Storck & Vanderwinckel (1955). The cells were grown in a synthetic medium with glucose as carbon source (Wiame & Storck, 1953). The protoplasts were obtained by treating cells with lysozyme (final concentration 0·1 %) in a medium containing 0·05 M-phosphate (pH 7·0) and 0·5 M-sucrose. These protoplasts seem to be more stable than those obtained from *B. megaterium*. Respiratory experiments lasting several hours are reported. The highest degree of stabilization was effected by 0·25–0·5 M-sodium chloride, but in this medium the action of lysozyme on the cells is inhibited.

STRUCTURE OF PROTOPLASTS

Bacillus megaterium. It has been shown by light and electron microscopy that isolated cell walls of this bacterium are dissolved by lysozyme (Welshimer, 1953; Salton, personal communication). Assuming that the action of the enzyme on the cell walls when isolated and *in situ* is the same, this indicates that the protoplast formation is due to the complete removal of the rigid envelope of the bacterium.

On lysis in the presence of sucrose a large amount of substances of high molecular weight goes into solution. This can be shown by analysis of the medium surrounding the cells before and after the treatment with lysozyme. The dissolved material shows, however, no specific light absorption in the ultraviolet spectral range, suggesting that protoplasmic constituents do not leak into the medium during lysis or afterwards. This is furthermore evidenced by the fact that at the same time no change of the inorganic phosphate content of the medium is observed (Weibull, 1955b). Therefore, the substances going into solution most probably represent cell-wall material exclusively. A quantitative estimate of the material has been made by means of gravimetric analyses of the medium before the addition of lysozyme and after the formation of protoplasts. When the volume change of the bacterial body accompanying the removal of the cell wall is taken into consideration, the analyses show that the cell wall represents about 45% of the total cell weight. About the same figure (38%) is obtained by a direct weighing of the cells and the corresponding protoplasts after fixation with formaldehyde.

The removal of the cell wall can also be demonstrated directly by comparing cells and fixed protoplasts suspended in Indian ink (Weibull 1955a). The intact cells are shown to consist of a central part, surrounded by an outer, somewhat brighter, envelope. Such an envelope, obviously representing the cell wall, does not surround the protoplasts.

When protoplasts are stained by an appropriate method and investigated in the light microscope it is seen that flagella are still attached to these bodies (Weibull, 1953a). This is also evidenced by electron micrographs of protoplasts fixed in formaldehyde. It can thus be concluded that the flagella are protoplasmic organelles piercing the cell wall.

As mentioned earlier the protoplasts rapidly undergo lysis unless the medium contains a stabilizing agent. Observations of such a lysate with the phase-contrast microscope reveal two kinds of remaining structures, namely, empty vesicles or 'ghosts' and small granules. The same structures are seen when cells are lysed directly with lysozyme, i.e. not via the formation of protoplasts.

The granules can be isolated by differential centrifugation (Weibull, 1953b). They are almost completely soluble in warm alkali and in warm chloroform. The solution in alkali shows no specific light absorption between 250 and 300 mμ. They contain about 0·25% nitrogen (Salton, personal communication) and are stainable with Sudan black B. These facts confirm the report of Lemoigne, Delaporte & Croson (1944) that the granules in the cells of *Bacillus megaterium* consist of lipid material, found by them to be polymerized β-hydroxy-butyric acid.

Like the granules described above, the 'ghosts' can also be separated from other cytoplasmic elements by centrifugation (Weibull, 1953b). They form dark yellow pellets in the centrifuge tubes. Electron micrographs of the 'ghost' fraction, fixed in osmic tetroxide vapour, reveal membrane-like bodies and granules, most of which are included within the membranes. When unfixed specimens are investigated only amorphous masses are seen. Evidently the membranes form a rather delicate kind of structure, probably partly consisting of lipids.

The 'ghost' fraction contains at least most of the pigmented material of the cells. The absorption spectra of 'ghosts' suspended in 70% glycerol before and after reduction with sodium hydrosulphite can be investigated with the 'Beckman' spectrophotometer (Weibull, 1953b). The resulting curve obtained from a reduced suspension shows maxima at 530, 558 and 600 mμ which correspond well to the absorption bands of whole cells of *Bacillus megaterium* (Keilin, 1934). This shows that the entire cytochrome system is present in the 'ghost' fraction.

Because of their membrane-like appearance it has been suggested that the 'ghosts' may represent cytoplasmic membranes, either intact or denatured (Weibull, 1953b). If they are equivalent to undamaged cytoplasmic membranes a numerical relationship of 1:1 would be expected when protoplasts and the corresponding 'ghosts' are counted.

The 'ghosts' usually exhibit a rather weak contrast in the phase-contrast microscope (see fig. 3b, Weibull, 1953a). Their size varies between rather wide limits compared to the relatively small variation in size of the protoplasts, and a large number of lipid granules are found free in the bacterial lysate. It has been found difficult to count these 'ghosts' accurately even with the aid of phase-contrast microscopy.

The situation changes when protoplasts are suspended for 4–8 hr. in a medium containing 0·2 M-sucrose and magnesium salts at a concentration greater than 0·005–0·01 M. When the protoplasts are lysed by diminishing the sucrose content of the medium, 'ghosts' are obtained. All are now, however, of about the same size as the corresponding protoplasts and most of the lipid granules are within the 'ghosts', as is shown in Pl. 1, figs. 1 and 2. These 'ghosts' may be counted in the light microscope, preferably using dark-field illumination. A count of protoplasts and the corresponding 'ghosts' obtained in the presence of magnesium ions showed that $1·00 \pm 0·015$ protoplasts gave rise to $0·98 \pm 0·015$ 'ghosts'. The ratio is thus equal to 1 within the statistical error limits.

'Ghosts' prepared in the presence and in the absence of magnesium ions have also been counted in the electron microscope by the method of Williams & Backus (1949). Experiments of this type have shown that 1·3–1·4 membrane-like bodies are obtained from each protoplast in the former case. Some of them give the impression of 'ghosts' split into halves. This would explain the value obtained (1·35 instead of the expected figure 1·0).

In the absence of magnesium ions, on the other hand, 3–5 'ghosts' are obtained together with many free lipid granules. In this case the size and shape of the 'ghosts' varies considerably, some of them being below the limit of resolution of the light microscope. Pl. 1, figs. 3 and 4, represent electron micrographs of the two types of 'ghosts'. The background material in the droplets consists essentially of soluble bacterial proteins; latex spheres are also present.

The data obtained from the counting experiments suggest that the 'ghosts' prepared in the presence of magnesium ions actually represent empty cytoplasmic membranes, perhaps including some additional structure, whereas in the absence of magnesium ions the membranes are split into fragments of varying size.

The presence of magnesium ions diminishes the amount of material released during the lysis of the protoplasts by 10–15 %.

The protoplasmic constituents other than the lipid granules and the 'ghosts' have been characterized by ultracentrifugal studies on the lysate obtained from protoplasts (Weibull, 1953 b). Similar results are obtained when whole cells are lysed. The macromolecular organisation of *Bacillus megaterium* cells and protoplasts thus fits into the general pattern characteristic of microbial cells as described by Schachman, Pardee & Stanier (1952). It may be mentioned, however, that the deoxyribonucleic acid (DNA) of *B. megaterium* sediments faster than all other macromolecular components in 0·15 M-sodium chloride. Apparently the DNA is obtained as a kind of gel in this medium.

Bacillus M. Tomcsik & Guex-Holzer have shown in an immunological study (1954) that an antiserum prepared by injecting protoplasts of this bacterium into rabbits does not agglutinate isolated cell walls or boiled bacteria. Protoplasts and live bacteria, on the other hand, are agglutinated. Cell wall antisera agglutinate boiled and live bacteria but not protoplasts. The experimental findings indicate that the cell wall is completely removed from the cell body by the lysozyme treatment except for a thermolabile surface antigen. This antigen probably represents the flagellar protein. Thus this investigation of the immunological properties of *Bacillus* M confirms the results obtained by analytical and morphological studies on *B. megaterium* (see above).

Bacillus subtilis. Wiame *et al.* (1955) report that flagella are attached to the protoplasts of this bacterium.

PERMEABILITY PROPERTIES OF PROTOPLASTS

In the present paper a description will be given of the permeability properties of protoplasts of *Bacillus* M and *B. megaterium* as manifested by a correlation between the volume of the protoplasts and the osmotic pressure of the surrounding medium. Some findings concerning the permeability properties of intact cells will also be discussed.

If one assumes that the protoplasts are surrounded by a semi-permeable membrane, a decrease of the volume of these bodies following an increase of the concentration of a solute in the medium indicates that they are less permeable to the solute than to water. In quantitative terms the volume changes should follow the law $P(V-b) = \text{const.}$ P represents the osmotic pressure of the medium and V the volume of the cell; b is equal to the 'dead space' within the cell filled with osmotically inert substances. This law has been found to hold for cells of higher organisms within certain concentration limits (Lucké, 1940). If the cells represented membrane-less gel bodies it is likely that the law would not be followed (Höber, 1945).

Bacillus M. The osmotic properties of protoplasts of this bacterium, obtained by plasmoptysis, have been investigated by Stähelin (1954). The volume changes of individual protoplasts could be followed and measured under the light microscope, since these showed a tendency to adhere to the coverslip.

Protoplasts were suspended in sucrose or sodium chloride solutions. When the solute concentration was increased, the volume of the proto-plasts decreased and vice versa. In other words, the protoplasts were plasmolysable, indicating a pronounced impermeability to the solutes studied. Stähelin showed that the volume changes of the protoplasts of *Bacillus* M follow the law $P(V-b) = \text{const.}$ approximately. The author points out, however, that, in order to obtain a good approximation, one has to assume an implausibly high value for the quantity b.

The average volume of the protoplasts in 10 % sucrose was found to be 0·76, the volume in 1 % sodium chloride being taken as unity. It is pointed out that the complicated physico-chemical conditions inside the cells make difficult a quantitative interpretation of these data.

In the same paper Stähelin reports the interesting observation that two protoplasts can be made to coalesce to form a greater spherical body when they are placed in a hypotonic solution or when the temperature is held above 40°.

Bacillus megaterium. The permeability properties of protoplasts of this bacterium have been studied by osmotic experiments in many respects similar to those described above (Weibull, 1955b). The average volume of the protoplasts was determined by measuring the diameters of 50–400 of these bodies with the aid of an ocular micrometer. The unexpected fact was then revealed that the osmotic pressure of the medium before the cell wall is removed has little or no influence on the volume of the protoplasts. The volume of protoplasts obtained per g. dry weight of whole cells was found to be 1·1 ml. in 0·1–0·2 M-sucrose and 1·3 ml. in 5·8–16% polyethylene glycol. The osmotic pressure inside the intact cell of B. megaterium cannot therefore be estimated from the experiments carried out so far.

Once the protoplasts have been formed they respond to changes in the osmotic pressure of the external medium.

The plasmolysis exhibited in polyethylene glycol solutions is reversible in a nearly quantitative way. Plasmolysis could be effected with sucrose, glucose and polyethylene glycol but not with urethane. Experiments with phosphate buffers did not give quite clear-cut results, since many protoplasts disintegrated. Determinations of the impermeable volume (see below) of the protoplasts have, however, indicated that the protoplasts are impermeable also to phosphate.

When the volume of the protoplasts is plotted against the reciprocal of the osmotic pressure of the medium a straight line is obtained. This shows that the law $P(V-b) = $ const. is valid, since it can be written in the form $V = $ const.$/P + b$. As pointed out previously, the existence of a semi-permeable membrane around the protoplasts is thus strongly suggested. The volume of the osmotically inert substances, i.e. the quantity b in the equation above, has been found to represent about 35% (v/v) of the protoplasm of the living cell. The remaining part of the protoplasm should then represent the 'free space' inside the cells, containing osmotically transferable water and dissolved substances of low molecular weight.

The independence of the protoplast volume of the osmotic pressure of the medium before the removal of the cell wall is not easy to explain. One could assume a more or less free passage of substances of low molecular weight into and out of the protoplasts during their formation. This explanation however, is not very probable, since no ultraviolet-absorbing substances or inorganic phosphates (Weibull, 1953a, 1955b) are found in the medium after the bacterial cells have been treated with lysozyme in sucrose solutions.

A comparison between the results obtained from the osmotic experiments described above makes it likely that the permeability of the protoplasts of Bacillus M and B. megaterium is fairly similar.

The permeability properties of resting, intact cells of *Bacillus mega-terium* in regard to various solutes under semi-anaerobic conditions were studied by adding to a heavy bacterial suspension a solution containing a known amount of the substance to be investigated. After some time the cells were removed by centrifugation and the concentration of the solute in the supernatant was determined.

The space not permeated by the solute in the final solution is given by the formula

$$V_{\text{impermeable}} = V_1 + V_2 - V_2 . c/c_s,$$

where V_1 represents the volume of the original bacterial suspension, V_2 the volume of the added solution, c and c_s the initial and final concentration of the solute. $V_{\text{impermeable}}$ may be called the impermeable volume of the bacterium.

The experimental results have shown (Weibull, 1955*a*) that under the given conditions the greater part of the bacterial body is impermeable to a number of solutes such as phosphate ions, sucrose and cozymase but permeable to urethane. In quantitative terms the impermeable volume is 2·9 ml./g. of dried bacteria.

This figure may be compared with the average volume of the whole bacterial cells and of the included protoplasm. These quantities were determined by measuring, under the light microscope, the length and width of a great number of bacteria and the width of the protoplasm. A good morphological differentiation between protoplasm and cell wall was obtained by suspending the bacteria in dilute Indian ink, as previously described. It was found that the volume of a quantity of live bacteria corresponding to a dry weight of 1 g. is 4·5 ml. and the volume of the protoplasm 2·5 ml. It can thus be concluded that the impermeable volume of *Bacillus megaterium*, 2·9 ml./g. of dried bacterial cells, is considerably smaller than the volume of the whole cells, 4·5 ml., but only slightly larger than the volume of the protoplasm, 2·5 ml. These facts are most easily explained by assuming the existence of a permeability barrier at the surface of the protoplasm. The difference between the morphologically determined volume of the protoplasm and the impermeable volume most probably represents the volume of the polypeptide and polysaccharide molecules of the cell wall.

It may be mentioned that it has been found impossible to plasmolyse *Bacillus megaterium* (strain KM) even by saturated sodium chloride or sucrose solutions.

As previously mentioned, the average volume of the protoplasts, determined by measuring the diameters of a large number of them, indicates that 1·1–1·3 ml. of protoplasts are obtained from a suspension of bacterial cells of dry weight 1·0 g. This means that the protoplasm shrinks to about half its original volume when the cell wall is removed.

A comparison between permeability properties of whole cells and protoplasts indicates that the permeability of the protoplasm is similar in regard to sucrose, urethane and phosphate before and after removal of the cell wall.

ENZYMOLOGY, METABOLISM AND FUNCTIONING OF PROTOPLASTS

The present author observed (Weibull, 1953 a) that whole cells and protoplasts have the same endogenous respiration and oxidize glucose at the same rate. This shows that at least many enzyme systems are left intact in the protoplasts. To the author's knowledge no enzyme activity has been found in isolated cell walls.

The complete cytochrome system is found in the protoplasts, more precisely in the 'ghost' fraction (see above). Storck (personal communication) has found that the total succinoxidase activity resides in the same fraction.

The biochemical capabilities of the protoplasts will be discussed in Dr McQuillen's contribution to this symposium. Only a short account will be given here.

Various nutrients are incorporated into the nucleic acid and protein fractions of the protoplasts. The rates of incorporation by the protoplasts are comparable to those shown by intact growing cells (McQuillen, 1955a).

Adaptive enzyme formation has been demonstrated in protoplasts of Bacillus subtilis (Wiame et al. 1955). The synthesis of the enzyme arabokinase was studied. Adaptive enzyme formation also takes place in protoplasts of B. megaterium (McQuillen, 1955b).

Salton & McQuillen (1955) and Brenner & Stent (1955) have shown that protoplasts of Bacillus megaterium are capable of supporting the growth of bacteriophages. The same is true also for protoplasts of B. subtilis (Mutsaars, 1955).

Salton (1955) has demonstrated that cells of Bacillus megaterium, committed to spore formation, can be converted to protoplasts which are then able to develop spores.

Recently McQuillen (this volume) has been able to demonstrate an increase of the volume and the dry weight of the protoplasts under aerobic conditions by incubating them at 28° in a medium containing sucrose (0·2 M), glucose and amino acids, and shaking the suspension gently. The growth of the protoplasts was comparable to that of intact cells. Furthermore, using 0·5 M-phosphate as stabilizing medium, McQuillen has found that after about 6 hr. dumbbell-shaped protoplasts appear. This very probably implies that the protoplasts can be brought to divide.

CONCLUSIONS AND PERSPECTIVES

It is apparent that the protoplasm of several bacterial species may be separated from the cell wall and still remain as a relatively stable structural unit. In addition to a mild method of separation, the presence of an agent stabilizing the naked protoplasm is essential for the success of the separation.

It is not easy to offer a simple explanation of the stabilization phenomenon. It can hardly be explained in exclusively osmotic terms. Equimolecular concentrations of sucrose, sodium chloride and cellobiose, for instance, give good, moderate and no stability, respectively, to the protoplasts of *Bacillus megaterium*. Moreover, the same protoplasts are less stable under aerobic than under anaerobic conditions.

From what has been said previously it should be evident that the removal of the bacterial cell wall from the cell in the presence of a stabilizing agent does not profoundly change the structure and capabilities of the bacterial protoplasm. The permeability properties of the protoplasts seem to be similar to those of intact cells. The protoplasts respire at about the same rate as do the cells and are capable of phage production and spore formation. Under special conditions they grow and probably also divide.

On the other hand, the protoplasts are hardly equivalent to intact cells. Active movements of the protoplasts have not been demonstrated as yet, in spite of the fact that flagella are still attached to them. The osmotic pressure experiments performed on protoplasts of *Bacillus megaterium* also suggest that the structure of the protoplasm is slightly changed when the cell wall is removed. Otherwise the volume of the protoplasts would not be independent of the initial osmotic pressure of the medium. The metabolism of protoplasts and cells seems to be very similar but is probably not identical. Further work in this field will certainly add new facts to our knowledge concerning the delicately balanced processes giving rise to growth and division. Refined comparative investigations of the structure of cells and protoplasts should also be of great value.

At the beginning of this paper the L forms of some bacteria were referred to as being of protoplasmic nature. Metabolic and serological studies together with growth experiments on cells, protoplasts, and L forms may disclose interesting relationships between these microbial structures.

REFERENCES

BELJANSKI, M. (1954). L'action de la ribonucléase et de la desoxyribonucléase sur l'incorporation de glycocolle radio-actif dans les protéines de lysats de *Micrococcus lysodeikticus*. *Biochim. biophys. Acta*, **15**, 425.

BRENNER, S. & STENT, G. S. (1955). Bacteriophage growth in protoplasts of *Bacillus megaterium*. *Biochim. biophys. Acta*, **17**, 473.

DIENES, L. (1946). Reproductive processes in *Proteus* cultures. *Proc. Soc. exp. Biol.*, *N.Y.*, **63**, 265.

DIENES, L. & WEINBERGER, H. J. (1951). The L forms of bacteria. *Bact. Rev.* **15**, 245.

FISCHER, A. (1900). Die Empfindlichkeit der Bakterienzelle und das baktericide Serum. *Z. Hyg. InfektKr.* **35**, 1.

FISCHER, A. (1906). Über Plasmoptyse der Bakterien. *Ber. deutsch. bot. Ges.* **24**, 55.

GARBOWSKI, L. (1907). Gestaltsänderung und Plasmoptyse. *Arch. Protistenk.* **9**, 53.

GLADSTONE, G. P. & FILDES, P. (1940). A simple culture medium for general use without meat extract or peptone. *Brit. J. exp. Path.* **21**, 161.

HÖBER, R. (1945). *Physical Chemistry of Cells and Tissues*, p. 272. Philadelphia and Toronto: The Blakiston Company.

HÖPKEN, W. & BARTMANN, K. (1955). Phasenkontrastmikroskopische Beobachtungen des durch Penicillin ausgelösten L-Cyclus von *Bact. proteus*. *Zbl. Bakt.* Abt. 1, Orig., **162**, 372.

KEILIN, D. (1934). Cytochrome and the supposed direct spectroscopic observation of oxidase. *Nature, Lond.*, **133**, 290.

KLIENEBERGER, E. (1935). The natural occurrence of pleuro-pneumonia-like organisms in apparent symbiosis with *Streptobacillus moniliformis* and other bacteria. *J. Path. Bact.* **40**, 93.

KLIENEBERGER-NOBEL, E. (1951). Filterable forms of bacteria. *Bact. Rev.* **15**, 77.

KNAYSI, G. (1951). *Elements of Bacterial Cytology*, 2nd ed. Ithaca, New York: Comstock Publishing Company.

LEMOIGNE, M., DELAPORTE, B. & CROSON, M. (1944). Contribution a l'étude botanique et biochimique des bactéries du genre *Bacillus*. *Ann. Inst. Pasteur*, **70**, 224.

LESTER, R. L. (1953). *In vitro* incorporation of leucine into the proteins of *Micrococcus lysodeikticus*. *J. Amer. chem. Soc.* **75**, 5448.

LUCKÉ, B. (1940). The living cell as an osmotic system and its permeability to water. *Cold Spr. Harb. Sym. quant. Biol.* **8**, 123.

MCQUILLEN, K. (1955a). Bacterial protoplasts. I. Protein and nucleic acid metabolism in protoplasts of *Bacillus megaterium*. *Biochim. biophys. Acta*, **17**, 382.

MCQUILLEN, K. (1955b). Protein, nucleic acid and adaptive enzyme formation in protoplasts of *Bacillus megaterium*. *J. gen. Microbiol.* **13**, iv.

MUTSAARS, W. (1955). *Ann. Inst. Pasteur*, **89**, 166.

RAICHEL, B. (1928). Über den Einfluss osmotisch wirksamer Mittel auf die Bakterienzelle. *Arch. Protistenk.* **63**, 333.

SALTON, M. R. J. (1952). Cell wall of *Micrococcus lysodeikticus* as the substrate of lysozyme. *Nature, Lond.*, **170**, 746.

SALTON, M. R. J. (1955). The formation of spores in protoplasts of *Bacillus megaterium*. *J. gen. Microbiol.* **13**, iv.

SALTON, M. R. J. & McQUILLEN, K. (1955). Bacterial protoplasts. II. Bacterio-phage multiplication in protoplasts of sensitive and lysogenic strains of *Bacillus megaterium*. *Biochim. biophys. Acta*, **17**, 465.

SCHACHMAN, H. K., PARDEE, A. B. & STANIER, R. Y. (1952). Studies on the macro-molecular organization of microbial cells. *Arch. Biochem. Biophys.* **38**, 245.

STÄHELIN, H. (1953). Über spontane sphärische Transformation von Milzbrand-bazillen. *Schweiz. Z. allg. Path. Bakt.* **16**, 892.

STÄHELIN, H. (1954). Über osmotisches Verhalten und Fusion nach der Proto-plasten von *Bact. anthracis*. *Schweiz. Z. allg. Path. Bakt.* **17**, 296.

STAPP, C. & ZYCHA, H. (1931). Morphologische Untersuchungen an *Bacillus mycoides*; ein Beitrag zur Frage des Pleomorphismus der Bakterien. *Arch. Mikrobiol.* **2**, 493.

STEMPEN, H. & HUTCHINSON, W. G. (1951). The formation and development of large bodies in *Proteus vulgaris* OX-19. *J. Bact.* **61**, 321.

TOMCSIK, J. & GUEX-HOLZER, S. (1952). Änderung der Struktur der Bakterienzelle im Verlauf der Lysozym-Einwirkung. *Schweiz. Z. allg. Path. Bakt.* **15**, 517.

TOMCSIK, J. & GUEX-HOLZER, S. (1954). Antikörperproduktion mit isolierter Bakterienzellwand und mit Protoplasten. *Experientia*, **10**, 484.

TULASNE, R. (1951). Les formes L des bactéries. *Rev. Immunol.* **15**, 223.

TULASNE, R. (1953). Le cycle L et les formes naines des bactéries. In *Bacterial Cytology, Symp. 6th Congr. Int. Microbiol.*, Rome, p. 144.

WARREN, G. H. & DURSO, J. G. (1952). Effect of lysozyme on the cell structure of *Achromobacter fischeri*. *J. Bact.* **64**, 483.

WEIBULL, C. (1953a). The isolation of protoplasts from *Bacillus megaterium* by controlled treatment with lysozyme. *J. Bact.* **66**, 688.

WEIBULL, C. (1953b). Characterisation of the protoplasmic constituents of *Bacillus megaterium*. *J. Bact.* **66**, 696.

WEIBULL, C. (1955a). The localisation of a permeability barrier in the cells of *Bacillus megaterium*. *Exp. Cell Res.* **9**, 139.

WEIBULL, C. (1955b). Osmotic properties of protoplasts of *Bacillus megaterium*. *Exp. Cell Res.* **9**, 294.

WELSHIMER, H. J. (1953). The action of lysozyme on the cell wall and capsule of *Bacillus megaterium*. *J. Bact.* **66**, 112.

WIAME, J. M. & STORCK, R. (1953). Métabolisme de l'acide glutamique chez *Bacillus subtilis*. *Biochim. biophys. Acta*, **10**, 268.

WIAME, J. M., STORCK, R. & VANDERWINCKEL, E. (1955). Biosynthèse induite d'arabokinase dans les protoplastes de *Bacillus subtilis*. *Biochim. biophys. Acta* **18**, 353.

WILLIAMS, R. C. & BACKUS, R. C. (1949). Macromolecular weights determined by direct particle counting. I. The weight of the Bushy Stunt Virus particle. *J. Amer. chem. Soc.* **71**, 4052.

EXPLANATION OF PLATE

Figs. 1 and 2. Phase-contrast micro-photographs of protoplasts and 'ghosts' of *Bacillus megaterium*. × 3000. The photographs were taken, developed and printed under identical conditions.

Fig. 1. Protoplasts.

Fig. 2. 'Ghosts' obtained by lysis of protoplasts in the presence of magnesium ions.

Figs. 3 and 4. Electron micrographs of droplets formed by bacterial lysates mixed with a polystyrene latex suspension and sprayed on specimen grids. × c. 3000.

Fig. 3. Protoplasts lysed in the absence of magnesium ions.

Fig. 4. Protoplasts lysed in the presence of magnesium ions.

PLATE 1

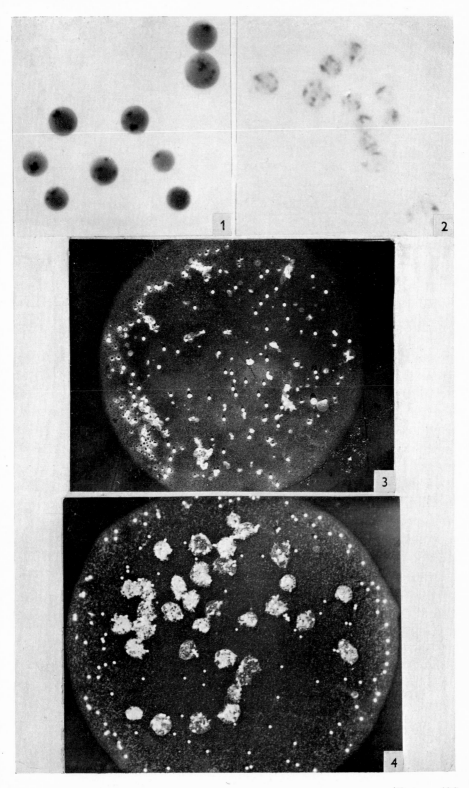

CAPABILITIES OF BACTERIAL PROTOPLASTS

K. McQUILLEN

Department of Biochemistry, University of Cambridge

An understanding of the bacterial cell as a biological entity presupposes detailed knowledge of the structure and function of the whole and of its parts. Other contributors to this symposium are dealing with specialized structures such as flagella, nuclei, cell walls and capsules, and it is abundantly evident what rapid advances are being made in the preparation and characterization of such cellular components. Cytological, histochemical and immunochemical investigations have provided some information on the anatomical localization of specific structures, but the capabilities of isolated subcellular fractions have been less fully studied. This is in part due to the smallness of bacteria and the consequent greater difficulty in taking them to pieces as compared with yeast cells and the cells of animals and plants. It is less than twenty years since the invention of the Booth-Green mill first provided a method for breaking bacteria and preparing cell-free enzymes (Booth & Green, 1938). Since that time other techniques have been devised (Hugo, 1954), but the study of physiological and biochemical properties of bacterial cell components is still rudimentary even when compared with the study of nuclei, mitochondria, microsomes and chloroplasts of higher organisms. It is known that certain enzyme systems and certain pigments are associated with specific 'particles' in some bacteria; it seems probable that the cell walls of certain species are essentially inert—none has ever been shown to possess any enzymic activity, and the chemical composition of some cell walls argues against the presence of protein in the generally accepted sense (see Salton, this volume); and it is certain that capsules can be removed from various organisms without impairing their viability in appropriate media. But much remains to be learned of the relationship between structure and function in the bacterial cell.

A major advance was recently made when Gale & Folkes (1954, 1955 *a, b*) showed that supersonically disrupted staphylococci are able to incorporate isotopically labelled amino acids and to synthesize proteins including certain enzymes. These preparations, which were still active after extraction by various means, seem to consist of the cell envelope (wall) inside which adheres a certain amount of debris. It is not possible yet to decide just which structures of the cell are essential for activity, but in view of the proof that the cell wall of other organisms can be removed without impairing protein and nucleic acid synthesis (see below) it may be that much of Gale's material is inert. The material isolated as the active fraction after disintegration represents only a very small fraction (less than 1 %) of the original dry weight of the cells so that the yield is relatively poor. Possibly these limitations are inherent in mechanical methods of breakage.

BACTERIAL PROTOPLASTS

An alternative method for preparing subcellular components of bacteria may be the use of specific enzymes. Unfortunately, there are few enzymes known which will attack living organisms, but Weibull (1953) has shown that lysozyme can be used to digest away the cell wall and cross-septa of *Bacillus megaterium*. If this is done under appropriate conditions, each rod of the original bacillus yields from one to four spherical 'protoplasts', ideal material for the study of subcellular capabilities at a level one stage below that of the intact cell.

The remainder of this paper is devoted to a discussion of some of the biochemical and physiological properties of these structures as compared with the corresponding properties of intact living bacteria. Although most of the work refers to protoplasts of *Bacillus megaterium*, analogous structures have been prepared from *B. subtilis*, *Micrococcus lysodeikticus*, *Sarcina lutea*, *Staphylococcus aureus* and other organisms (McQuillen, 1955*a*; Mitchell, this volume; Wiame, Storck & Vanderwinckel, 1955).

The preparation and characterization of protoplasts are described in detail in an adjoining paper by Weibull, and it suffices to say that they can be made in excellent yield, comprise 60–80 % of the dry weight of the original cells and consist essentially of an organized structure which when present in the living organism is possibly modified only in shape by the presence of the rigid cell wall. The sequence of events observable by phase-contrast microscopy during the dissolution of the cell wall by lysozyme is represented diagrammatically in Text-fig. 1 (cf. the electron micrographs in Wiame *et al.* 1955).

The principal difficulty in handling protoplasts and studying their behaviour is their extreme fragility and sensitivity to osmotic shock, mechanical treatments such as shaking and centrifuging, and to aeration. Suspension media which provide some protection include sucrose, 0·15– 0·5 M; sodium chloride, 0·25–0·5 M; 'Carbowax 4000', a polythene glycol, 7·5 % (w/v); and phosphate buffer, pH 7·0, 0·5 M (Weibull, 1953; Wiame *et al.* 1955; McQuillen, 1955*c*). The problem of providing air to maintain the metabolism of protoplasts of highly aerobic organisms such as *Bacillus megaterium* has been investigated by McQuillen (1955*a*). Aeration by bubbling or by rotating flasks results in rapid lysis, and ultimately the least damaging technique was found to be gentle rocking of half-filled stoppered test-tubes. For larger scale work, Roux bottles provided with an air vent through a stopper and containing up to 250 ml. have been rocked in metabolic experiments lasting over 6 hr. (McQuillen unpublished).

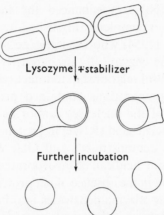

Lysozyme +stabilizer

Further incubation

Text-fig. 1. Formation of spherical protoplasts by lysozyme treatment of rod-shaped cells of *Bacillus megaterium*.

According to Wiame *et al.* (1955) protoplasts of *Bacillus subtilis* are more robust than those from other species, but since Salton (personal communication) has shown that lysozyme does not completely digest the isolated cell walls of this organism, it may be that the spheres formed by lysozyme treatment of *B. subtilis* still bear part of the cell wall.

RESPIRATION

Protoplasts of *Bacillus megaterium* have a high endogenous respiration ($Q_{O_2} = 66$) and can oxidize glucose ($Q_{O_2} = 128$, uncorrected for endogenous). These values are virtually the same as those for intact bacteria (Weibull, 1953). Similarly, preparations from *B. subtilis* were shown by Wiame *et al.* (1955) to oxidize glucose at a constant rate for 3 hr. Osmotic lysis resulted in complete loss of activity in the case of protoplasts of *B. subtilis*, but protoplasts of *B. megaterium* after lysis still oxidized glucose ($Q_{O_2} = 27$). Lysozyme 'lysates' of *Micrococcus lysodeikticus* in sucrose were also able to respire (Beljanski, 1954). Weibull (unpublished) found that 0·005 M-Mg^{++} inhibited both endogenous and glucose respiration of *Bacillus megaterium* protoplasts.

9

SYNTHESIS OF PROTEIN AND NUCLEIC ACID

The presence of a respiratory mechanism in a subcellular preparation is not remarkable, and it is of interest to see what more intricate, synthetic, processes can be carried out. When highly concentrated suspensions of *Micrococcus lysodeikticus* were treated with lysozyme in the presence of sucrose, it was found by Lester (1953) that the 'lysates' could still incorporate ^{14}C-labelled leucine into the protein fraction. Addition of deoxyribonuclease (DNA-ase) enhanced the incorporation, whereas ribonuclease (RNA-ase) completely abolished it. Similar findings were reported by Beljanski (1954) who used glycine in place of leucine, but in neither case was the enzymically prepared 'lysate' characterized at all fully as to its structural relationship to intact cells. It seems probable, however, that these preparations contained protoplasts of *M. lysodeikticus*. The action of the nucleases cannot be taken to indicate the involvement of ribonucleic acid (RNA) in protein synthesis. Firstly, no protein synthesis was demonstrated, and Gale & Folkes (1953) have shown that a single amino acid can be incorporated into bacterial protein by an exchange reaction in the absence of net protein synthesis. Secondly it is unlikely that either enzyme penetrates into intact protoplasts since substances of low molecular weight such as nucleotides and sucrose do not readily pass in or out. Thirdly, Brenner (personal communication) has shown that protoplasts of *Bacillus megaterium* are rapidly lysed by RNA-ase although unaffected by DNA-ase. The stimulatory action of DNA-ase may well have been due to degradation of deoxyribonucleic acid released from bursting organisms rather than to action on protoplasts as such. The highest rates of incorporation of labelled amino acids into protein in these experiments were in the range $0.001-0.0025 \mu$mole/ mg. of protein/hr. at 37°.

A more detailed study of the incorporation of ^{14}C-labelled substrates into protoplasts of *Bacillus megaterium* has been made by McQuillen (1955*a*, *b*, and unpublished). The strain KM was first trained to grow in a glucose-NH$_3$-salts medium and suspensions of washed intact cells and protoplasts were incubated in this medium supplemented with sucrose and the radioactive substrate. In some cases a mixture of amino acids was also added. The preparations were fractionated into lipid, nucleic acid and protein and each was assayed for radioactivity. Samples of protein and nucleic acid were also hydrolysed, chromatographed and radio-autographed. In this way it was possible to determine into which amino acids and purines and pyrimidines the tracer carbon had become incorporated.

It was found that the rates of incorporation of ^{14}C into protoplast constituents were usually between 50 and 100 % of the rates of incorporation into the corresponding fractions of intact cells, even under conditions such that the intact cells were rapidly growing. Using labelled glycine, for instance, the rate of incorporation in a representative experiment amounted to 0.2μmole/mg. protein/hr. i.e. about 1 % of the dry weight of the protoplasts per hour. Such rates were maintained or increased during 3 hr. incubations. There was no incorporation into osmotically lysed protoplasts.

The tracers used have included glucose, acetate, glycine, aspartic acid, uracil and thymine. Table 1 lists the major fractions into which radioactivity becomes incorporated and Tables 2 and 3 indicate specific end products.

The almost exact similarity in behaviour of intact cells and protoplasts is apparent from these tables, but there is one striking difference— protoplasts do not incorporate radioactivity into diaminopimelic acid in their protein fraction, whereas whole cells do. Moreover, this amino acid appears to be absent from protoplasts. This is consistent with its presence as a constituent of the cell wall of *Bacillus megaterium* (Salton, 1953) and with the apparent inability of protoplasts to form a new cell wall. It seems extremely unlikely that protoplasts are unable to synthesize this amino acid, and it may well be that diaminopimelic acid will be found as an excretion product, but this has not yet been investigated.

The pattern of incorporation of acetate carbon into amino acids and pyrimidines is very similar to that found in *Escherichia coli* (McQuillen & Roberts, 1954), where the tricarboxylic acid cycle operates mainly to provide intermediates for amino acid synthesis (Roberts, Abelson, Cowie, Bolton & Britten, 1955).

The diversity, rate and extent of incorporation of carbon from the various tracers make it certain that *de novo* synthesis of most of the cellular components is occurring in this protoplast system rather than that only exchange incorporation is involved. This is confirmed by subsequent work on enzyme synthesis, etc. (see below).

All of the reactions which were tested were found to be inhibited by 2:4-dinitrophenol, which had a comparable effect on both protoplasts and intact cells. On the other hand, uranyl chloride inhibited incorporation of glycine carbon into protoplast nucleic acid but not incorporation into protein (Text-fig. 2). Moreover, neither protein nor nucleic acid synthesis by intact cells was inhibited by this reagent. This may be related to the known interaction of uranyl chloride with the cell walls of various species of bacteria (McQuillen, 1950).

Table 1. *Incorporation of* [14]*C into major fractions of protoplasts*
of Bacillus megaterium

	Fraction		
[14]C substrate	Lipid	Nucleic acid	Protein
Glucose (random)	+ + +	+ + +	+ + +
CH_3[14]COONa	+ + +	+	+ + +
[14]CH_3COONa	+ + +	+	+ + +
CH_2NH_2[14]COOH	.	+ + +	+ + +
Aspartic acid (random)	.	+ + +	+ + +
Uracil (random)	.	+ + +	.
Thymine (random)	.	−	.

Protoplasts were incubated with aeration in a medium containing glucose, sucrose (as stabilizer), NH_3 and inorganic salts as well as the radioactive substrate. Intact cells of *Bacillus megaterium* showed the same pattern of labelling. Symbols + + +, + and − indicate strong, weak and no labelling, respectively. Data of McQuillen (1955*a*, *b*).

Table 2. *Incorporation of* [14]*C into amino acids of the proteins of*
Bacillus megaterium *and its protoplasts*

	[14]C substrate							
	Glucose		Acetate		Aspartic acid		Glycine	
Amino acid	KM	PP	KM	PP	KM	PP	KM	PP
Alanine	+	+	+	+	+	+	−	−
Arginine	+	+	+	+	+	+	−	−
Aspartic acid	+	+	+	+	+	+	(+)	(±)
Glutamic acid	+	+	+	+	+	+	(+)	(±)
Glycine	+	+	−	−	−	−	+	+
Leucine(s)	+	+	+	+	+	+	−	−
Lysine	+	+	+	+	+	+	−	−
Proline	+	+	+	+	+	+	(+)	−
Serine	+	+	−	−	−	−	(±)	(±)
Threonine	+	+	+	+	+	+	−	−
Diaminopimelic acid	+	−	+	−	+	−	(+)	−

Intact cells (KM) or protoplasts (PP) incubated as described in Table 1. Symbols +, (+) and − indicate strong, weak and no labelling, respectively; (±) indicates occasional traces of activity. Data of McQuillen (1955*a*, *b*).

Table 3. *Incorporation of* [14]*C into nucleic acid constituents of*
Bacillus megaterium *and its protoplasts*

	[14]C substrate									
Nucleic acid constituent	Glycine		Acetate		Aspartic acid		Uracil		Thymine	
	KM	PP	KM	PP	KM	PP	KM	PP	KM	PP
Adenine	+	+	−	−	(+)	(+)	−	−	−	−
Guanine	+	+	−	−	(+)	(+)	−	−	−	−
Cytidylic acid	−	−	(+)	(+)	+	+	+	+	−	−
Uridylic acid	−	−	(+)	(+)	+	+	+	+	−	−
Thymidylic acid	−	−	−	−	(+)	(+)	(+)	(+)	−	−

Intact cells (KM) or protoplasts (PP) incubated as described in Table 1. Symbols +, (+) and − indicate strong, weak and no labelling, respectively. Data of McQuillen (1955*a*, *b* and unpublished).

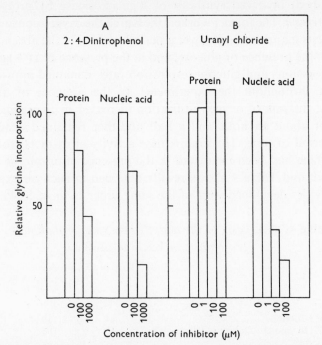

Text-fig. 2. Inhibition of glycine incorporation into protein and nucleic acid of protoplasts of *Bacillus megaterium*. Results expressed relative to 100 for the control in the absence of inhibitor. (Data from McQuillen, 1955a.)

SYNTHESIS OF ENZYMES

Constitutive enzymes

The studies described in the previous section established the considerable synthetic abilities of protoplasts. Some investigations have also been made of the synthesis of specific enzymes by these subcellular preparations. McQuillen (unpublished) has assayed the succinic dehydrogenase activity of protoplasts of *Bacillus megaterium* incubated in the presence of glucose and amino acids with sucrose as stabilizer. Enzyme activity was determined on the sedimentable material using the methylene-blue-Thunberg-tube technique. Increases in activity of up to five-fold were observed during incubations lasting several hours. In general the results were approximately similar to those obtained with intact cells treated in the same way.

Adaptive enzymes

Two studies have been made on the induced biosynthesis of adaptive enzymes by protoplasts. Wiame *et al.* (1955) followed the formation of arabokinase in protoplasts of *Bacillus subtilis*; McQuillen (1955*b*, and unpublished) observed synthesis of β-galactosidase by protoplasts of *B. megaterium*. The former workers measured the oxygen consumption of protoplasts manometrically over a period of 3 hr. in the absence of substrate, in the presence of glucose, and in the presence of L($+$)arabinose. The endogenous and glucose respiration rates remained approximately constant throughout the experiment. In the presence of arabinose, however, the rate of oxygen utilization increased in two stages over a period of about an hour and a half and then remained steady for an equal period of time. The arabokinase activity of extracts from protoplasts which had been incubated in the presence of arabinose was also measured, and Table 4 shows results obtained in such an experiment. The activities developed were of the same order as those in whole cells.

Table 4. *Synthesis of the adaptive enzyme, arabokinase, by protoplasts of* Bacillus subtilis

	Rate of CO_2 production (μl./hr.) after pre-incubation for		
Substrate	0 hr.	1 hr.	2 hr.
ATP (10 μmole)	24	19	28
ATP (10 μmole) + arabinose (20 μmole)	46	106	220
Arabokinase activity	22	87	192

Protoplasts were shaken with arabinose (0·02M) for various periods of time in a solution containing NaCl (0·5M), $(NH_4)_2SO_4$ (0·005M) and yeast extract (0·1 %). Enzyme activity was determined on extracts of lyophilized preparations. Data of Wiame *et al.* (1955).

McQuillen (1955*b*, and unpublished) worked with strain KM of *Bacillus megaterium* used for the tracer studies mentioned above. Both the intact cells and the protoplasts derived from them had relatively low β-galactosidase activity when the organism was grown in a glucose-NH_3-salts medium. However, incubation of either system in the presence of galactose (10 mg./ml.) induced synthesis of the adaptive β-galactosidase, which was estimated using *o*-nitrophenyl-β-D-galactopyranoside as substrate (Lederberg, 1950; Creaser, 1955*a*). The adaptation occurred readily in washed suspensions and was about as rapid in protoplasts as in intact cells. In view of the fragility of protoplasts and the fact that the enzyme is a soluble one, there are some disadvantages in studying this system since, to carry out the assay, the preparations must be centrifuged and washed to remove the galactose and then resuspended in the presence of the *o*-nitrophenyl galactoside. (More recently, thiomethyl-β-D-galactoside has been found to act as an inducer at a concentration of 1 mg./ml.; it appears not to interfere with the assay so that centrifuging and washing can be omitted.)

The synthesis of enzyme continues for some hours, and the final activities may be a hundred times greater than the initial. Several factors influence the adaptation. Aeration is essential, as has been found for all metabolic activities of this organism. Small amounts of glucose (100μg./ml.) are stimulatory but higher concentrations inhibit enzyme formation. Addition of an amino-acid mixture (18 amino acids, each 50μg./ml., see McQuillen & Salton, 1955) or peptone (2 mg./ml.) enhances β-galactosidase synthesis. 2:4-Dinitrophenol inhibits, as do 'aureomycin' (1μg./ml.) and 'puromycin' (25μg./ml.). Uranyl chloride (0·001 M) had no effect on enzyme synthesis although it flocculated the protoplasts, inhibited glycine incorporation into nucleic acid (Text-fig. 2) and reduced bacteriophage multiplication (see below). Creaser (1955b) has shown that β-galactosidase synthesis by intact staphylococci can be inhibited by the purine analogues (8-azaguanine and 2:6-diaminopurine), but not by the pyrimidine analogues (5-nitrouracil, 5-bromouracil, 2-thiouracil and isocytosine). In the supersonically disrupted staphylococci studied by Gale & Folkes (1955b) formation of various enzymes including β-galactosidase was shown. After extraction of much of the nucleic acid from these preparations, the synthesis of enzymes was found to be enhanced to a greater or less extent by addition of purines and pyrimidines, ribonucleic acid or deoxyribonucleic acid. In much other work, too, there are indications of a close interrelationship between protein and nucleic acid metabolism. It will be interesting to determine whether or not protein synthesis in protoplasts can occur without concomitant synthesis of nucleic acid.

MULTIPLICATION OF BACTERIOPHAGES
The virulent bacteriophage system

In view of the considerable structural integrity maintained in protoplasts and the fact that the cell wall is not essential for protein, nucleic acid and enzyme synthesis, it is perhaps not surprising that bacteriophages can multiply in protoplasts.

Phage active against the intact cell is not adsorbed by protoplasts of *Bacillus megaterium* (Weibull, 1953) as might have been anticipated, since the primary interaction between host and virus is probably a specific reaction of the phage tail with the bacterial cell wall. In at least some bacterium-bacteriophage systems, after adsorption the DNA of the phage passes into the bacterial cell leaving the phage protein coat outside. Most of this protein can be removed without impairing the ability of the host/phage DNA system to continue the normal course of intracellular phage development, lysis of the bacteria and liberation of many mature bacteriophage particles from each organism. Text-fig. 3 represents diagrammatically the possible course of events.

It has been shown independently by Brenner & Stent (1955) and Salton & McQuillen (1955) that bacteriophage multiplication can occur in protoplasts of *Bacillus megaterium* if the bacteria are infected with virulent phage before removal of their cell walls by lysozyme. This sequence also is represented in Text-fig. 3.

Brenner & Stent (1955) infected *Bacillus megaterium* strain KM with phage C in a peptone medium and, after centrifuging and washing, resuspended the cells in sucrose buffer. One portion of the suspension

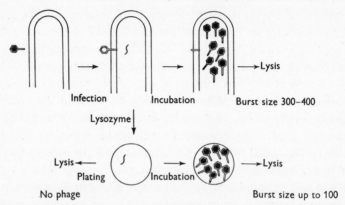

Text-fig. 3. Representation of current hypotheses concerning multiplication of virulent bacteriophage together with implications of conversion of cells to protoplasts.

was treated with lysozyme, and after protoplast formation was complete, as indicated by microscopic examination, both this and the other portion, consisting of infected whole bacteria, were diluted in sucrose-buffer-peptone and incubated at 25°. Samples were plated at intervals to assay the number of infective centres. The intact cells exhibited a normal one-step growth curve with a latent period of 90 min. and a burst size of 230. The initial counts in the protoplast system were, however, less than 1 % of the input, presumably because during the 'eclipse period' plating of protoplasts results in immediate lysis and prevents maturation of the phage. Later the number of infective centres increased and ultimately reached a value fourteen times greater than the input level.

Single-burst experiments were also carried out by Brenner & Stent (1955) to determine whether the phage multiplication in protoplasts results from most protoplasts giving small bursts or a minority only giving large bursts. Table 5 shows shows the distribution of numbers of infective centres among forty tubes which originally contained an average of one infected protoplast per tube. It seems that only small bursts were occurring from most of the protoplasts.

Table 5. *Single-burst experiment on bacteriophage-infected protoplasts of* Bacillus megaterium

No. of plaques	No. of tubes	No. of plaques	No. of tubes
0	24	5	1
1	5	12	2
2	2	23	1
3	4	25	1

Forty tubes containing an average of one infected protoplast per tube were incubated and the whole contents of each tube eventually plated to determine the number of infective centres.

Fraction of tubes without burst	$24/40 = 0.60$
Average number of bursts per tube	$-\ln 0.60 = 0.51$
Average number of infected protoplasts per tube	1.0
Fraction of protoplasts yielding bursts	$0.51/1.0 = 0.51$

Data of Brenner & Stent (1955).

This small burst size is not invariably found with protoplasts; Salton & McQuillen (1955; see below) using a glucose-sucrose-salts medium obtained values of about 100, or 30 % of those obtained with intact cells. They were, however, unable to get satisfactory results in peptone media and, moreover, they aerated their suspensions which Brenner & Stent (1955) did not. More recently Brenner (personal communication), using an asparagine-phosphate-sucrose medium in shaken tubes, obtained a burst size of 45 for intact *Bacillus megaterium* and 30 for protoplasts. He also showed that DNA-ase did not affect the burst size from either preparation, and that while RNA-ase had no effect on intact cells it abolished phage multiplication in protoplasts. Microscopic examination showed that the protoplasts were lysed by treatment with RNA-ase. Unpublished experiments of Brenner have also indicated that uranyl acetate consistently inhibits bacteriophage production in protoplasts by 80 % or more. This may be related to McQuillen's finding that uranyl chloride causes inhibition of glycine incorporation into protoplast nucleic acid.

Salton & McQuillen (1955) infected the same strain (KM) of *Bacillus megaterium* with phage C in peptone water and then studied virus multiplication in intact cells, protoplasts and osmotically lysed protoplasts in a glucose-sucrose-salts medium—this synthetic medium was not suitable for adsorption. Using high multiplicities of infection they found no evidence of the 'eclipse period' and the rate of phage release was comparable in protoplasts and intact cells (Text-fig. 4). The lysed protoplasts, which were included as a control in case any intact cells survived lysozyme treatment, showed no increase in phage titre.

When low multiplicities of infection were used the 'eclipse period' was readily apparent, and again the final yield from protoplasts was up to 25 % of that from the intact organisms (Text-fig. 5). In these experiments the only sources of carbon and nitrogen were glucose, sucrose and ammonia.

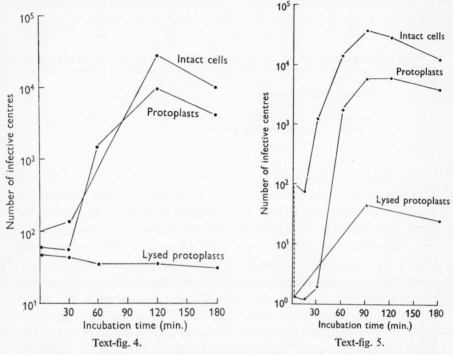

Text-fig. 4.   Text-fig. 5.

Text-fig. 4. Bacteriophage production after high-multiplicity infection of *Bacillus megaterium* KM with phage C. Intact cells were infected before washing and conversion to protoplasts. (Data from Salton & McQuillen, 1955.)

Text-fig. 5. Bacteriophage production after low-multiplicity infection of *Bacillus megaterium* KM with phage C. Intact cells were infected before washing and conversion to protoplasts. Note the 'eclipse period' which lasts for the first 30 min. (contrast text-fig. 4). (Data from Salton & McQuillen, 1955.)

The lysogenic system

Bacteriophage multiplication can also be studied in lysogenic bacteria. These are believed to carry prophage as a genetic component (Lwoff, 1953). Cultures of such organisms often exhibit 'spontaneous' phage production which is thought to be due to lysis of a small proportion of the cells in which prophage has for some unknown reason developed through the vegetative phase to become mature phage. Various inducing agents such as ultraviolet light, certain reducing agents and hydrogen peroxide may cause most or all of the lysogenic bacteria in a growing culture to produce mature phage and eventually lyse. In many respects the course of events after induction of a lysogenic culture resembles that after infection of a non-lysogenic culture with virulent phage. It is represented diagrammatically in Text-fig. 6.

Suitable media are necessary both for maintenance of the condition of lysogeny in the culture and also for conferring a condition of 'aptitude' for induction on the cells. Simple synthetic media were developed by

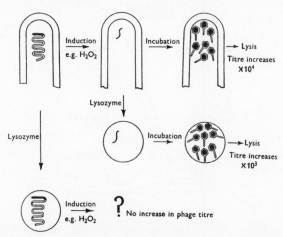

Text-fig. 6. Representation of current hypotheses concerning induction of a lysogenic organism together with implications of conversion of cells to protoplasts.

McQuillen & Salton (1955) for the lysogenic strain 899(1) of *Bacillus megaterium*. Hydrogen peroxide (final concentration 67 μM.) was used as inducing agent. Two types of experiment were attempted—induction prior to conversion of cells to protoplasts and direct induction of protoplasts (Text-fig. 6). Only the former were successful. The procedure was as follows (Salton & McQuillen, 1955). An exponentially growing culture of *B. megaterium* 899(1) in a glucose-sucrose-amino-acids medium was divided into two parts, one of which was treated with hydrogen peroxide. After 15 min. aeration, samples of the induced and non-induced cultures were converted to protoplasts by treatment with lysozyme. Half of each of these samples was lysed by dilution and shaking. Six preparations were then incubated with gentle aeration by rocking—intact cells, protoplasts and lysed protoplasts of both induced and non-induced cultures. Phage titres were determined at intervals for 3 hr. Text-fig. 7 shows one such experiment. The rate of appearance of infective centres in protoplasts formed from induced cells is similar to that in the induced whole cells. Although protoplasts showed 100 to 1000-fold increase in phage titre, the maximum yield was always smaller than from intact cells—about 1/7 in the most successful experiments. No increase in titre occurred in lysed protoplasts from induced or uninduced organisms.

Attempts to induce protoplasts themselves were uniformly unsuccessful despite trials with hydrogen peroxide concentrations varying from 167 to 16·7 μM.

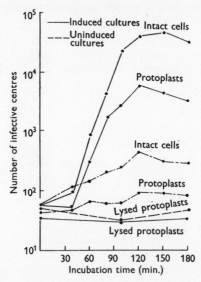

Text-fig. 7. Bacteriophage production by the lysogenic strain 899(1) of *Bacillus megaterium* with and without induction by 67 μM-H_2O_2. Protoplasts formed 15 min. after induction. (Data of Salton & McQuillen, 1955.)

SPOROGENESIS

Members of the genus *Bacillus* form endospores. Hardwick & Foster (1952) have shown that under appropriate conditions there is almost 100% conversion of vegetative cells to spores. Further, once the process has proceeded to a certain stage, the cells are 'committed' to sporogenesis and it is impossible to reverse the process. These workers shook suspensions of *B. mycoides* in distilled water and found that although the phase of rapid appearance of spores occurred between the 10th and the 12th hour, the suspension was irrevocably committed much earlier.

Salton (1955) has carried out similar experiments with strains of *Bacillus megaterium*. He found wide day-to-day variations in the degree of sporulation achieved in distilled water, but he obtained more consistent results when the suspending medium was a solution of sucrose (7·5 % w/v) in phosphate buffer (0·033 M, pH 7) containing 0·01 M-Mg++. After 4½ hr. shaking the cells were committed to sporogenesis and a part of the suspension was treated with lysozyme; the resulting protoplasts were shaken for a further period. Viable spores developed and their numbers were estimated by plating on 5 % peptone/0·1 % starch agar. In a typical experiment the number of viable spores per millilitre obtained from intact cells was 10^7, from protoplasts 10^5 and from osmotically lysed protoplasts 10^1. The formation of spores was confirmed by the observation in the phase-contrast microscope of highly refractile bodies within the protoplast membrane. Text-fig. 8 illustrates the course of events.

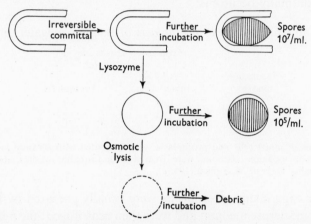

Text-fig. 8. Representation of sporogenesis of *Bacillus megaterium* and implications of conversion of cells to protoplasts.

GROWTH OF PROTOPLASTS

As far as the writer is aware, bacterial protoplasts have never been shown to form colonies. The closest approach has been the work on spores by Salton just mentioned. In an adjoining paper Weibull has drawn attention to possible similarities between L-forms and protoplasts, and Dr Klieneberger-Nobel in conversation has also remarked on this possibility.

Recently it has been found that protoplasts of *Bacillus megaterium* can increase markedly in size, optical density and dry weight during the course of incubation in suitable media (McQuillen, 1955c). Parallel experiments have been carried out on intact cells and protoplasts suspended in 250 ml. of a glucose-sucrose-peptone medium in Roux bottles fitted with air vents and gently rocked in an incubator at 28°. Samples were removed at intervals, treated with formaldehyde and centrifuged. The pellets were well washed with distilled water and dried to constant weight. The peptone could be replaced by a mixture of amino acids, but it is not known whether the synthetic medium, glucose-sucrose-NH_3-salts, which supports growth of the intact cells, will suffice. Table 6 shows the results of a typical experiment carried out in the presence of peptone. Control suspensions of protoplasts which were incubated without aeration showed no change in dry weight.

Both intact cells and protoplasts more than doubled in weight during the first 2 hr., but the former continued to grow exponentially while protoplasts increased approximately linearly. Whether this is significant of major differences in growth or whether it is due to gradual lysis of the fragile protoplasts has not been established, but similar results have been obtained on many occasions.

Table 6. *Growth of protoplasts of* Bacillus megaterium

Incubation time (hr.)	Suspension density, mg. dry weight/100 ml.	
	Intact cells	Protoplasts
0	10·4	8·2
2	23·4	17·2
4	52·4	24·8

Suspensions of intact cells and protoplasts were incubated with aeration in a glucose-sucrose-peptone medium. Samples were treated with formalin, washed and dried to constant weight. Data of McQuillen (1955 c).

In these experiments protoplasts were usually prepared by lysozyme treatment in sucrose medium and were then centrifuged; the pellets were rinsed twice with the sucrose medium before suspension in the incubation fluid. Despite careful standardization of conditions, some batches of protoplasts are very difficult to resuspend, and if this is the case they are usually unstable and rapidly lyse. An alternative protection medium has been tried in recent weeks. Instead of sucrose (7·5–10 %, w/v), phosphate buffer (0·5 M, pH 7·0) has been used. Protoplast formation is slower but fewer unstable preparations have been obtained and phosphate may have advantages over sucrose as a stabilizer. Using protoplasts prepared, centrifuged, rinsed and incubated in media containing 0·5 M-phosphate, increases in size, optical density and dry weight comparable with those found in sucrose media have been obtained.

DIVISION OF PROTOPLASTS

Some of the growth experiments just mentioned have been prolonged for many hours and a new characteristic of protoplasts has been discovered. During all the writer's studies on these subcellular forms it has been customary to make repeated examinations of the experimental material with the phase-contrast microscope. In this way it is possible to keep track of lysis and changes in size or appearance of the protoplasts. It has now been found that after 4–6 hr. incubation in the presence of glucose and amino acids, there appear among the greatly enlarged protoplasts a number which are no longer spherical. Normally there is some variation in size of freshly prepared protoplasts, but all are more or less spherical. The new forms had a small protuberance. As the incubation continued, the prevalence of this type increased and the nodules appeared larger until eventually symmetrical dumbbell-shaped forms were present. Very rarely more than one 'bud' was seen on a single protoplast. Preparations were unchanged in appearance after treatment with formaldehyde, and many phase-contrast photomicrographs and electron micrographs have been taken which illustrate the various forms. Some representative pictures appear in Pls. 1 and 2, and Text-fig. 9 shows diagrammatically what seems to be the sequence of development.

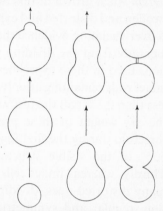

Text-fig. 9. Representation of possible sequence of growth and division of protoplasts of *Bacillus megaterium* on continued incubation in a suitable medium.

The appearance of the dumbbell forms and even of 'ghosts' of corresponding shape leaves no doubt that division of protoplasts can occur. At present it has not been established whether or not such dumbbells finally separate into two discrete units. This is mainly because (*a*) total counts have not yet been made and in any case might be inconclusive owing to concomitant lysis of some protoplasts, and (*b*) it is not yet possible to observe continuously a single protoplast during its growth. Active aerobic metabolism is a prerequisite of most of the capabilities of protoplasts, and no one has so far succeeded in cultivating them on solid media. It is hoped to devise a small chamber in which these preparations can be watched continuously while they are immobilized in a viscous medium.

One piece of circumstantial evidence which suggests that separation may follow division of the protoplasts is that after 8–10 hr. incubation there appear to be protoplasts and protoplast 'ghosts' which are smaller than those observed at an earlier stage and which are about the size of one-half of the dumbbell forms. But in view of the scatter in sizes it would be unwise to infer that they have arisen by division of dumbbell forms.

The growth and division of protoplasts requires the presence of a growth medium. In one experiment, after 6 hr. protoplasts reached a stage where about 5% showed early signs of budding. During 3 hr. further incubation there was no appreciable change in appearance. A portion of the suspension was then transferred to fresh medium and within 2 hr. more than 50% of the protoplasts had developed protuberances.

It should be mentioned that normal rod-shaped cells of *Bacillus megaterium* when grown in this medium containing 0·5 M-phosphate become swollen and distorted and exhibit some grotesque forms. However, there is overwhelming evidence that these intact bacterial forms differ fundamentally from the dividing protoplasts. First, the protoplast preparations used in these experiments have been examined for the presence of intact rods remaining after lysozyme treatment. The incidence of such was less than 0·1%; all the rest were typical spherical protoplasts. Secondly, the dry weight of these protoplast preparations increased more than threefold during the first few hours of incubation, and later as many as 50% of the visible structures appeared to be dividing protoplasts. Thirdly, whereas intact cells showed a wide variety of shapes including many distorted ones, dividing protoplasts were, almost without exception, regular and symmetrical. Fourthly, a cross-wall is usually discernible between the segments in the swollen intact cells but not in dividing protoplasts. Finally, the intact cells are resistant to dilution of the medium, whereas the dividing protoplasts, like single protoplasts, are very sensitive to osmotic shock. Moreover, protoplast membranes or 'ghosts' in the form of dumbbells have been seen.

Although protoplasts have not been shown to be capable of producing new cell-wall material, and although in the dividing forms there is no direct evidence of a cross-membrane, there is some indication that the cytoplasm may not form a continuous plasmodesma between the two halves of the dumbbells. The connecting bridge is often much less electron-dense than the two spheres which in some cases show an abrupt demarcation suggestive of a limiting membrane round each. Further, on one occasion partial lysis of a dumbbell was seen to result in a structure which consisted of one dense spherical protoplast connected by a bridge to a circular 'ghost'. It will surely not be long before someone demonstrates conclusively that complete separation can occur.

MOTILITY

Most of the capabilities of intact living bacteria are also possessed by protoplasts, although in many instances early experiments gave negative results. This situation still obtains so far as attempts to demonstrate motility of protoplasts is concerned. Admittedly, so far as the writer is aware, no very strenuous efforts in this direction have been made, and there is little doubt but that flagella still remain attached to protoplasts (Weibull, 1953; Wiame *et al.* 1955; McQuillen, unpublished).

PROPERTIES OF LYSED PROTOPLASTS

When suspensions of protoplasts are vigorously shaken or when the osmotic pressure of the medium is reduced by dilution, lysis occurs and the soluble components and the DNA leak out. 'Ghosts,' which probably consist of the protoplast membranes, and lipid granules as well as other debris can be seen in the phase-contrast microscope. The respiration of such lysates is reduced or abolished according to the species of organism used (Weibull, 1953; Wiame *et al.* 1955). Many experiments (McQuillen, 1955*a*, *b*; Salton & McQuillen, 1955; Salton, 1955; McQuillen, unpublished) have shown that osmotic lysis results in abolition of ability to incorporate ^{14}C into proteins and nucleic acids, to form adaptive enzymes and spores and to support the multiplication of bacteriophage.

McQuillen (unpublished) has evidence, however, that if the lysis is carried out by shaking in the stabilizing medium (10% sucrose), a preparation is obtained which contains very few intact protoplasts but which retains the ability to carry out a wide range of syntheses of amino acids and to incorporate these amino acids into protein. As yet these experiments are in a preliminary stage, but it seems possible that the protoplast membrane may be a site of protein synthesis. If so, this could be correlated with Gale & Folkes's (1955*a*) finding that in staphylococci, a cell envelope fraction (which may carry with it the protoplast membrane) is such a site. It may be significant that both Gale & Folkes and McQuillen find activity in preparations made in 10% sucrose but little or none in the absence of the stabilizer. This may mean that osmotically shockable organelles are involved—perhaps analogous to microsomes which are now believed to be associated with membranous material in animal cells and which have been implicated in protein synthesis.

DISCUSSION

Intact bacteria and the protoplasts derived from them have closely parallel capabilities. Both forms respire; both synthesize proteins and nucleic acids and form adaptive enzymes; both can support the multiplication of virulent and temperate bacteriophages; both can support the development of endospores; both grow in appropriate media; and both can divide. Moreover, many of these activities are carried out at approximately similar rates and to similar extents by the two forms, the whole and the part. And yet the part is not the whole; there are differences in behaviour. To what extent some of these differences are due to use of unsuitable conditions is not yet known.

Let us list the differences in capability of intact cells and protoplasts of *Bacillus megaterium* and indulge in some speculation about them.

(*a*) Protoplasts no longer have a cell wall, do not seem to contain diaminopimelic acid, a known constituent of the wall of the intact *Bacillus megaterium*, and have not been shown to be able to build a wall. Whole cells can incorporate ^{14}C from glucose, from acetate or from aspartic acid into diaminopimelic acid of the protein fraction. This does not happen with protoplasts. The incorporation must occur into new cell wall material, and it may be that this is formed in protoplasts but is excreted or degraded because of inability to lay it down as a finished structure. Why this should be so is unknown. Rejecting as unlikely the possibility that protoplasts are unable to synthesize some simple cell-wall component such as acetyl glucosamine or diaminopimelic acid, there remains the possibility that a 'starter' or 'key' of cell-wall material must be present before more can be laid down, just as the enzyme phosphorylase needs a short-chain dextrin before it can build on more glucose units. To test such an hypothesis it would be profitable to arrest the action of lysozyme before cell-wall dissolution is complete and determine how far the process can be taken before the ability to make new wall is lost. Also, it would be worth while to try to provoke synthesis by supplying bits and pieces such as partially degraded cell-wall material. Another possibility is that cell-wall synthesis is an extra-protoplastic activity, in which case the necessary enzymes, etc., must be released or digested by lysozyme action. If this is so, then it is unlikely that the cell-wall synthesizing apparatus is present in the cell wall as isolated by Salton (this volume), since his analyses suggest absence of typical protein—unless the enzymes are non-protein in nature. Finally, there is always the possibility that protoplasts carry some lysozyme with them after they are formed and that it degrades new cell-wall material as fast as it is laid down.

(*b*) Protoplasts cannot be infected with virulent bacteriophage. Since the cell wall is an essential participant in the primary interaction this is understandable. But since neither the bacterial cell wall nor the phage protein coat is necessary for the subsequent development of mature virus, there is conjured up the tantalizing question, can the phage DNA be persuaded to enter the naked protoplast? Is the micro-syringe function of the phage tail essential? Brenner (personal communication) has made some unsuccessful attempts to procure such a penetration. Salton (personal communication) has suggested that an artificial wall might be built on to protoplasts by a series of antibody-antigen reactions, culminating in a layer of cell wall material. Possibly, also, at some stage the protoplast membrane may become amenable to entry of phage DNA —for instance, at the time of division or under conditions of protoplast fusion which Stähelin (1954) has claimed can occur.

The failure to induce protoplasts from lysogenic bacteria directly with hydrogen peroxide may not be due to the absence of the cell wall. Only a few experiments have been performed and it seems more likely that conditions suitable for induction have not been established.

(*c*) Although bacteria which have been committed to sporogenesis can be converted to protoplasts which go on to form endospores (albeit only 1 % of the yield from intact cells), it has not been shown that protoplasts themselves can be induced to spore. The biochemical events leading to spore formation by intact bacilli are little understood, and it is quite possible that cell-wall material is withdrawn or modified during the committal period. Until more is known it would be rash to speculate further.

(*d*) So far as motility is concerned, it seems to the writer that unless the flagella themselves are in some way affected by lysozyme, it will be possible to demonstrate motile protoplasts.

Mechanism of cell division

Bisset (1951) quotes a very eminent American cyto-geneticist as saying, in connexion with bacterial cytology, that there are two stages in the progress of a scientific problem: the first, in which the findings are highly improbable, and the second, in which they are obvious. The observation that protoplasts can apparently divide in the absence of a cell wall was surprising but is, after all, consistent with current theories of the mechanism of cell division. The process is usually described as occurring in three stages—division of the cytoplasm by growth of a transverse plasma membrane, formation of a cross-wall and finally separation of the sister cells. If the events occurring during protoplast division have their counterpart in intact bacilli, constriction of the cytoplasm into two separate units is a potentiality of the protoplast independent of cross-wall formation.

It is not clear why, when protoplasts are prepared by lysozyme treatment of *Bacillus megaterium*, no division forms are observed—all are spherical. This may be because stable protoplasts are best prepared from cultures in the stationary phase of growth when cell division has more or less ceased. If it becomes possible to work with protoplasts of actively dividing cells, dumbbell forms may be found. Another subject which it will be interesting to investigate is the distribution of nuclear material in dividing protoplasts.

SUMMARY

Protoplasts, formed by digestion of the cell wall from *Bacillus megaterium*, are able to synthesize proteins, nucleic acids and enzymes, including adaptive enzymes; they can support the multiplication of both virulent and temperate bacteriophages and allow the development of endospores; they can also grow and divide.

REFERENCES

BELJANSKI, M. (1954). L'Action de la ribonucléase et de la desoxyribonucléase sur l'incorporation de glycocolle radioactif dans les protéines de lysats de *Micrococcus lysodeikticus*. *Biochim. biophys. Acta*, **15**, 425.

BISSET, K. A. (1951). The morphology and cytology of bacteria. *Annu. Rev. Microbiol.* **5**, 1.

BOOTH, V. H. & GREEN, D. E. (1938). A wet-crushing mill for micro-organisms. *Biochem. J.* **32**, 855.

BRENNER, S. & STENT, G. S. (1955). Bacteriophage growth in protoplasts of *Bacillus megaterium*. *Biochim. biophys. Acta*, **17**, 473.

CREASER, E. H. (1955*a*). The induced (adaptive) biosynthesis of β-galactosidase in *Staphylococcus aureus*. *J. gen. Microbiol.* **12**, 288.

CREASER, E. H. (1955*b*). Inhibition of induced enzyme formation by purine analogues. *Nature, Lond.*, **175**, 899.

GALE, E. F. & FOLKES, J. P. (1953). The assimilation of amino acids by bacteria. 18. The incorporation of glutamic acid into the protein fraction of *Staphylococcus aureus*. *Biochem. J.* **55**, 721.

GALE, E. F. & FOLKES, J. P. (1954). Effect of nucleic acids on protein synthesis and amino-acid incorporation in disrupted staphylococcal cells. *Nature, Lond.*, **173**, 1223.

GALE, E. F. & FOLKES, J. P. (1955*a*). The assimilation of amino acids by bacteria. 20. The incorporation of labelled amino acids by disrupted staphylococcal cells. *Biochem. J.* **59**, 661.

GALE, E. F. & FOLKES, J. P. (1955*b*). The assimilation of amino acids by bacteria. 21. The effects of nucleic acids on the development of certain enzymic activities in disrupted staphylococcal cells. *Biochem. J.* **59**, 675.

HARDWICK, W. A. & FOSTER, J. W. (1952). On the nature of sporogenesis in some aerobic bacteria. *J. gen. Physiol.* **35**, 907.

PLATE 1

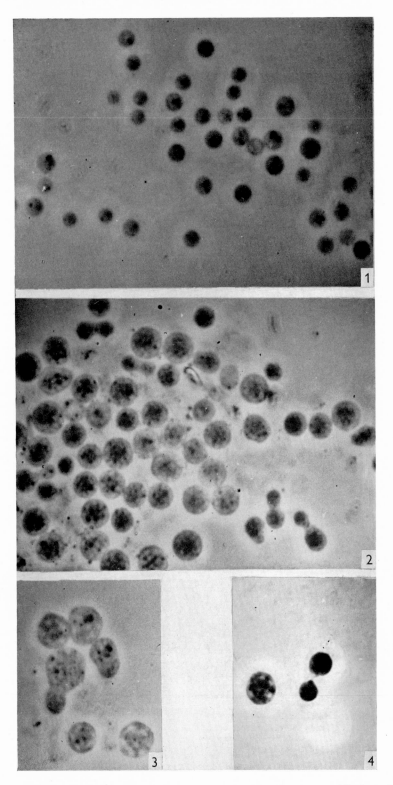

PLATE 2

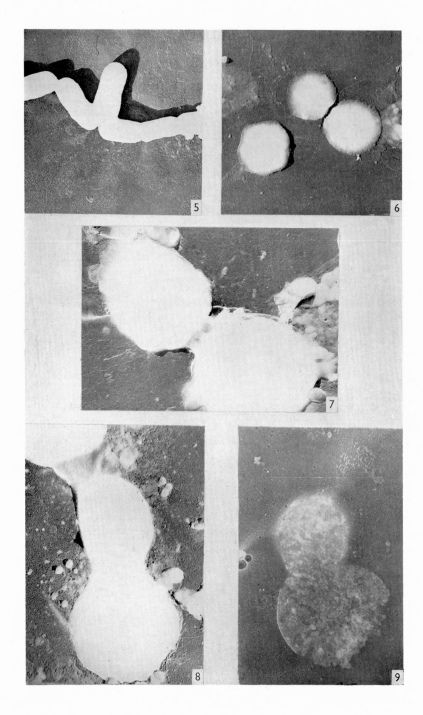

HUGO, W. B. (1954). The preparation of cell-free enzymes from micro-organisms. *Bact. Rev.* **18**, 87.

LEDERBERG, J. (1950). The beta-D-galactosidase of *Escherichia coli*, strain K-12. *J. Bact.* **60**, 381.

LESTER, R. L. (1953). *In vitro* incorporation of leucine into the proteins of *Micrococcus lysodeikticus*. *J. Amer. chem. Soc.* **75**, 5448.

LWOFF, A. (1953). Lysogeny. *Bact. Rev.* **17**, 269.

McQUILLEN, K. (1950). The bacterial surface. II. Effect of uranyl chloride on the electrophoretic mobility of bacteria. *Biochim. biophys. Acta*, **6**, 66.

McQUILLEN, K. (1955 a). Bacterial protoplasts. I. Protein and nucleic acid metabolism of protoplasts of *Bacillus megaterium*. *Biochim. biophys. Acta*, **17**, 382.

McQUILLEN, K. (1955 b). Protein, nucleic acid and adaptive enzyme synthesis in protoplasts of *Bacillus megaterium*. *J. gen. Microbiol.* **13**, iv.

McQUILLEN, K. (1955 c). Bacterial protoplasts: Growth and division of protoplasts of *Bacillus megaterium*. *Biochim. biophys. Acta*, **18**, 458.

McQUILLEN, K. & ROBERTS, R. B. (1954). The utilisation of acetate for synthesis in *Escherichia coli*. *J. biol. Chem.* **207**, 81.

McQUILLEN, K. & SALTON, M. R. J. (1955). Synthetic media for maintenance and induction of lysogenic *Bacillus megaterium*. *Biochim. biophys. Acta*, **16**, 596.

ROBERTS, R. B., ABELSON, P. H., COWIE, D. B., BOLTON, E. T. & BRITTEN, R. J. (1955). *Studies of Biosynthesis in* Escherichia coli. Carnegie Institution of Washington Publication no. 607. Washington, D.C., U.S.A.

SALTON, M. R. J. (1953). Studies on the bacterial cell wall. IV. The composition of the cell walls of some Gram-positive and Gram-negative bacteria. *Biochim. biophys. Acta*, **10**, 512.

SALTON, M. R. J. (1955). The formation of spores in protoplasts of *Bacillus megaterium*. *J. gen. Microbiol.* **13**, iv.

SALTON, M. R. J. & McQUILLEN, K. (1955). Bacterial protoplasts. II. Bacteriophage multiplication in sensitive and lysogenic strains of *Bacillus megaterium*. *Biochim. biophys. Acta*, **17**, 465.

STÄHELIN, VON H. (1954). Über osmotisches Verhalten und Fusion nackter Protoplasten von *Bac. anthracis*. *Schweiz. Z. allg. Path. Bakt.* **17**, 296.

WEIBULL, C. (1953). The isolation of protoplasts from *Bacillus megaterium* by controlled treatment with lysozyme. *J. Bact.* **66**, 688.

WIAME, J. M., STORCK, R. & VANDERWINCKEL, E. (1955). Biosynthèse induite d'arabokinase dans les protoplastes de *Bacillus subtilis*. *Biochim. biophys. Acta*, **18**, 353.

EXPLANATION OF PLATES

Plate 1 consists of phase-contrast photomicrographs of protoplasts of *Bacillus megaterium* (magnification, × 1450). (Reproduced from *Biochimica et Biophysica Acta*.)

Fig. 1. Protoplasts at beginning of experiment.

Figs. 2, 3 and 4. Protoplasts after 8–9 hr. incubation.

Plate 2 consists of electron micrographs of *Bacillus megaterium* and protoplasts derived therefrom (fixed with formaldehyde: magnification, × 8000). (Reproduced from *Biochimica et Biophysica Acta*.)

Fig. 5. Whole cells at beginning of experiment.

Fig. 6. Protoplasts at beginning of experiment.

Figs. 7, 8. Dividing protoplasts after 9 hours' incubation.

Fig. 9. 'Ghost' of dividing protoplast (9 hours' incubation).

The author is indebted to Mr R. W. Horne for making the electron micrographs.

OSMOTIC FUNCTION AND STRUCTURE IN BACTERIA

P. MITCHELL* AND JENNIFER MOYLE*

Department of Biochemistry, University of Cambridge

The anatomical identity of a living cell, unlike that of most inanimate objects, is maintained by an interchange of matter between the interior of the cell and the external medium. The molecules of nutrient pass inwards through the cell surface, the end-products of metabolism pass out, the substances of the cytoplasm are retained and many of the substances of the external medium are excluded. It is the main object of this paper to consider the cause of the forces which are thus responsible for separating the cell from the external medium with respect to most substances, and for specifically connecting the cell with the external medium for the reception of molecules of nutrient and the expulsion of molecules of waste. Some of the osmotic factors involved in the expansion and change of shape of the cytoplasm and cell envelopes during growth and cell division will also be considered.

Two alternative views have been held about the seat of the osmotic forces in bacteria. The shape of bacteria, like the shape of plant cells, may depend mainly upon the structural rigidity of the cell wall, while the osmotic relationship between the protoplasm and the external medium may depend upon the plasma membrane lying close within the cell wall. The cell wall would thus be the ultimate seat of the mechanical forces which result from the osmotic communication of the cell with its environment. On the other hand, the protoplasm may possess sufficient rigidity to play a part in determining the shape of the cell, and the movement of solutes between the protoplasm and the external medium may be controlled not only by the cell envelopes but also by adsorption within the protoplasmic gel. The mechanical forces accompanying the osmotic communication of the cell with its environment would thus be borne at least in part by the mechanical rigidity of the protoplasmic gel. The static anatomy of the cell would be the same in either case, but functionally the two alternatives differ profoundly and can be distinguished only by studying the mechanical and osmotic properties of the intact cell and its component parts.

* Present address: Department of Zoology, University of Edinburgh.

At the first symposium of the Society for General Microbiology, Mitchell (1949) described the functional unit which effects the osmotic separation of the cell interior and the external environment of bacteria by the term 'osmotic barrier'. Since the existence of such a barrier for small molecular weight solutes has recently been seriously disputed in the case of *Bacterium coli* and of some other organisms (Roberts, Abelson, Cowie, Bolton & Britten, 1955) it will be necessary to consider the evidence for the existence of an osmotic barrier in bacteria before attempting to place it anatomically.

OSMOTIC PROCESSES IN RESTING CELLS

The case for the existence of an osmotic barrier in bacteria

In general, bacteria are not very exacting about the media in which they will remain viable. They will often tolerate suspension in distilled water or in strong salt or non-electrolyte solutions of which the solute composition may be varied within extremely wide limits. However, the tolerance towards the external medium is affected profoundly by the 'age' of the cells—that is to say, upon the rate at which the cells were growing when harvested. The more rapid the rate of growth at harvesting, the more fragile the cells are (see Winslow & Walker, 1939). *Bacterium coli*, for instance, will remain viable in distilled water if harvested in the stationary phase of growth, but if harvested in the exponential phase the cells undergo rapid plasmoptysis, loss of internal diffusible constituents (Mitchell & Moyle, 1954 and unpublished observations) and loss of viability (Hershey, 1939) in distilled water. The different osmotic fragility of cells of different 'age' may be due to differences in the internal osmotic pressure, to differences in the tensile strength of the cell as a whole, or to differences in the activity of the autolytic systems. We need to consider what is the cause of the so-called osmotic pressure of the bacterial cell and how the cell as a whole resists the tendency to swell in media of low osmotic pressure.

Causes of internal 'osmotic pressure' and swelling: osmotic barrier .versus protoplasmic gel

Many years ago Jacques Loeb (1922) compared the osmotic pressure of a solution of gelatin with the same weight-concentration of gelled gelatin particles and found that the osmotic pressure of the latter was negligible in comparison to that of the former. The explanation is that the osmotic pressure of the gelled particle is compensated for by the mechanical pressure due to the cohesion of the gel. Obviously we must not overlook the possibility that the cohesion of the protoplasm may play a part in resisting the swelling of bacteria in media of low osmotic pressure, especially as other unicellular organisms such as amoebae are known to possess a cortical gel which imparts rigidity to the cell. Indeed, the fact that a bacterium shrinks in media of high solute content and swells in distilled water does not constitute evidence for the existence of a true osmotic system, for a gelled particle may behave in the same way, as Harman & Kitiyakara (1955) have pointed out for the case of muscle mitochondria. If the swelling and shrinkage is due to a true osmotic pressure acting across a semipermeable membrane, it will be dependent upon the permeability of the membrane to the solute used for controlling the osmotic pressure of the external medium. Only those solutes which do not permeate the membrane should be effective in preventing true osmotic swelling. Of course, since one wishes to draw conclusions about the internal osmotic pressure and permeability of normal cells, it is essential that the solutes used should not disrupt the osmotic barrier or materially affect its permeability.

At the end of the last century, Alfred Fischer observed that while many Gram-negative organisms could be plasmolysed in salt solutions or in sucrose, they were not plasmolysed by the same concentration of glycerol, urea, chloral hydrate and other substances of low molecular weight or high lipid solubility (see Fischer, 1903). This constituted excellent evidence for the existence of a plasma membrane, permeable to glycerol, etc., but impermeable to sucrose or electrolyte solutions, which was free to retract from within a rigid relatively permeable cell wall. The idea that the plasma membrane acted as the main osmotic barrier in many Gram-negative bacteria was strengthened by the observation that plasmolysis was prevented or was made to subside if the cells were treated with reagents that would destroy the semipermeability of a lipid membrane such as that proposed by Overton (1899)—for example, methyl or ethyl alcohol, chloroform, phenol, acetic acid (Eisenberg, 1910), or methylene blue (Vahle, 1910). The threshold concentration of external solute required to cause plasmolysis indicated that the effective internal osmotic pressure of Gram-negative bacteria was from 2 to 3 atmospheres in old cells. According to Knaysi (1951) the internal osmotic pressure of *Bacterium coli* rises to 15 atmospheres during rapid growth. But the fact must not be overlooked that the plasmolysis threshold may depend upon the adhesion of the plasma membrane to the cell wall as well as upon the internal osmotic pressure of the protoplast (vide infra).

During plasmolysis of Gram-negative bacteria, the cell wall does not collapse with the protoplast, and there is therefore little doubt that the cell wall possesses structural rigidity and must play a part in determining the shape of the normal cell (Fischer, 1903; Ellis, 1903; Swellengrebel, 1909; Eisenberg, 1910; Vahle, 1910; Raichel, 1928)—a fact which has been confirmed by studies with the electron microscope reviewed by Salton at this Symposium. However, since the osmotic pressure is exerted against the plasma membrane of a plasmolysing cell and not against the cell wall, it is not possible to infer from the collapse of the protoplast that the plasma membrane or protoplasm exerts no resistance to the osmotic strain and that they make no contribution to the rigidity of the cell. In the case of *Spirillum volutans*, there is evidence that the cytoplasm is not gelled, for King & Beams (1942) observed that after centrifuging at 400,000 G for 10–20 min., the internal granules, which had been forced to the side of the cell, became redistributed in the protoplasm in 30–60 min. But there are no other measurements bearing on the physical state of the protoplasm of bacteria except under conditions which might cause the destruction of a protoplasmic gel. The microdissection experiments of Wámoscher (1930) in which the protoplasm was observed to stream out of a ruptured cell in a series of droplets, and the disintegration techniques by which the 'particulate fractions' can be separated from the 'soluble' components (e.g. Dawson, 1949; Mitchell & Moyle, 1951; Weibull, 1953b) cannot be held to show that the protoplasm of bacteria is normally liquid.

The fact that Gram-positive organisms cannot in general be plasmolysed, even in strong sucrose solutions, was considered to show that the Gram-positive group of bacteria had relatively permeable plasma membranes (Fischer, 1903; Brudny, 1908; Eisenberg, 1910; Baumgärtel, 1924), and that the osmotic function was shared more or less equally between the plasma membrane and cell wall (Fischer, 1903). The 'plasmolysis' of certain *Bacillus* species is possible (Knaysi, 1930; Robinow & Murray, 1953) in very strong salt solutions (e.g. 25 % NaCl), but it is questionable whether 'plasmolysis' in such experiments is due only to contraction of the protoplast or whether the dehydrating conditions due to the high solute concentration may not play a part by severing the normal bonding between the cell wall and the surface of the protoplast and allowing the cell wall to expand away from the protoplast. An effect of the latter type, which resembles osmotic plasmolysis only in appearance, is caused by exposure of the cells to ether vapour (Robinow & Murray, 1953). Generally Gram-positive bacteria contract as a whole in media of high osmotic pressure. *B. megaterium*, for instance, contracts by some 14–25 % when transferred from normal broth to broth containing 2 M-NaCl (Dutky, 1933), while *Staphylococcus aureus*, harvested near the stationary phase of growth, contracts by 6–9 % by volume (phosphate-impermeable volume) or 2–3 % linearly when transferred from 0·1 to 1·0 M-NaCl (Mitchell & Moyle, 1955a). Thus, the cell wall of some bacteria is elastic, a fact established directly by microdissection (Wámoscher, 1930).

The reason for the failure of most Gram-positive organisms to plasmolyse might be their permeability to the small molecular weight solutes used for raising the osmotic pressure of the medium, as suggested by Fischer (1903). If this were the case, the contraction observed in place of plasmolysis must represent the equivalent of a syneresis of the protoplasm due to a lowering of the water activity. However, although young cells of *Staphylococcus aureus*, *Micrococcus lysodeikticus*, *Sarcina lutea* and *Bacillus megaterium* can be seen to contract by phase-contrast microscopy when transferred from 0·1 M-NaCl to 0·1 M-NaCl containing 1·2 M-sucrose, they do not contract when transferred from 0·1 M-NaCl to 0·1 M-NaCl containing 1·2 M-glycerol, the implication being that they possess an osmotic barrier permeable to glycerol but not to sucrose (Mitchell & Moyle, 1955a). The osmotic behaviour of these Gram-positive organisms is thus analogous to that of the Gram-negative group, except that the plasma membrane does not separate from the cell wall in the former. The separation of the plasma membrane from the cell wall of Gram positive bacteria might be prevented by a very high internal osmotic pressure or by strong adhesion between the plasma membrane and the cell wall. In the latter case, the protoplasm would be under a negative pressure while the material of the cell wall would be under compression when the cells were in hyperosmotic media. This has been shown to be the case for the large sulphur organism *Beggiatoa mirabilis*, for the cell wall buckles when the osmotic pressure of the external medium exceeds a certain value. Moreover, the cell wall expands away from the protoplast if the cells are treated with reagents that destroy the adhesion between the protoplast and the cell wall (Ruhland & Hoffman, 1926). It is relevant that when Gram-negative bacteria are plasmolysed the plasma membrane presents a concave face towards the cell wall as it pulls away from it, showing that there is adhesion between the plasma membrane and cell wall (Fischer, 1903; Ellis, 1903; Swellengrebel, 1909; Raichel, 1928). Evidently the adhesion of the plasma membrane to the cell wall may vary greatly in different organisms, and in certain organisms it may play a part in preventing plasmolysis or in determining the plasmolysis threshold.

The observations on plasmolysis and swelling of bacteria constitute excellent evidence for the existence of an osmotic barrier, very permeable to glycerol, but relatively impermeable to sucrose and certain electrolytes. However, the question of the importance of the part played by the binding of small molecular weight solutes by large molecular weight constituents of the protoplasm, and by the cohesion of the large molecular weight constituents to one another in resisting the osmotic stress, can be answered only by more quantitative measurements of permeability and osmotic pressure.

Retention of internal solutes

It was not until comparatively recently that bacteria were found to contain high concentrations of 'free' internal solutes of low molecular weight that could be released by treatment with cold trichloracetic acid, detergents, organic solvents or by heating. This conception received much of its impetus from Gale's observations on the accumulation of 'free' amino acids in bacteria. In a recent review of this subject, however, Gale (1953) pointed out that there was very little evidence to show that the amino acids are actually free to diffuse within the osmotic barrier. Moreover, Roberts and his collaborators have presented evidence against the existence of an osmotic barrier for small molecular weight solutes in *Bacterium coli* and *Staphylococcus aureus*. Roberts & Roberts (1950) observed that suspensions of *Bacterium coli* in saline containing inorganic phosphate marked with ^{32}P would exchange phosphate rapidly with the medium, the exchange being confined to the so-called free internal inorganic phosphate fraction of the cells extracted by cold trichloracetic acid. They proposed that the internal 'inorganic phosphate' was a labile adsorption complex or compound which remained constant in amount because the number of adsorption sites remained constant, but that each site could readily exchange one phosphate for another, giving rise to the process of 'exchange adsorption' observed with ^{32}P-marked phosphate in the suspension medium. Evidence was also presented to show that the surface of *B. coli* is permeable to several inorganic cations (Cowie, Roberts & Roberts, 1949; Roberts, Roberts & Cowie, 1949) and to sugar phosphates (Roberts & Wolffe, 1952), and that the surface of *Staphylococcus aureus* is permeable to glutamic acid (Britten, 1951–2). It seemed, therefore, that many of the internal 'free' solutes might normally exist as adsorption complexes or labile compounds in bacteria. According to this conception we should visualize the protoplasm either as a gel within which all the 'free' solutes are adsorbed, or as a solution of high molecular weight substances (proteins, nucleic acids, etc.) which adsorb the 'free' internal solutes. In the first case the protoplasmic gel might partly resist the osmotic stress directly, while in the second case the liquid protoplasm would be retained only by an envelope permeable to the small molecular weight solutes but impermeable to the large molecular weight substances that adsorb them.

Estimation of internal osmotic pressure

The total weight of the internal solutes extracted in cold trichloracetic acid represents c. 18% of the cell dry weight in *Staphylococcus aureus* (Mitchell, 1953) and c. 6% of the cell dry weight in *Bacterium coli* (Mitchell & Moyle, 1955b), when harvested near the stationary phase of growth. The protoplasmic water amounts to c. 1·5 and 2·4 ml./g. respectively (vide infra) and the internal solutes would therefore give about a 12% (w/v) solution in *Staphylococcus aureus* and a 2·5% solution in *Bacterium coli*. If the mean particle weight of the internal solutes were about 100, the internal osmotic pressure would be some 20–30 atmospheres in *Staphylococcus aureus* and some 5–6 atmospheres in *Bacterium coli*, provided that the solutes were able to move independently in the internal water. If, on the other hand, the internal solutes were bound to components of high molecular weight, their osmotic pressure would be much reduced. The figure of 2–3 atmospheres given for the internal osmotic pressure of *B. coli* by studies of plasmolysis threshold indicates that a large proportion of the internal solutes may diffuse freely in the protoplasm. *Staphylococcus aureus*, being unplasmolysable, a new vapour-pressure equilibrium method was used for measuring its effective internal osmotic pressure (Mitchell & Moyle, 1955a). A very thick washed suspension of *S. aureus* (strain Duncan), harvested near the stationary phase of growth, was prepared in distilled water. Equal samples of this suspension were smeared rapidly on to thin pieces of polythene, covered by watch-glasses and weighed. They were then equilibrated to constant weight in small desiccators over sucrose solutions of known molality *in vacuo* at 20°. Equilibration was achieved within 5 hr. by placing the pieces of polythene, smear downwards, as close as possible to the surface of the sucrose solutions. The results of such an experiment are shown in Fig. 1, the reciprocal of the molality of each sucrose solution being plotted against the weight of the cells equilibrated over it. The cell dry weight, at zero vapour pressure, was obtained by equilibrating smears over P_2O_5. It will be understood that this type of experiment is analogous to an osmotic equilibrium experiment in which the swelling (uptake of water) of the cells is plotted against the reciprocal of the osmotic pressure of their suspension medium, the communication between the cells and the medium being through the vapour phase instead of by direct contact. For concentrations of sucrose greater than molal (reciprocal less than 1), the weight of water held by the cells varies linearly with the reciprocal of the molality of the sucrose, but for lower sucrose concentrations the weight of water retained by the cells rapidly reaches a limit. The discontinuity at *c.* 1 molal sucrose corresponds to the point at which the internal cohesion or hydrostatic pressure of the cells begins to resist the further uptake of water. In this experiment it represents an uptake of

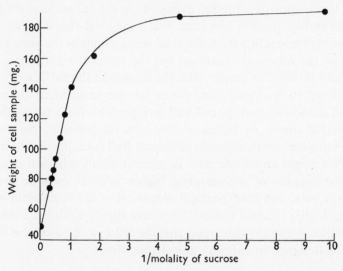

Fig. 1. Vapour-pressure equilibrium data for *Staphylococcus aureus* (strain Duncan) after equilibration of the cells over sucrose solutions for 5 hr. at 20°.

1·9 ml. water per g. cell dry weight, in reasonably good agreement with the value of 1·5–1·6 obtained by direct permeability measurements (Mitchell, 1953). Since the water uptake for sucrose concentrations greater than 1 molal obeys the van't Hoff law (osmotic pressure × volume of water = constant) strictly, it is probable that this water is freely miscible with the internal solutes. At all events, when the cells contain the normal amount of water, the cell solutes cause a vapour-pressure depression corresponding to that of about 1 molal sucrose, and to an osmotic pressure of some 20–25 atmospheres. There is therefore little doubt that a large proportion of the internal solutes must be free to diffuse within the osmotic barrier.

Mechanical implication of internal osmotic pressure

A pressure of some 20 atmospheres appears at first sight to be very large for the structure of the cell to withstand. An osmotic pressure of this magnitude has been reported for *Achromobacter harveyi* (Johnson & Harvey, 1937; Johnson, Zworykin & Warren, 1943), but this marine organism bursts without swelling when placed in distilled water. We can readily calculate that for a spherical cell 0.7μ in diameter—the approximate size of the above staphylococcus—a pressure of 20 atmospheres corresponds to a tension of some 300 dynes/cm. in the cell surface, about four times the surface tension of water. For a long rod-shaped organism of diameter of cross-section 0.7μ, the axial stress would be the same as in the surface of the spherical organism, but the stress at right angles to the axis would be twice as great. Also, the tension at the surface of a cell is proportional to its linear dimensions for the same internal pressure. We shall show later that the cell wall is responsible for resisting this very considerable stress. In media of low osmotic pressure, plasmoptysis occurs when the tensile strength of the cell wall is insufficient to take the stress. We might anticipate that, in general, small spherical organisms would be capable of withstanding higher internal osmotic pressures than large ones, and that spherical organisms would be capable of withstanding higher internal osmotic pressures than cylindrical ones of the same radius. We might also expect that the cell wall of cylindrical bacteria would be designed to carry an anisotropic stress.

EXCLUSION OF OUTER MEDIUM COMPONENTS

Intact cells. Thick suspension technique

The most unequivocal method of determining whether bacteria possess osmotic barriers is to determine whether the water within the cell is available to externally added solutes. This can readily be done by taking an extremely thick cell suspension, adding a known weight of a solute in a small quantity of water to the suspension, centrifuging down the cells and measuring the concentration of the solute in the supernatant medium. Knowing the weight of solute added and the total volume of the suspension used, the final concentration of solute in the suspension medium allows one to calculate the volume of water available to the solute and, by difference, the effective volume of the cells. This method (Mitchell, 1953) gave an effective phosphate-impermeable cell volume of 2.42 ± 0.05 ml./g. cell dry weight for *Staphylococcus aureus* (strain Duncan) suspended in 0.1 M-NaCl, and this volume did not decrease significantly in 30 min. at 25°. Since we know the specific volume of the cell constituents to be between 0·7 and 1·0, there must be a considerable volume of water inaccessible to the externally added phosphate, namely, about 1·5 ml./g. cell dry weight. The phosphate ion at pH 7 carries between one and two negative charges, and most of the cell constituents are also negatively charged. It is possible, therefore, that the inaccessibility to phosphate ion might be due to electrical repulsion and not to an osmotic barrier. However, if the phosphate ion is excluded by an osmotic barrier, reagents expected to break the barrier should make the internal cell water accessible. After treatment with 5% (w/v) butanol or trichloracetic acid, the cell volume inaccessible to inorganic phosphate falls to only 0·76 ± 0·07 ml./g. cell dry weight. While the trichloracetic acid might have made the internal space accessible by neutralizing the electrical repulsion between the cell interior and the phosphate ion, the butanol could not act in this way. There can therefore be little doubt that the internal water space is bounded by an osmotic barrier impermeable to phosphate ions. The average volume of the centrifuged pad of intact cells in these experiments was 3·61 ± 0·01 ml./g. cell dry weight. Of this, 2·42 ± 0·05 ml./g. cell dry weight represented the phosphate-impermeable volume of the cells, leaving an interspace volume of 33% of the cell pad volume. This interspace is only 7% greater than the interspace volume for close-packed spheres (26%), and consequently we may infer that the outer surface of the osmotic barrier of *S. aureus* is close to the external surface of the cells. It may be that the extra 7% interspace, corresponding to 0·25 ml. water/g. dry weight, represents the water held in the pores of the cell wall. This is in agreement with measurements of the cell volume impermeable to a dextran of average molecular weight 10,000 which cannot penetrate the cell wall (Mitchell & Moyle, 1955a). The dextran-impermeable volume is 8% greater than the phosphate-impermeable volume, giving an extra water space of 0·18 ml./g. dry weight.

Since Britten (1951–2) had claimed that *Staphylococcus aureus* was freely permeable to glutamic acid on the basis of measurements with a thick suspension technique similar to that described by Mitchell (1953) but employing radioactive glutamic acid and relying only upon a Geiger counter for its estimation, it was desirable to measure the permeability of *S. aureus* to some other solutes to see whether phosphate might be exceptional in its behaviour.

Measurements were made with glutamic acid, glutamine, sodium chloride, sodium thiocyanate and a dextran (Mitchell & Moyle, 1955a). The volume of the cells impermeable to phosphate was measured at the same time as the volume impermeable to each of these solutes, as a check on the variations in cell size which were found to occur from one culture to another. The measurements on the amino acids were made at pH 7 in 0·1 M-NaCl. Glutamic acid and glutamine were measured manometrically by the decarboxylase method (Gale, 1945); glycine was measured by oxidation with ninhydrin, distillation of the formaldehyde produced and colorimetric estimation with chromotropic acid (Alexander, Landwehr & Seligman, 1945); chloride and thiocyanate were estimated volumetrically by adding excess silver nitrate and back-titrating with thiocyanate in dilute nitric acid, using ferrous ammonium sulphate as indicator.

Table 1. *Amino-acid- and phosphate-impermeable volumes o,*
Staphylococcus aureus (*strain Duncan*)

Amino-acid in suspension medium (approx. concn.)	Time and temperature of equilibration	Amino-acid-impermeable volume/g. cell dry weight (ml.)	Phosphate-impermeable volume/g. cell dry weight (ml.)	Mg. cell dry weight/ml. suspension	μmole amino acid disappearing from external phosphate space/g. cell dry weight
Glutamic acid (0·02M)	5 min. at 25°	2·25	} 2·34	} 203	1·7
Glutamine (0·02M)	5 min. at 25°	2·01			6·0
Glutamic acid (0·02M)	5 min. at 2°	1·93			0·4
Glutamic acid (0·02M)	30 min. at 25°	1·87		} 242	0·8
Glutamine (0·02M)	5 min. at 2°	1·55			6·4
Glutamine (0·02M)	30 min. at 25°	1·51	} 1·91		7·2
Glutamic acid (0·04M)	5 min. at 2°	1·87			1·5
Glutamic acid (0·04M)	30 min. at 25°	1·89		} 230	0·7
Glutamine (0·04M)	5 min. at 2°	1·76			5·1
Glutamine (0·04M)	30 min. at 25°	1·72			6·2
Glycine (0·02M)	5 min. at 2°	1·60			8·9 (23·4)*
Glycine (0·02M)	30 min. at 25°	−2·38	} 2·17	} 235	29·3 (29·6)*
Glycine (0·04M)	5 min. at 2°	1·86			10·6 (41·3)*
Glycine (0·04M)	30 min. at 25°	−0·25			45·7 (51·1)*

* Values after breaking the osmotic barrier with 5 % (w/v) butanol.

Table 1 shows values for the glutamic acid-, glutamine- and glycine-impermeable volumes of two different batches of cells. It will be observed that neither glutamic acid nor glutamine penetrate the osmotic barrier to a significant extent during 30 min. at 25°, but, whereas glutamic acid behaves almost exactly like inorganic phosphate, some 5–7 μmole glutamine disappear from the external phosphate space within 5 min. (the time required for centrifuging) at 2°. Since the amount of glutamine disappearing is approximately the same whether the external concentration is 0·02 or 0·04 M and the amount increases very little in 5 or 30 min. at 25°, it is probable that this glutamine is adsorbed on the cell wall or on the surface of the osmotic barrier. These results appear to be in direct conflict with those of Britten (1951–2). However, the 'cell-water space' with which Britten found the glutamic acid of the external medium to equilibrate may simply have represented the interspace medium in a centrifuged cell pad of which he took no account (Britten, 1955).

The value for the glycine-impermeable volume is similar to that for glutamine at 2°, but at 25° it rapidly becomes negative. This means that the amount of glycine disappearing from the suspension medium is greater than can be accounted for by completely uniform distribution even within the substance of the cells. The cells therefore appear to occupy a negative volume. This shows that the glycine is either being metabolized or adsorbed. On adding butanol to give a 5% solution so as to break the osmotic barriers of the cells, an amount of glycine is taken up from the medium which is near to that taken up by intact cells in 30 min. at 25°, even in the suspensions held at 2° (values in brackets, Table 1). The results suggest that at 2° the cells are impermeable to glycine, but that some 10 μmole glycine are adsorbed outside the osmotic barrier. If the cells are treated with butanol, or if the temperature is raised to 25°, the glycine probably passes through the osmotic barrier. Since the cell materials must occupy some 0·9 ml./g. cell dry weight, the total amount of glycine disappearing when the osmotic barrier is broken with butanol at 2° are 15 and 24 μmole/g. cell dry weight when the final glycine concentrations are respectively 8 and 18 mM. It is unlikely that this glycine is metabolized at 2° in the presence of 5% butanol, and hence it is probably adsorbed, partly in the surface where it adsorbs before penetration and partly in the cell interior. This is in accord with Gale's observation of a spontaneous uptake of radioactive glycine by this organism (Gale, 1953). In order to throw more light on the relative rates of permeation of glycine at 2° and at 25°, the time course of the glycine-impermeable volume has been measured, using an initial glycine concentration of 0·04 M (Fig. 2). At 2°, glycine does not permeate significantly in 2 hr., but at 25° half-equilibration occurs in about 30 min. The fact that glycine permeation has a high temperature coefficient suggests that it may involve a specific carrier mechanism.

The chloride- and thiocyanate-impermeable volumes are plotted against time at 2° in Fig. 3, with phosphate for comparison. The chloride and thiocyanate were present at an initial concentration of 0·1 M as the sodium salts, and the pH of the suspensions was 7·2. Evidently *Staphylococcus aureus* is somewhat permeable to sodium chloride, and very permeable to sodium thiocyanate. The thiocyanate ion does not damage the osmotic barrier at this concentration, for even 1 M-NaCNS was found not to cause leakage of phosphate across the osmotic barrier. Since the anion and cation probably penetrate independently, these

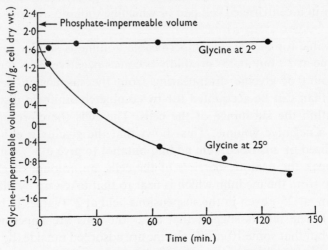

Fig. 2. Time course of glycine-impermeable volumes of *Staphylococcus aureus* (strain Duncan) at 2° and at 25°.

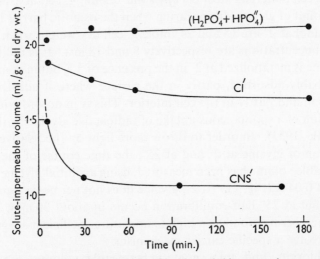

Fig. 3. Time course of phosphate-, chloride- and thiocyanate-impermeable volumes of *Staphylococcus aureus* (strain Duncan) at 2°.

results indicate that Na^+ penetrates readily while the ease of penetration for the anions is in the order $CNS' > Cl' > (H_2PO_4' + HPO_4'')$.

The phosphate-impermeable volume was compared with the volume impermeable to a *Leuconostoc* dextran of mean molecular weight 10,000 in normal cells and in cells which had been treated with 5% butanol to break the osmotic barrier, the dextran being estimated by the anthrone reaction (Mitchell & Moyle, 1955a). The volumes impermeable to phosphate and dextran in normal cells were respectively 2·21 and 2·39 ml./g. dry weight, while after treating with butanol they were 0·78 and 2·15 ml./g. cell dry weight. Thus, the osmotic barrier for phosphate is not the same as that for the dextran. Probably the osmotic barrier for phosphate is the plasma membrane, while the osmotic barrier for dextran is the cell wall.

The observations on the penetration of salts and amino acids into *Staphylococcus aureus* establish two main facts: an osmotic barrier impermeable to certain small molecular weight solutes exists near the cell surface; although this barrier may be sufficient to confine a given solute within the cell (e.g. glycine at 2°), the solute may in addition be bound by constituents of the cell both inside and on, or beyond, the surface of the osmotic barrier.

Using the thick suspension technique, Weibull (1955) has shown that *Bacillus megaterium* in general resembles *Staphylococcus aureus* in structure and permeability properties. *B. megaterium* is impermeable to phosphate, sucrose and diphosphopyridine nucleotide, the osmotic barrier to these solutes most probably lying at the plasma membrane rather than at the cell wall.

The experiments of Roberts *et al.* (1955) on the permeability of the surface of *Bacterium coli* to inorganic phosphate, sulphate, sugar phosphates, amino acids and inorganic cations using radioactive tracer techniques led them to the view that 'the protoplasm may be likened to a sponge, the cell membrane to a surrounding hair net unable to exclude the entrance or emergence of small molecules'. In view of our observations on *Staphylococcus aureus*, it would seem that the two organisms might differ profoundly in their structure, general permeability properties and in the mode of uptake of solutes from their nutrient medium. The permeability to phosphate of the same strain of *Bacterium coli* (American strain B), grown in the same inorganic salts-glucose medium as employed by Roberts and his group, was therefore measured, using the same technique as previously described (Mitchell, 1953) with the exception that the cells were washed and suspended in 1% (w/v) NaCl in place of distilled water. A large number of experiments gave phosphate-impermeable volumes lying between 3·34 and 3·09 ml./g. cell dry weight, and an interspace volume of *c.* 22%. There can be little doubt that the plasma membrane is impermeable to inorganic phosphate. The microscopic observations on the suspensions which were made as a routine check on their normal morphology showed that the cell size was visibly affected by the salinity of the suspension medium. As the NaCl concentration was raised from 1 to 2%, the cells showed a small but definite shrinkage, but at concentrations above 2%, plasmolysis occurred quite sharply. The phosphate-impermeable volume was therefore measured over a range of salinities. The results are shown in Table 2. In order to see more clearly the relationship between external osmotic pressure and the phosphate-impermeable volume, the concentrations of NaCl have been converted to equivalent osmolalities of sucrose (by consulting the vapour-pressure equilibrium data of Robinson & Sinclair (1934)) and the phosphate-impermeable volume has been plotted against the reciprocal

Table 2. *Phosphate-impermeable volume of* Bacterium coli (*strain B*) *in various concentrations of* NaCl *at* 25°

% (w/v) NaCl	Phosphate impermeable volume (ml./g. cell dry weight)
1·0	3·09
1·4	2·88
2·2	2·40
3·3	2·08
4·7	1·85
8·8	1·62

of the osmolality in Fig. 4. It is evident that below the plasmolysis threshold the van't Hoff law is obeyed by the protoplast and that above it the hydrostatic pressure exerted by the cell wall begins to resist the further swelling of the protoplast. This implies that the plasma membrane and protoplasm exert little if any resistance to the uptake of water by the internal solutes in plasmolysed cells and that the cell wall is normally responsible for exerting a hydrostatic pressure equal to the difference of osmotic pressure between the media inside and outside the plasma membrane. As the reciprocal of the external osmolality rises from 0 to 1·0, the phosphate-impermeable volume rises from 1·33 to 2·03, or by 0·7 ml./g. cell dry weight. In 1·0% saline, therefore, when the phosphate-impermeable volume is 3·09 the equivalent internal osmolality must be $0·7/1·06 = 0·66$, while the external osmolality is 0·30. Thus in 1% saline the cell wall must exert a hydrostatic pressure of $0·36 \times 22·4 = 8·1$ atmospheres against the plasma membrane. The fact that the intercept on the vertical axis of Fig. 4 occurs at a volume of 1·33 ml./g. cell dry weight, whereas the volume occupied by the cell constituents would not be expected to exceed 0·9 ml./g. implies either that water corresponding to 31% of the cell volume is not freely accessible to the internal solutes or to the external phosphate, or alternatively that this water is accessible to chloride but not to phosphate ion. This water might be bound to constituents of the protoplasm, be held within the osmotic barrier or within the cell wall. It is difficult to escape the conclusion that *B. coli* possesses an osmotic barrier that is relatively impermeable to sodium phosphates and to sodium chloride, and, moreover, that this osmotic barrier is represented by the plasma membrane. The protoplasm and plasma membrane can contribute little if any mechanical resistance to contraction down to a volume of 1·33 ml./g. cell dry weight. If there is a gelled region in the protoplasm, this gel cannot therefore contribute much rigidity to the protoplast, and consequently it would be unlikely to play an important part in determining the shape of the resting cell. We cannot reconcile our results with those of Roberts *et al.* (1955).

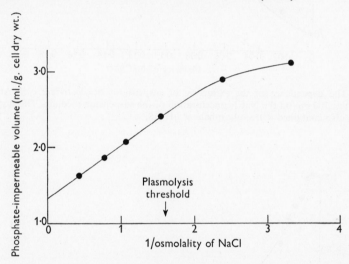

Fig. 4. The dependence of the phosphate-impermeable volume of *Bacterium coli* (American strain B) on the NaCl concentration of the suspension medium.

Swelling of intact cells in dilute suspensions

The swelling and shrinkage of dilute suspensions of bacteria in media of different osmotic pressures can conveniently be observed by measurements of light scattering (Mitchell & Moyle, 1955b), for, as bacteria swell, they scatter less light. Fig. 5 shows a plot of the relative extinctions of suspensions of *Bacterium coli* (American strain B) in a range of concentrations of NaCl in 0·01 M-phosphate at pH 6·8. The change of light scattering over the range of this curve was found to be strictly reversible and did not involve lysis of the cells. It was therefore possible to determine whether *B. coli* was permeable to a given solute at a concentration

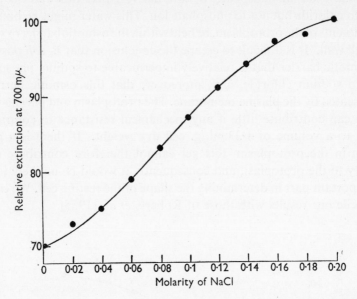

Fig. 5. The dependence of the extinction of suspensions of *Bacterium coli* (American strain B) at 700 mμ on the NaCl concentration of the suspension medium. The suspension medium also contained 0·01 M-phosphate at pH 6·8.

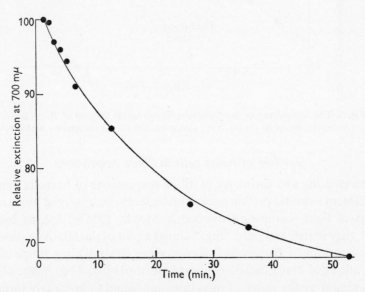

Fig. 6. Time course of the permeation of erythritol into *Bacterium coli* (American strain B) at 20° measured by the change in extinction at 700 mμ. Cells suspended in 0·36 molal erythritol containing 0·01 M-phosphate pH 6·8.

corresponding to 0·2 M-NaCl (0·36 osmolal) in 0·01 M-phosphate by observing the change in the extinction; for, if the solute permeated, the cells swelled and the extinction approached the relative value observed in 0·01 M-phosphate. Fig. 6 shows the change in light scattering during permeation of erythritol at 20°. By this technique it was observed that the following salts did not permeate to a measurable extent in 1 hr. at 20°: NaCl, KCl, NH_4Cl, $MgCl_2$, NaBr, NaCNS, KCNS, NH_4CNS, Na_2SO_4, $(Na_2HPO_4 + NaH_2PO_4)$; Na-acetate (pH 9), K-acetate (pH 9).

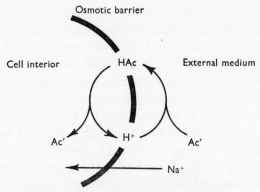

Fig. 7. Mechanism of acetate-ion transport.

Glycerol reached equilibrium across the osmotic barrier within 3 min., erythritol in *c.* 1 hr. as shown in Fig. 6, and lactose did not permeate to a significant extent in 1 hr. In some suspensions sodium acetate and potassium acetate, if adjusted to pH 7 with acetic acid, appeared to permeate rapidly. The explanation for this might be that the plasma membrane is permeable to Na^+, K^+, H^+ and HAc, but not to Ac′. Hence, in the presence of a significant concentration of H^+ (i.e. at pH 7 as opposed to pH 9) the H^+ might carry in Ac′ as HAc and return through the membrane as H^+ to pick up another Ac′, and thus, cyclically, catalyse the entry of Ac′ as HAc, as shown in Fig. 7.

Protoplasts

It was observed by Weibull (1953*a*) that spherical bodies, which appeared to be intact protoplasts, emerged from the cells of *Bacillus megaterium* when the walls were digested by lysozyme in 0·2 M-sucrose. The 'protoplasts' would not remain intact unless the water activity of the medium was lowered by sucrose, polyethylene glycol or certain other solutes, and they were shown by electron microscopy to possess an external membrane (Weibull, 1953*b*). It was not known, however, whether the mechanism of action of the solutes was to exert an osmotic pressure across the membrane thus preventing osmotic explosion of the 'protoplast', or whether the solutes simply prevented the swelling of hydrated constituents of the protoplasm which would otherwise have ruptured the external membrane. It was therefore of interest to measure the permeability of isolated 'protoplasts' to a range of solutes.

In order to obtain data for comparison with those already described, it was desirable to prepare the 'protoplasts' of *Staphylococcus aureus*. However, the lysozyme sensitivity of *S. aureus* being very low, attention was first turned to *Micrococcus lysodeikticus*. Since there was not likely to be a change of shape on release of the 'protoplasts' from cocci, some other criterion of 'protoplast' formation was required. The method adopted was to pipette 0·1 ml. samples of the cell suspension undergoing 'protoplast' formation into paired 5 ml. samples of 1·2 M-NaCl in 0·01 M-phosphate and 0·01 M-phosphate alone at pH 6·8, and compare the turbidities (Mitchell & Moyle, 1955c). 'Protoplast' formation was indicated by lysis in 0·01 M-phosphate and stability in 1·2 M-NaCl. Grula & Hartsell (1954) had attempted to prepare the 'protoplasts' of *M. lysodeikticus* by Weibull's method in 0·2 M-sucrose, but most of the 'protoplasts' swelled and disintegrated. In view of our osmotic pressure measurements on *S. aureus* it seemed probable that a much higher concentration of sucrose than 0·2 M would be required to keep the 'protoplasts' intact. A few preliminary experiments showed that *M. lysodeikticus* (NCTC 2665) harvested towards the stationary phase of growth and washed in distilled water would readily form 'protoplasts' if incubated for 2 hr. at 25° at a dry-weight concentration of 10 mg./ml. in 1·2 M-sucrose buffered with 0·04 M-phosphate at pH 6·8 and containing 10 μg. crystalline egg-white lysozyme/ml. The 'protoplasts' appeared similar to the original cells under phase-contrast microscopy, but they were somewhat paler and were generally separated from one another instead of clumped. The 'protoplasts' of *Sarcina lutea* were obtained in the same way using 0·02 mg. lysozyme/ml. in place of 0·01 mg. Fig. 8 shows the sensitivity of the 'protoplasts' of *M. lysodeikticus* to suspension in NaCl and sucrose solutions for 30 min. at 25°. The stability of the 'protoplasts' was measured by the extinction at 700 mμ of samples pipetted into 1·2 M-NaCl, in which the 'protoplasts' had been found to be stable. The extinction values have been plotted against molality of sucrose and the equivalent osmolality of NaCl so that the two curves can be compared. Evidently not more than 10 % of the 'protoplasts' break in 30 min. at 25° at an osmolality of 1·5, while 50 % break at an osmolality of 0·9 whether the solute is NaCl or sucrose. Essentially the same results were obtained with *S. lutea* harvested at the same phase of growth.

These results show that the proportion of 'protoplasts' breaking depends upon the activity of water whether sucrose or NaCl be the solute. When, however, glycerol is used as the solute the breakage of the 'protoplasts' is almost complete and is independent of the glycerol concentration, as shown in Fig. 8. Consequently it can be inferred that the stability of the 'protoplast' depends upon a membrane which is very permeable to glycerol but relatively impermeable to sucrose or NaCl, and

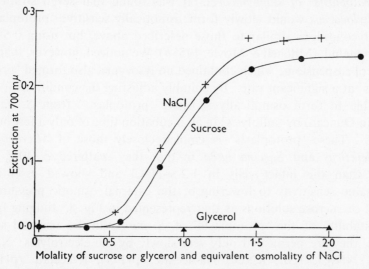

Fig. 8. Stability of the 'protoplasts' of *Micrococcus lysodeikticus* (NCTC 2665) to suspension in NaCl, sucrose and glycerol solutions over a range of solute concentration. Extinction measured in 1·2M-NaCl containing 0·01 M-phosphate pH 6·8.

that some 50% of the 'protoplasts' of *Micrococcus lysodeikticus* have an internal osmotic pressure of 20 atmospheres or greater. There was no evidence for any structural rigidity within the 'protoplast' of *M. lysodeikticus* or *Sarcina lutea*, and there is therefore little doubt that the cell wall must be capable of withstanding a hydrostatic pressure of 20 atmospheres or more.

By observing the rate of lysis of 'protoplast' suspensions in various solutes at a concentration of 1·5 molal, it was possible to obtain a relative measure of the permeability of the 'protoplast' membrane to the solutes. Thus, the 'protoplasts' of *Micrococcus lysodeikticus* and *Sarcina lutea* appeared to be permeated only very slowly by the following solutes: NaCl, KCl, NH_4Cl, $MgCl_2$, Na-acetate (pH 9), K-acetate (pH 9), NaBr, K_2SO_4, ($KH_2PO_4 + K_2HPO_4$), sodium glutamate, lysine hydrochloride, glucose, and sucrose. The 'protoplasts' broke almost instantaneously in glycerol at 20°; the time for *c.* 50% lysis was 20 sec. for erythritol, 5 min. for ribose and more than 1 hr. for sorbitol. The 'protoplasts' also broke instantaneously in 1·5 molal glycine or urea, but it is probable that the latter two substances would in any case seriously affect the 'protoplast' membrane at this high concentration. Indeed, a serious criticism of this method of observing permeation is that the high concentrations of the solutes may well affect the permeability of the membrane even when the solute is a relatively unreactive one.

'*Protoplasts*' *of staphylococci.* It was found that seven strains of *Staphylococcus* would slowly form osmotically sensitive 'protoplasts' under conditions similar to those described above, but using 0·5 mg. lysozyme/ml. (Mitchell & Moyle, 1955*d*). We noticed, however, that the control suspensions, which contained no lysozyme, also formed 'protoplasts' at a significant rate. By suitably adjusting the conditions it was possible to form osmotically sensitive 'protoplasts' from *S. aureus* (strain Duncan) by 'autolysis' in an incubation time of only a few hours at 25°. These 'protoplasts' resembled closely those of *Micrococcus lysodeikticus* and *Sarcina lutea* in that they scattered *c.* 40% less light than the intact cells in 1·2 M-NaCl and showed essentially the same sensitivity to lowering of the external osmotic pressure in NaCl or sucrose solutions as that represented in Fig. 8. Judging from the stability of the 'protoplasts' of *S. aureus* in 1·5 osmolal solutions, they are permeated only very slowly by the electrolytes: NaCl, KCl, NH_4Cl, KBr, KNO_3, Na-acetate (pH 9), K-acetate (pH 9), K_2SO_4, ($KH_2PO_4 + K_2HPO_4$), sodium glutamate, and lysine hydrochloride. In KCNS, however, the 'protoplasts' break in the course of a few minutes as shown in Fig. 9, the rate of breakage being very sensitive to pH. In NaCNS, similar curves show a rate of lysis *c.* 0·8 that observed in the corresponding KCNS solution. The more rapid lysis at lower pH values could not be due simply to an increase in the fragility of the 'protoplasts', for there was no lysis in NaCl solutions at corresponding pH values. These results are in accord with the observations described above on the permeability of intact *S. aureus* to thiocyanate. The time for half-lysis of the 'protoplasts' of *S. aureus* was less than 3 sec. for glycerol, 20 sec. for erythritol, 5 min. for ribose, 30 min. for arabinose and 20 min. for sorbitol. Lysis in glucose, sorbose, mannose, galactose, fructose and sucrose was extremely slow.

Thus the permeability properties of the 'protoplasts' of *Micrococcus lysodeikticus*, *Sarcina lutea* and *Staphylococcus aureus* are essentially the same, and closely resemble those of the intact cells. Consequently it seems very likely that the 'protoplast' membrane is the same structure as the plasma membrane of the intact cell, but whereas the 'protoplast' membrane must be prevented from expanding by the osmotic pressure of a non-penetrating solute, in the intact cell it is prevented from expanding by a hydrostatic pressure exerted by the cell wall. This leads to an important difference between the isolated 'protoplast' and the intact cell, for in the isolated 'protoplast', the protoplasm and plasma membrane must be near atmospheric pressure, but in the intact cell the protoplasm and plasma membrane are under a hydrostatic pressure corresponding to the osmotic pressure difference across the plasma membrane, and often of the order of some 20 atmospheres.

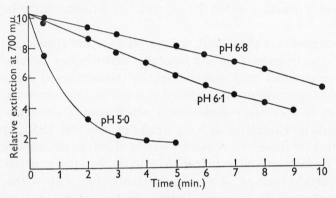

Fig. 9. Time course of the permeation of KCNS into 'protoplasts' of *Staphylococcus aureus* (strain Duncan) at three pH values at 20°. 'Protoplasts' suspended in 1·5 molal KCNS.

Lysis by cooling. The 'protoplasts' of *Staphylococcus aureus* lyse almost instantaneously in 1·5 molal glycine at 25°, at which temperature the intact cells are known to be permeable to glycine. If the breakage of the 'protoplasts' in glycine were due simply to penetration of the glycine and not to damage of the 'protoplast' membrane, the 'protoplasts' should have remained intact at 2°, for at this temperature the intact cells are known to be impermeable to glycine. It was found, however, that the 'protoplasts' were rapidly lysed in glycine at 2°, but that they were also lysed in NaCl or sucrose at 2°. This lysis was almost complete if the suspension was cooled from 25° to 2° at the rate of 10° per min., and was only slightly less if the rate of cooling was reduced to 1° per min. In this respect the intact cells differ profoundly from the 'protoplasts', for there was no detectable loss of internal solutes when the intact cells were cooled. Cold shock has been reported to kill rapidly growing *Bacterium coli* (Sherman & Albus, 1923; Sherman &

Cameron, 1934; Hegarty & Weeks, 1940), but it was not known whether the cause of death was the breakage of the osmotic barrier. At all events, the presence of the external wall of *S. aureus* appears to decrease the sensitivity of the underlying plasma membrane to the disorganizing effect of cooling.

THE CELL WALL AND PLASMA MEMBRANE AS A UNIT

It cannot seriously be doubted, in face of the experimental evidence, that both Gram-positive and Gram-negative bacteria possess an osmotic barrier impermeable to many small molecular weight solutes. The osmotically functional part of this barrier corresponds to the plasma membrane which lies close within the cell wall and is mechanically supported by it.

Measurements of the weight, the morphology and chemical composition of the fragments of mechanically disintegrated *Staphylococcus aureus*, segregated into morphologically homogeneous fractions by differential centrifugation, suggested that the plasma membrane of this organism is a complex lipo-protein which readily disintegrates into small particles containing 41 % by weight protein and 22·5 % lipid, and accounting for some 10 % of the dry weight of the cell (Mitchell & Moyle, 1951). Experiments now in progress show that the material of this 'small particle fraction' is practically identical to that of the 'protoplast' membrane of *S. aureus*, isolated by lysis of the 'protoplasts' in dilute saline containing deoxyribonuclease, followed by differential centrifugation. There is therefore little doubt that the 'small particle fraction' represents the plasma membrane of the intact organism. The weight of the 'small particle fraction' is such as to give a membrane *c*. 15 mμ thick if hydrated to the same extent as the whole cell (Mitchell & Moyle, 1951) but *c*. 5 mμ thick if unhydrated. Thus, the facts would be in accord with the conception of a classical lipo-protein membrane (Davson & Danielli, 1943) containing one or two sheets of molecules of lipid and protein.

The plasma membrane possesses very little mechanical strength, and since it receives the hydrostatic pressure corresponding to the osmotic pressure across it, it is forced against the cell wall with a pressure which may often be as great as 20 atmospheres. The cell wall must therefore be so designed as to exert a fairly even thrust over the surface of the plasma membrane; the pores in the cell wall must be fairly small. The fact that, when the continuity of the plasma membrane of *Staphylococcus aureus* is destroyed by detergents or organic solvents, diffusible substances of molecular size not usually exceeding that of nucleotides escape through the cell wall, suggested that the cell wall consists of a network of chains or fibres with an effective pore diameter of c. 1 mμ (Mitchell & Moyle, 1951); and this conception is supported by the observation that a dextran of which the molecules are c. 2·5 mμ in diameter will not penetrate the cell wall from outside (Mitchell & Moyle, 1955a). Thus we would conceive the plasma membrane as a close-packed lipo-protein sheet two to four molecules thick, having a low affinity for water and containing very few water-filled pores, supported by the cell wall, a more hydrated framework of considerable tensile strength containing pores with an effective diameter of c. 1 mμ.

The question arises as to what extent the plasma membrane is built into the pores in the cell wall, for in Gram-positive bacteria there generally appears to be strong adhesion of the plasma membrane to the cell wall, and the two envelopes cannot generally be separated except by enzymic digestion of the wall or by mechanical disintegration. It is relevant, however, that more than 90% of an acid phosphatase which acts outside the osmotic barrier of intact *Staphylococcus aureus* can be recovered in the material of the plasma membrane of disintegrated cells, while less than 3% of it remains in the cell-wall fraction. The plasma membrane material also contains the bulk of the cytochrome system and many other enzyme activities, while only very small traces of these can be found in the cell-wall fraction (Mitchell, 1954b). Moreover, while the plasma-membrane fraction contains some 20% lipid the cell-wall fractions contain less than 0·5% lipid in clean preparations. Consequently, even if some constituents of the plasma membrane penetrate the pores of the cell wall in the intact cell, the lipid and many protein components probably do not since they are not strongly bound to the cell wall. The fact that the permeability of the 'protoplasts' to small molecular weight solutes does not differ substantially from that of intact cells suggests that the pores of the cell wall are filled mainly with water. But the most potent argument against the entry of the material of the plasma membrane into the pores of the cell wall is the fact that the plasma membrane might thus be extruded through the cell wall when the internal osmotic pressure was high. We may, therefore, regard the osmotically functional part of the plasma membrane as exhibiting more lateral cohesion than adhesion to the cell wall. On the other hand, the cell wall must be associated with the plasma membrane in a sufficiently intimate manner to stabilize the latter to the lytic effect of cooling. It may be that the lysis of the plasma membrane of the 'protoplast' on cooling is due to a rearrangement (crystallization) of parts of the membrane to give areas permeable to sucrose or chloride ion so that the 'protoplast' inflates and bursts. The protective effect of the cell wall could thus be explained by bonding between the two envelopes which would be expected to inhibit the lateral movement or rearrangement of parts of the plasma membrane.

Although they can be separated artificially, we should not regard the cell wall and plasma membrane as independent entities, but as constituting a well-integrated unit, responsible for most of the osmotic properties of the cell. Moreover, while the plasma membrane acts as the osmotic barrier to small molecular weight solutes, for solutes of molecular weight 10,000 or more the cell wall acts directly as the osmotic barrier. This may perhaps have survival value in as much as lytic substances (antibodies or enzymes) in the environment of the organism do not gain access to the delicate plasma membrane. Although the evidence concerning the functional properties of the cell envelopes of other bacteria is less complete than for *Staphylococcus aureus*, it is sufficient to suggest that a similar division of function and structure occurs.

In certain *Spirilla* and in an unidentified Gram-positive rod (Houwink, 1953; Labaw & Mosley, 1954) the cell wall has been shown by electron microscopy to consist, in part, of a sheet of spherical particles packed hexagonally in the first case and perhaps rectangularly in the second. It is interesting to estimate the possible pore size of these walls simply from geometrical considerations. For a hexagonally packed array of spheres 100 units in diameter, a sphere 13 units in diameter can just slip through, while for rectangular packing a sphere 40 units in diameter can slip through. In the *Spirilla* the particles of the wall were c. 14 mμ in diameter giving a 'pore size' of c. 2 mμ, while in the unidentified Gram-positive organism the particles of the wall were c. 11 mμ in diameter, giving a 'pore size' of c. 1·5 mμ for hexagonal packing or c. 5 mμ for rectangular packing. These figures are near to the estimated pore size of 1 mμ for the wall of *Staphylococcus aureus* from permeability measurement. Unfortunately, no fine structure has yet been demonstrated in the cell wall of *S. aureus*.

There is no evidence to suggest that the protoplasm or plasma membrane generally contributes significantly to the retention of the normal shape of the cell against the osmotic and mechanical stress to which the organism is subjected in its normal environment, and one must therefore assume that the cell wall performs this function. In the case of *Spirilla*, however, the cells round up during cell division and a cleavage process occurs (Ellis, 1922) which may well involve the action of a mitotic spindle, asters and cortical gel as in many Protozoa. One must not dismiss, therefore, the possibility that a structural rigidity of the protoplasm of bacteria may play a part in the determination of bacterial form at least at some stages of growth and division.

EXCHANGE DIFFUSION AND THE MECHANISM OF SPECIFIC PERMEATION

It has been observed that an exchange of inorganic phosphate occurs across the surface of *Staphylococcus aureus* (Mitchell & Moyle, 1953) just as it does in *Bacterium coli* (Roberts & Roberts, 1950). The phosphate exchange may be explained by a type of mechanism, called exchange diffusion by Ussing (1947), in which the ions pass across the plasma membrane on carrier groups which can be regarded as ferryboats carrying an equal number of passengers in either direction. There are two main facts which support the exchange diffusion mechanism and oppose the alternative mechanism which Roberts & Roberts (1950) called exchange adsorption: first, the permeability measurements show that the plasma membrane is impermeable to inorganic phosphate; and secondly, the exchange of inorganic phosphate is inhibited by an amount of phenyl mercuric chloride corresponding to only 3 % of the number of internal inorganic phosphate molecules (Mitchell, 1953, 1954 *a*). It is not easy to see how each phenyl-mercury ion could prevent phosphate exchange on more than thirty hypothetical adsorption sites. On the other hand, the inhibitor might readily prevent the movement of the relatively few ferryboats or the entry or exit of their phosphate passengers. Moreover, the specificity of the exchange reaction towards phosphate ions, the specificity of action of inhibitors and the effect of changing the pH, phosphate concentration and temperature confirm the idea that the phosphate ions move through the osmotic barrier in combination with specific carrier groups, and that the movement of these carrier groups involves a reversible deformation of parts of the plasma membrane which resembles reversible protein denaturation (Mitchell, 1954 *c*). The plasma membrane of *Staphylococcus aureus* has also been found to contain the bulk of the cytochrome system (like that of *Bacillus megaterium* (Weibull 1953 *b*)) and many other enzyme activities (Mitchell, 1954 *b*). These and other observations which have been reviewed in detail elsewhere (Mitchell & Moyle, 1956) lead to a view of the plasma membrane, not only as a static barrier to the free diffusion of small molecular weight solutes, but also as a mosaic of specific carriers which may allow the free movement of certain solutes with a specificity equal to that of enzyme-substrate combination—some of the carriers being enzymes themselves.

Although the carriers probably move to and fro across the osmotic barrier simply by thermal agitation, when metabolism is proceeding within the cell this movement may be coupled to the formation and breakage of the bonds that attach the solute passengers to the carriers in such a way that the solutes are actively transported inwards or outwards across the plasma membrane.

These considerations help to resolve a long-standing obstacle to the acceptance of the idea that bacteria possess membranes that are impermeable to small molecular weight solutes, namely, that bacteria, having a very vigorous metabolism, must be freely permeable to their nutrients and waste products. We propose the hypothesis that the permeability of bacteria to many of their nutrients and waste products is a specific one, dependent upon the presence of the enzymes which adsorb the nutrients and desorb the end-products of metabolism in the surface of the plasma membrane.

OSMOTIC PROCESSES DURING GROWTH

We have pointed out above that the shape of bacteria appears to be determined by the mechanical rigidity (and shape) of the cell wall. The cell must be regarded as a highly organized kind of crystal. During growth and division, the plasma membrane and cell wall expand and change shape in a way that must ultimately be determined by the location of enzymes and the packing of the units of which the plasma membrane and cell wall are made.

The plasma membrane is in contact with the protoplasm, and it seems probable that the substances of which it is constituted are in equilibrium with reserves of these substances at their site of synthesis in the cytoplasm, either directly or through the mediation of enzymes. Similarly, the cell wall is in contact with the plasma membrane, and one might expect that the units of which the cell wall is built are in equilibrium with reserves of these units at their site of synthesis in the protoplasm or in the plasma membrane. In the latter case, however, the situation is particularly interesting from an osmotic point of view because the cell wall is outside the plasma membrane. The problem that we have to consider is how the cell wall can be carried outside the plasma membrane without making a hole in the plasma membrane (osmotic barrier) and while maintaining the tensile strength of the cell wall so that it can resist the large internal hydrostatic pressure.

It has been found that the cells of seven strains of *Staphylococcus*, *Sarcina lutea*, *Micrococcus lysodeikticus* and *Bacillus megaterium* will spontaneously form 'protoplasts' if harvested from rapidly growing cultures, and that the rate of 'protoplast' formation is approximately proportional to the rate of growth of the culture at harvesting. Moreover the walls of these organisms, if separated from the rest of the cell by the usual techniques of mechanical disintegration and centrifugation (Mitchell & Moyle, 1951), become partially or completely digested at a rate approximately corresponding to that of 'protoplast' formation, and at the same time these isolated cell walls liberate a lysozyme-like factor which will lyse *Micrococcus lysodeikticus* and digest the isolated cell walls of old cultures of this organism (Mitchell & Moyle, unpublished). We therefore propose the hypothesis that the walls of these organisms are built up through the mediation of a lysozyme-like enzyme which will reversibly catalyse the formation of links between the 'relatively small molecular weight units' of which the cell wall is made.

It has been also observed that if the 'protoplasts' of *Staphylococcus aureus* formed from cells harvested shortly after the end of the exponential phase of growth are lysed in dilute saline containing deoxyribonuclease and the cell-wall fraction is isolated, the cell walls are observed by electron microscopy to have broken into hemispherical parts. Moreover, when an equatorial ridge is visible in the wall, it runs at right angles to the edge of the hemisphere. We therefore suggest that the lysozyme-like factor which is responsible for condensing the substance of the cell wall is situated on an equatorial ring in the wall. The lysozyme-like enzyme molecules may be imagined as acting like the clasps on a set of zip-fasteners which are extruded through the plasma membrane and become zipped together outside to form a continuous wall.

It is possible that the condensation of the units forming the cell wall might occur by virtue of the fact that the cell wall material is insoluble in water, just as an insoluble peptide (e.g. benzoyl-leucyl-leucyl-anilide) is formed by the action of a proteolytic enzyme (cysteine-papain) (Bergmann & Fraenkel-Conrat, 1938). If this were the case, one would expect that unless some cell wall were already present on the surface of the plasma membrane, the formation of cell wall would be impossible, for until an aggregate sufficiently large to be insoluble in water had formed, the equilibrium would not lie in favour of cell-wall formation. Thus, a protoplast with all the necessary intermediates and enzymes required for cell-wall formation might be unable to synthesize a cell wall until provided with a fragment of 'starter' (see paper by McQuillen at this symposium). To conclude this paragraph of speculation we suggest that the shape of the cell may be regulated by an appropriate fluctuation in the number of active lysozyme-like enzyme molecules during the cycle of cell division and growth.

REFERENCES

ALEXANDER, B., LANDWEHR, G. & SELIGMAN, A. M. (1945). A specific micromethod for the colorimetric determination of glycine in blood and urine. *J. biol. Chem.* **160**, 51.

BAUMGÄRTEL, P. T. (1924). *Grundriss der theoretischen Bakteriologie.* Berlin: Springer.

BERGMANN, M. & FRAENKEL-CONRAT, H. (1938). The enzymatic synthesis of peptide bonds. *J. biol. Chem.* **124**, 1.

BRITTEN, R. (1951–2). Report of Biophysics Section, Dept. of Terrestrial Magnetism. *Yearb. Carneg. Instn,* p. 92.

BRITTEN, R. (1955). Discussion in *Symposium on Amino acid Metabolism,* p. 120, ed. McElroy & Glass. Baltimore: Johns Hopkins Press.

BRUDNY, V. (1908). Über die Beziehung zwischen der Färbbarkeit der Bakterien nach Gram und ihrer Permeabilität. *Zbl. Bakt.,* Abt. II, **21**, 62.

COWIE, D. B., ROBERTS, R. B. & ROBERTS, I. Z. (1949). Potassium metabolism in *Escherichia coli.* 1. Permeability to sodium and potassium ions. *J. cell. comp. Physiol.* **34**, 243.

DAVSON, H. & DANIELLI, J. R. (1943). *The Permeability of Natural Membranes.* Cambridge: University Press.

DAWSON, I. M. (1949). Discussion in *The Nature of the Bacterial Surface,* p. 119, ed. A. A. Miles & N. W. Pirie. Oxford: Blackwell.

DUTKY, S. R. (1933). Unpublished, quoted by KNAYSI, G. (1938). Cytology of bacteria. *Bot. Rev.* **4**, 83.

EISENBERG, P. (1910). Über die Tuschedifferenzierung gramnegativer Bakterien. *Zbl. Bakt.* Abt. I, Orig., **56**, 183.

ELLIS, D. (1903). Untersuchungen über Sarcina, Streptococcus und Spirillum. *Zbl. Bakt.* Abt. I, Orig., **33**, 1, 81 and 161.

ELLIS, D. (1922). The intimate structure of the bacterial cell. *Brit. med. J.* ii, 731.

FISCHER, A. (1903). *Vorlesungen über Bakterien,* 2nd ed. Jena: Fischer.

GALE, E. F. (1945). Studies on bacterial amino-acid decarboxylases. 5. The use of specific decarboxylase preparations in the estimation of amino-acids and in protein analysis. *Biochem. J.* **39**, 46.

GALE, E. F. (1953). Assimilation of amino-acids by Gram-positive bacteria and some actions of antibiotics thereon. *Advanc. Prot. Chem.* **8**, 285.

GRULA, E. A. & HARTSELL, S. E. (1954). Lysozyme and morphological alterations induced in *Micrococcus lysodeikticus. J. Bact.* **68**, 171.

HARMAN, J. W. & KITIYAKARA, A. (1955). Studies on mitochondria. 6. The relationship between the structure, osmotic reactivity and ATPase activity of mitochondria from pigeon skeletal muscle. *Exp. Cell Res.* **8**, 411.

HEGARTY, C. P. & WEEKS, O. B. (1940). Sensitivity of *Escherichia coli* to cold shock during the logarithmic growth phase. *J. Bact.* **39**, 475.

HERSHEY, A. D. (1939). Factors limiting bacterial growth. 4. The age of the parent culture and the rate of growth of transplants of *Escherichia coli. J. Bact.* **37**, 285.

HOUWINK, A. L. (1953). A macromolecular monolayer in the cell wall of *Spirillum* spec. *Biochim. biophys. Acta,* **10**, 360.

JOHNSON, F. H. & HARVEY, E. N. (1937). The osmotic and surface properties of marine luminous bacterial *J. cell. comp. Physiol.* **9**, 363.

JOHNSON, F. H., ZWORYKIN, N. & WARREN, G. (1943). A study of luminous bacterial cells and cytolysates with the electron microscope. *J. Bact.* **46**, 167.

KING, R. L. & BEAMS, H. W. (1942). Ultracentrifugation and cytology of *Spirillum volutans*. *J. Bact.* **44**, 597.

KNAYSI, G. (1930). The cell structure and cell division of *Bacillus subtilis*. *J. Bact.* **19**, 113.

KNAYSI, G. (1951). *Elements of Bacterial Cytology*, 2nd ed. Ithaca, New York: Comstock.

LABAW, L. W. & MOSLEY, V. M. (1954). Periodic structure in the flagella and cell walls of a bacterium. *Biochim. biophys. Acta*, **15**, 325.

LOEB, J. (1922). On the influence of aggregates on the membrane potentials and the osmotic pressure of protein solutions. *J. gen. Physiol.* **4**, 769.

MITCHELL, P. (1949). The osmotic barrier in bacteria. In *The Nature of the Bacterial Surface*, p. 55, ed. A. A. Miles & N. W. Pirie. Oxford: Blackwell.

MITCHELL, P. (1953). Transport of phosphate across the surface of *Micrococcus pyogenes*: nature of the cell 'inorganic phosphate'. *J. gen. Microbiol.* **9**, 273.

MITCHELL, P. (1954*a*). Transport of phosphate across the osmotic barrier of *Micrococcus pyogenes*: specificity and kinetics. *J. gen. Microbiol.* **11**, 73.

MITCHELL, P. (1954*b*). The mechanism of transport of phosphate across the osmotic barrier of *Staphylococcus aureus*. *J. gen. Microbiol.* **11**, x.

MITCHELL, P. (1954*c*). Transport of phosphate through an osmotic barrier. *Symp. Soc. exp. Biol.* **8**, 254.

MITCHELL, P. & MOYLE, J. (1951). The glycerophospho-protein complex envelope of *Micrococcus pyogenes*. *J. gen. Microbiol.* **5**, 981.

MITCHELL, P. & MOYLE, J. (1953). Paths of phosphate transfer in *Micrococcus pyogenes*: phosphate turnover in nucleic acids and other fractions. *J. gen. Microbiol.* **9**, 257.

MITCHELL, P. & MOYLE, J. (1954). The Gram reaction and cell composition: nucleic acids and other phosphate fractions. *J. gen. Microbiol.* **10**, 533.

MITCHELL, P. & MOYLE, J. (1955*a*). Permeability of the osmotic barrier of *Staphylococcus aureus* to some salts, amino-acids and non-electrolytes (in the Press).

MITCHELL, P. & MOYLE, J. (1955*b*). Permeability of the osmotic barrier of *Bacterium coli* to small molecular weight solutes (in the Press).

MITCHELL, P. & MOYLE, J. (1955*c*). Preparation and osmotic properties of 'protoplasts' from *Micrococcus lysodeikticus* and *Sarcina lutea* (in the Press).

MITCHELL, P. & MOYLE, J. (1955*d*). Autolytic preparation and osmotic properties of 'protoplasts' from *Staphylococcus aureus* (in the Press).

MITCHELL, P. & MOYLE, J. (1956). Permeation mechanisms in bacterial membranes. *Faraday Soc. Symp.* (in the Press).

OVERTON, E. (1899). Über die allgemeinen osmotischen Eigenschaften der Zellen, ihre vermutlichen Ursachen und ihre Bedeutung für die Physiologie. *Vjschr. naturf. Ges. Zürich*, **44**, 88.

RAICHEL, B. (1928). Über den Einfluss osmotisch wirksamer Mittel auf die Bakterienzelle. *Arch. Protistenk.* **63**, 333.

ROBERTS, R. B., ABELSON, P. H., COWIE, D. B., BOLTON, E. T. & BRITTEN, R. J. (1955). *Studies on Biosynthesis in* Escherichia coli. Washington: Carnegie Institution.

ROBERTS, R. B. & ROBERTS, I. Z. (1950). Potassium metabolism in *Escherichia coli*. 3. Interrelationship of potassium and phosphorus metabolism. *J. cell. comp. Physiol.* **36**, 15.

ROBERTS, R. B., ROBERTS, I. Z. & COWIE, D. B. (1949). Potassium metabolism in *Escherichia coli*. 2. Metabolism in the presence of carbohydrates and their metabolic derivatives. *J. cell. comp. Physiol.* **34**, 259.

ROBERTS, R. B. & WOLFFE, E. L. (1952). Utilization of labelled fructose-6-phosphate and fructose-1,6-diphosphate by *Escherichia coli*. *Arch. Biochem.* **33**, 165.

ROBINOW, C. F. & MURRAY, R. G. E. (1953). The differentiation of cell wall, cytoplasmic membrane and cytoplasm of Gram-positive bacteria by selective staining. *Exp. Cell Res.* **4**, 390.

ROBINSON, R. A. & SINCLAIR, D. A. (1934). The activity coefficients of the alkali chlorides and of lithium iodide in aqueous solution from vapour pressure measurements. *J. Amer. chem. Soc.* **56**, 1830.

RUHLAND, W. & HOFFMANN, C. (1926). *Beggiatoa mirabilis.* Ein Beitrag zur Ultrafiltertheorie des Plasmas. *Planta*, **1**, 1.

SHERMAN, J. M. & ALBUS, W. R. (1923). Physiological youth in bacteria. *J. Bact.* **8**, 127.

SHERMAN, J. M. & CAMERON, G. M. (1934). Lethal environmental factors within the natural range of growth. *J. Bact.* **27**, 341.

SWELLENGREBEL, N. H. (1909). Neuere Untersuchungen über die vergleichende Cytologie der Spirillen und Spirochäten. *Zbl. Bakt.* Abt. I, **49**, 529.

USSING, H. H. (1947). Interpretation of the exchange of radio-sodium in isolated muscle. *Nature, Lond.*, **160**, 262.

VAHLE, C. (1910). Vergleichende Untersuchungen über die Myxobakteriazeen und Bakteriazeen, sowie die Rhodobakteriazeen und Spirillazeen. *Zbl. Bakt.* (Abt. II), **25**, 178.

WÁMOSCHER, L. (1930). Versuche über die Struktur der Bacterienzelle. *Z. Hyg. InfektKr.* **111**, 422.

WEIBULL, C. (1953*a*). The isolation of protoplasts from *Bacillus megaterium* by controlled treatment with lysozyme. *J. Bact.* **66**, 688.

WEIBULL, C. (1953*b*). Characterisation of the protoplasmic constituents of *Bacillus megaterium*. *J. Bact.* **66**, 696.

WEIBULL, C. (1955). The localisation of a permeability barrier in the cells of *Bacillus megaterium*. *Exp. Cell Res.* **9**, 139.

WINSLOW, C.-E. A. & WALKER, H. H. (1939). The earlier phases of the bacterial culture cycle. *Bact. Rev.* **3**, 147.

THE CHROMATIN BODIES OF BACTERIA

C. F. ROBINOW

Department of Bacteriology and Immunology, University of Western Ontario, Canada

Living rod-shaped bacteria from young cultures appear faintly patterned. In ordinary transmitted light or with phase-contrast illumination they are relatively dense at the poles and across the middle (Knoell, 1944; Knoell & Zapf, 1951; Stempen, 1950; Stempen & Hutchinson, 1951; Clifton & Erhard, 1952). On either side of the dark central band there are two or more vague shapes which are less dense. It has often been shown that the relatively transparent regions are the site of structures which give a positive Feulgen reaction (Stille, 1937; Piekarski, 1937; Neumann, 1941; and others since (Pl. 1, fig. 2). In this article these structures will be referred to as 'chromatin bodies'.

Entities of this kind have been demonstrated in many species of bacteria, but only in a few of them are they large enough for detailed study with the light microscope. Relatively large well-spaced chromatin bodies are regularly found in cells from very young cultures of various *Bacillus* species (Pl. 1, figs. 2–9). Similar arrangements of chromatin bodies have also frequently been demonstrated in cells from young cultures of *Escherichia coli* and *Proteus*. Irregular arrangements of chromatin bodies which are difficult to interpret have been described in the luminous bacterium, *Achromobacter fischeri* (Johnson & Gray, 1949), in *Azotobacter* (Truant, 1954), in strain C of *E. coli* K 12 (Kellenberger, 1953; Lieb, Weigle & Kellenberger, 1955) and in *Shigella dysenteriae* (Whitfield & Murray, 1954).

TECHNIQUE

(a) Fixation

The chromatin bodies in fixed and stained preparations of relatively large bacteria such as *Bacillus cereus*, *B. mycoides and B. megaterium* are not all alike; some are solid, some are hollow, some are split down the middle, others appear as clusters of three or four granules. Very little of this detail is visible during life. It is therefore uncertain how much of the detail reflects the living organization of chromatin bodies and how much is the result of fixation. This uncertainty is at present most acutely felt in the interpretation of electron micrographs of thin sections of bacteria.

There is not room to discuss the merits of the many fixatives that have been used in studies of bacteria. But one or two matters of special interest will be mentioned. The widely used osmium tetroxide, as it has recently been learned, acts more slowly on bacteria than has been supposed and leaves their chromatin material in a very labile and far from 'fixed' condition. Experiments of Murray (1955) and Whitfield & Murray (1955) have shown that under the ordinary conditions of OsO_4 vapour fixation the chromatin remains susceptible to manipulations of the ionic environment.

Osmium, as experiments suggest, damages the mechanisms which maintain the cell's normal internal ionic milieu. An influx of sodium ions into the dying cell affects the electric charge of the chromatin, which the authors regard as an anionic gel, and may cause it to aggregate into a solid axial cord. This artifact explains the results of experiments in which bacteria were fixed for electron microscopy by the addition of osmium tetroxide to the salt-containing liquid culture medium (Birch-Andersen, Maaløe & Sjöstrand, 1953).

Of great interest is the observation (Whitfield, 1955) that a similar, but reversible, aggregation of the chromatin structures takes place in *living* bacteria growing on a salt-containing medium whenever their powers of osmo-regulation are put under the strain of having to deal with a sudden increase in the concentration of sodium ions in the environment or are temporarily weakened by various inimical influences such as cold, ultraviolet light, phage infection or the presence of streptomycin or tetracycline antibiotics.

More valuable than osmium as a fixative for bacteria, in certain respects, is Bouin's fluid (picric acid, formalin, acetic acid). This mixture seems to achieve more nearly life-like preservation of *Bacillus* cells and enteric bacteria in the logarithmic phase of growth than other common fixatives. The appearance of the chromatin bodies in bacteria fixed *in situ* with Bouin's fluid (Pl. 1, figs. 3, 3a) (Robinow, 1944, Pl. 7, fig. 24; Pl. 8, fig. 28) agrees remarkably well with their appearance in living bacilli studied with phase-contrast optics or with ultraviolet light (Hedén, 1951) and equally well with the conformation and relatively low density of chromatin bodies in electron micrographs of whole and of thinly sectioned bacteria. Bouin preparations retain the soft wavy contours and uniform texture of chromatin bodies seen during life, but the usefulness of Bouin fixation is limited by the fact that the chromatin bodies are rendered practically unstainable by this treatment and are visible only because they are silhouetted against the strongly basophilic, readily stainable cytoplasm. Anaerobic Gram-negative bacteria are a notable exception to this rule; their chromatin bodies can be directly stained with Giemsa solution after Bouin fixation (Dienes & Smith, 1944).

Comparison with living bacteria suggests that all fixatives, Bouin's included, coarsen and exaggerate the features of chromatin bodies. This impression is confirmed by the study of electron micrographs of ultra-thin sections of bacteria in which the chromatin bodies are most diffuse and vaguely delimited in those specimens which, for independent reasons, must be regarded as optimally preserved (unpublished observations of R. G. E. Murray).

(b) Staining

Chromatin bodies are neither obvious in heat-fixed films of bacteria stained by the accepted methods of diagnostic bacteriology, nor can haematoxylin or aceto-carmine, the two most generally useful stains in studies of plant and animal chromosomes, be relied upon to demonstrate them at all stages of the life cycle. In other words, the chromatin bodies usually remain hidden from those who constantly examine stained bacteria in the course of their daily work and are not at all readily found by those who may be searching for them with the standard methods of general cytology. This accounts for some of the doubts of the reality of chromatin bodies which still exist in many minds.

The Feulgen process, one of the few techniques common to general and bacterial cytology, stains the chromatin bodies neatly but rather faintly. Fortunately, there are other stains with a peculiar affinity for the chromatin of bacteria. It was found long ago that bacterial chromatin, especially in Gram-negative species, is more brilliantly stained by compound dyes of the Romanowsky series (Giemsa, Leishman, Wright) than by most other stains (Dobell, 1911; Douglas & Distaso, 1912; Neumann, 1941; Hartman & Payne, 1954). Romanowsky dye-complexes stain bacterial chromatin bodies red. This is not always sufficient to make them clearly visible in the dark blue cytoplasm, but the contrast between chromatin bodies and cytoplasm can be increased by treating fixed bacteria with N/1 HCl at 60° or by digesting them with ribonuclease (Tulasne & Vendrely, 1947) before staining them.

It is generally thought that acid hydrolysis is useful because it removes ribonucleic acid from the cytoplasm of the bacteria (Vendrely & Lipardy, 1946), but this is not the whole story. Hydrolysis has also a *direct* effect on the chromatin bodies. It greatly increases their normally very low affinity for ordinary basic stains. Digestion with ribonuclease does not have this effect on the nuclei. Thus, chromatin bodies of *Bacillus* species may be stained with basic fuchsin after hydrolysis but not after digestion with ribonuclease. Chromatin bodies are now usually stained with Giemsa and not with fuchsin, and that is why the direct effect of hydrolysis on the staining properties of the chromatin bodies has not attracted more attention. Giemsa stains these structures even before hydrolysis, and with this stain the gain from either hydrolysis or ribonuclease is the same, and is partly a matter of greater visibility.

Chromatin bodies of *Escherichia coli*, *Proteus* and *Bacillus* species are coloured cherry-red when they are stained directly with Giemsa (or May-Gruenwald Giemsa) solution (Hartman & Payne, 1954). After digestion with deoxyribonuclease they stain red no longer (Tulasne, 1953; Peters & Wigand, 1953). In accordance with the findings of Jacobson & Webb (1952) the red stain is interpreted as indicating the presence of deoxyribonucleic-acid protein in the chromatin bodies, and this in turn is in agreement with the positive Feulgen reaction given by these structures.

Chromatin bodies are often more voluminous after hydrolysis than before and are stained dark blue or purple by Giemsa after this treatment, not red. The identity of the bluish purple material is less certain than that of the previously mentioned red-staining component. At present it seems not improbable that materials are deposited on the chromatin bodies during acid hydrolysis or digestion with ribonuclease which are not there normally. This assumption would also explain the abnormally high electron density of the chromatin bodies in bacteria that have been hydrolysed (Mudd & Smith, 1950) or digested with ribonuclease followed by pepsin (Peters & Wigand, 1953; Wigand & Peters, 1954).

Vexing as they are, these cytochemical uncertainties have no immediate bearing on the *morphological* problem presented by the chromatin bodies, structures which, after all, are clearly visible already in unstained preparations.

The acid-Giemsa method just outlined is useful in general work but it is less discriminating than the Feulgen procedure. For the photographic recording of fine chromatin detail a modification of the Feulgen technique is now often used which DeLamater (1951a) introduced into bacterial cytology. It is based on experiences of Atwood & Orinstein (1949). In this procedure thionin or azure A (one of the constituents of Romanowsky stains) is substituted for the fuchsin in the Schiff reagent of the standard Feulgen technique. Very sharply and delicately stained preparations of bacterial chromatin bodies are obtained with De-Lamater's technique. The writer has found a similar method by

Huebschman (1952) quite as useful and less likely to leave dye precipitates on the preparation. DeLamater insists that there is an increase in visible detail when cells stained by this method are dehydrated in deeply cooled alcohol, but this has never been proved. In experiments in which the same stained bacteria were first examined in water and then again after dehydration by DeLamater's method, I have found faithful preservation but no increase of visible chromatin detail.

(Special problems arising in the staining of bacterial nuclei are pointed out in a very recent paper by Cassel & Hutchinson (1955), of which the writer became aware too late for discussion in the present article.)

BEHAVIOUR AND CYTOLOGICAL STATUS OF CHROMATIN BODIES

(a) Cytological terminology

The constant presence of chromatin bodies in vegetative bacteria and spores suggests that they are integral parts of the bacterial cell. The positive Feulgen reaction of chromatin bodies coupled with the demonstration that their numbers increase by growth and division has inclined many to the belief that they are the bacterial cell's equivalent of a nucleus. Protozoologists, than whom nobody has a wider knowledge of varieties of nuclear organization, have been critical of this idea on morphological grounds. Geneticists have tolerated it because it does not disagree with their findings, others again have expressed doubt whether caryological studies of bacteria can have any significance at all (Oginski & Umbreit, 1954).

A fruitful discussion of this matter can only be conducted when it is recognized that in biological writings the term 'nucleus' is used in three different and overlapping contexts by chemists, geneticists and morphologists, and that of these three it is the morphologist whose description of nuclei are the most discriminating, the least ambiguous and the most easily verifiable.

Cytologists define a nucleus as something that arises from a set of chromosomes. They regard the general morphology of the resting phase as a matter of secondary importance but sharply distinguish different varieties of nuclei according to *the behaviour of the chromosomes during division*. Most of the nuclei in growing tissues of higher plants and animals divide by mitosis, but chromosome nuclei of higher organisms and protista may also grow and multiply by other means, including direct division or *amitosis* (Geitler, 1942, 1953; Grell, 1953*b*). The macronuclei of ciliate protozoa and of suctorians regularly divide in this

manner. The effectiveness of amitosis is still often undervalued outside
the circles of protozoologists. It is important to know that recent
experiments of Sonneborn (1947; review by Beale, 1954) and the
experiences of other workers have shown that macronuclei are genetically active, dominant over the micronucleus, which has the leading role
only in conjugation, and adequate by themselves for the multiplication of animals of normal structure and activity, short of mating.
Macronuclei are cytologically remarkable because they are formed
from chromosomes by repeated endo-mitotic divisions (Grell, 1953a)
but do not give rise to chromosomes when they divide.

Cytologists hold that all organisms have nuclei with the exception of
the blue-green algae and the bacteria. These two classes of organism
have enigmatic chromatin structures, but no chromosomes, hence, in the
strict sense, no nuclei.

This greatly simplified outline of accepted concepts of types of nuclei
indicates that before we can relate bacterial chromatin bodies to known
types of nuclei we must find out how they divide and whether they have
chromosomes.

(b) Observations on living cells

The division of living chromatin bodies has been studied in *Escherichia
coli* (Knoell & Zapf, 1951; Stempen, 1950) and *Proteus* (Tulasne, 1949;
Stempen & Hutchinson, 1951), and in every instance has given the impression of being a simple, direct process (Text-fig. 1). Nothing has

Text-fig. 1. Changes in the structure of living *Escherichia coli* as seen in the phase-
contrast microscope. Drawn at intervals of 20 min. After Knoell & Zapf (1951).

been seen that resembles the alternation of nuclear vesicles and sets of
chromosomes in mitosis, familiar from motion pictures of tissue cultures
of, say, mammalian fibroblasts or grasshopper spermatocytes. On the
contrary, it is characteristic of living chromatin bodies of bacteria that
they always seem to be in the *same* physical state. However, the vague-
ness of detail in even the best phase-contrast photomicrographs makes
it impossible to be certain that component parts of chromatin bodies,
invisible in life, are not going through intricate division manoeuvres
(Clifton & Erhard, 1952).

(c) General remarks on the behaviour of chromatin bodies as inferred from stained preparations

The process of division of chromatin bodies will ultimately be reconstructed from electron micrographs of serial ultra-thin sections. Meanwhile an approximation to the truth can be obtained from the analysis of fixed and stained preparations.

Early helpful observations by Stille (1937) and Piekarski (1937) were made on Feulgen preparations of *Bacillus subtilis* and *Salmonella paratyphi*. At the growth stage selected for study the chromatin bodies of both species occur in regular numbers and are widely and symmetrically spaced. Comparison of bacilli of different length revealed that the chromatin bodies increased in numbers as the bacilli grew longer. A plausible reconstruction of the course of division of chromatin bodies could be worked out in this material because division was related in a simple manner to a set of directly determined reference points, i.e. the different lengths of the bacilli composing a given sample. In species in which the behaviour of the chromatin bodies is not related in a simple manner to the growth of the cell, the reconstruction of their division manoeuvres must always be more or less arbitrary.

In those early experiments nothing useful was learned about the *structure* of the chromatin bodies, which were very small. The belief that chromatin bodies are something akin to nuclei thus rests solely on their positive Feulgen reaction and the correlation of their division with cell division. From the morphological point of view these properties are inadequate for the identification of nuclei. The cytological status of chromatin bodies can only be determined from detailed information on the *structure* and behaviour of individual bodies at rest and in division. In *Bacillus cereus* this information can be obtained, but with poor resolution at present, from preparations of vegetative bacilli because their chromatin bodies are relatively large and often symmetrically spaced (Pl. 1, figs. 2–5). The task is more difficult in vegetative forms of *B. megaterium* because there the chromatin bodies are often arranged at random and packed very densely (Smith, 1950; and Pl. 1, fig. 9).

The most satisfactory material for the study of individual chromatin bodies would obviously be a cell with a single chromatin body of sufficiently large size whose division could be induced at will. A spore is such a cell, and the study of the behaviour of chromatin bodies in samples of synchronously germinating spores has provided the most useful information on their mode of division that has so far been obtained with the light microscope.

(d) *The behaviour of chromatin bodies during spore germination*

Independent studies of resting spores of *Bacillus megaterium* and *B. cereus* by two direct methods, sectioning and shattering (Robinow, 1953; Fitz-James, 1953), have shown that their chromatin 'is arranged in a ring, or variation thereof, composed of at least three segments. Although in a few cases these segments seem so closely associated as to form an unbroken circular band, the majority are arranged more loosely in a beaded ring. Many of these latter structures are broken at one particular point, possibly as a result of the disintegration. One notes also triangular forms, and in some, three radiating arms form a claw-like structure. In a few, S-shaped and figure of eight patterns are encountered' (Fitz-James, 1953). There is a striking resemblance between the range of configurations of the spore chromatin (Text-fig. 2) and

~2 μ

Text-fig. 2. Disposition of chromatin in resting spores of *Bacillus megaterium*. Top row: sectioned spores; bottom row: mechanically disintegrated spores. Drawn from photo-micrographs of ribonuclease-Giemsa preparations (Fitz-James, 1953; Robinow, 1953). Magnification only approximate.

the variety of shapes of the (non-chromosomal) nucleus of the avian malaria parasite *Plasmodium elongatum* described by Chen (1944) and illustrated in Text-fig. 3. I am not suggesting that there is a direct relationship between bacteria and sporozoa. The chromatin body of *P. elongatum* is here referred to only in the character of a geometrical model to help us visualize the spatial arrangement of the chromatin in resting bacterial spores.

The same configurations, henceforth 'rings' for short, have also repeatedly been described in whole spores in the earliest stages of preparation for germination (Robinow, 1942, 1945; Hunter & DeLamater, 1952). On the subsequent behaviour of the spore chromatin several recent studies are in satisfactory agreement. After some 10 min. at 37° on any medium adequate for germination, rings of chromatin are no longer found. In its place one now sees in the centre of every spore a single solid round chromatin body (Robinow, 1942, 1945; Piekarski, 1952; Hunter & DeLamater, 1952).

All chromatin bodies of the vegetative bacilli are descendants of the single body in the germinating spore and are therefore homologous. Successive divisions of the single original body during germination and early vegetative growth of *Bacillus megaterium* are illustrated in Text-fig. 4 and Pl. 2, figs. 7–9. The chromatin bodies in this material and else-where in vegetative bacilli tend to be in either one or the other of two states. One type of body is a simple solid bar or has a dumbbell shape. Another, less frequently encountered, simple type is shaped like a small c or narrow oval (Text-fig. 5, Pl. 1, figs. 3, 5 and 9). It is possible that ovals and rodlets are merely two different aspects, full face and profile, of a single elemental disk-like body, but this is not certain.

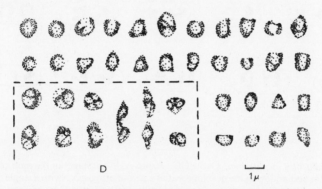

Text-fig. 3. Nuclei of *Plasmodium elongatum*. D = dividing nuclei
in schizonts. After Chen (1944).

The other type of body is complex and may have the shape of an open angular beaded ring, thicker than the ring in resting spores, or it may be a three- or four-cornered cluster of interconnected chromatin granules. U and V shapes and butterfly silhouettes also belong to this class.

In sequences of comparable bacteria arranged according to length it is usually found that complexes of this kind are replaced in bacilli of the next higher length class by two bodies of the simple type. The complex shapes must therefore be regarded as stages in the division of the simple ones. That this is indeed their relationship has very recently been proved by direct observations of dividing chromatin bodies in the living cells of a bacterium with unusually favourable optical properties isolated from cow dung, shortly to be described elsewhere.

In addition to *dividing* and *recently divided* bodies it is also possible to distinguish bodies that are *preparing* to divide (Pl. 1, fig. 8). Transition from one type to another is continuous. All phases are equally chroma-tinic and there is no distinct resting stage.

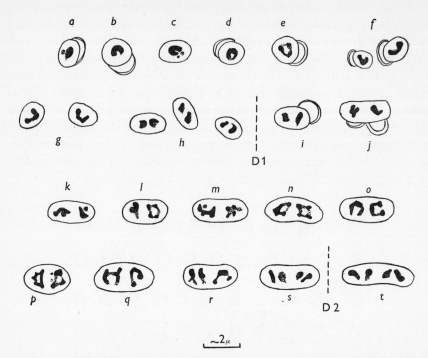

Text-fig. 4. *Bacillus megaterium*. OsO_4, HCl, Azure-A, SO_2. Stages in the multiplication of the chromatin bodies during the development of a germinating spore with a single chromatin body (*a*) into a bacillus with four chromatin bodies (*t*). Drawn from photomicrographs which will be published elsewhere. Cells *p* and *q* are also shown in Pl. 2, fig. 7. The sequence is continued in Pl. 2, fig. 9. D1 indicates the end of the first division. Constellations *j* to *r* represent chromatin bodies undergoing the second division. The process is completed at D2.

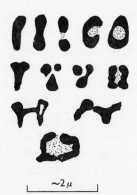

Text-fig. 5. Diagrams of types of chromatin bodies commonly seen in *Bacillus* cells. Top row: recently divided bodies. The first three may be side views of the last two. Remainder: division figures. The two constellations in the centre of the second row have sometimes been interpreted as resting nuclei with three chromosomes. Stippling indicates problematic 'cores', referred to in the text. Compare with Pl. 1, figs. 3–9.

Precisely what happens during division is not yet clear. The ingenious three-dimensional models constructed by Fitz-James (1954) reflect some of the features of division figures but do not account for the shape of recently divided bodies. Recent observations suggest that the author's 'original triad' of chromatin granules is itself a stage in the division of a simpler structure. It should also be borne in mind that most fixatives coarsen and exaggerate the proportions of chromatin bodies. The triads of seemingly distinct chromatin granules which are common in hydro-lysed osmium preparations and which are the basic configuration in Fitz-James's model sequence are probably artificially accentuated thickenings in a continuous chromatin structure.

(e) Accessory chromatic granules

DeLamater & Mudd (1951) and DeLamater (1953a) have made the important discovery that one or two minute granules, visible but beyond the limits of resolution, are very often found close to the much larger

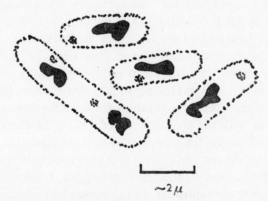

~2 µ

Text-fig. 6. Accessory granules ('centrioles') rendered visible by the contraction of the chromatin bodies. 2½ hr. culture of *Bacillus cereus* on Difco heart infusion agar. Fixed 10 min. after transfer to heart infusion agar with 3 % salt. In the remainder of the culture the chromatin bodies soon rearranged themselves into normal patterns. Drawn from a photomicrograph by Dr R. G. E. Murray.

chromatin bodies. The granules are usually round but sometimes elongated. The existence of these structures in Giemsa preparations of *Bacillus cereus* has been confirmed by R. G. E. Murray (Text-fig. 6) and they have been seen in *B. megaterium* by the writer and C. L. Hannay. The tiny accessory granules are often clearly visible in the voluminous cells of the first generation of bacilli issuing from germinating spores of *B. megaterium* (Pl. 1, figs. 6, 7). It has been suggested that the granules have a function connected with the laying down of transverse septa

(Bissett, 1953), but this seems unlikely, since they are often found by the side of the single chromatin body of germinating spores long before the first partition wall is laid down across the young bacillus. Moreover, in rod forms one or two accessory granules are frequently found between a distal chromatin body and the end of the cell, i.e. at a point where septa are not formed. It seems probable that DeLamater and Bisset are not in all instances discussing the same structures. The accessory granules are not always easily seen in fully grown multiplying vegetative bacilli. That they are there nevertheless and are merely hidden among the much larger ordinary chromatin bodies may be inferred from experiments of Whitfield & Murray (1955) in which chromatin bodies, aggregated in the centre of the cell owing to a sudden rise in the salt concentration of the environment from 0·5 to 3%, were found to have left the accessory granules behind in the clear cytoplasm where they now stood out very distinctly (Text-fig. 6). In these experiments the bacilli adapted themselves quickly to life in the new environment and their chromatin bodies reverted within minutes to arrangements of the normal kind.

We have not seen fibres between accessory granules and chromatin granules, and in our preparations their position relative to dividing and recently divided chromatin bodies varies unpredictably. But information on the behaviour of these elements must needs be incomplete, since they are often hidden by the much larger chromatin bodies and our experience does not rule out the possibility that changes in the numbers and position of the accessory granules are in reality connected in a systematic manner with the growth and division of the chromatin bodies.

The positive Feulgen reaction of the small granules (Pl. 1, fig. 2), and the fact that they do not move along with the chromatin bodies when the latter are shifted about in the cell (Text-fig. 6), renders it improbable that they function as 'centrioles' in the sense in which this term is used in general cytology (Schrader, 1953). No well-founded alternative interpretation can be advanced at present.

(f) Random arrangements of chromatin bodies

The description of chromatin bodies in the preceding sections is based on preparations from cultures in the earliest phases of growth. It is not necessarily true of chromatin bodies in bacteria from older cultures. The structure of bacteria in cultures with limited food is, in many instances, liable to change visibly with age (Delaporte, 1950). These changes, which include spore formation, are due to the action of the bacteria on their environment, and can be indefinitely delayed by stabilizing the supply of food and other factors of the environment. Thus they do not have the significance of stages of an inexorable 'life cycle' of the kind characteristic of the plasmodia of malaria and other parasites. A knowledge of changes in bacterial morphology with increasing age is, nevertheless, essential to a balanced view of the nature of chromatin bodies.

The symmetrical grouping and synchronous division movements of chromatin bodies in bacteria from young cultures plead persuasively for their nuclear nature and divert the student's attention from reflexion on the properties of the *individual* body. By contrast, the odd shapes and random distribution of chromatin bodies in cells from older cultures (of many species) emphasize the primitive, rather non-nuclear, bearing of these elements.

Differences in appearance between cells from very young cultures and cells from older cultures are particularly striking in the large *Bacillus* species which are often used for cytological studies. In *B. megaterium* and *B. mycoides*, two historically important examples, the difference is due to the accumulation of many brightly refractile granules in the cytoplasm after a few hours of growth on all common media (de Bary, 1884; Bayne-Jones & Petrilli, 1933). The bright granules are droplets of lipid (Lewis, 1934; Delaporte, 1939). The lipid, which has been identified as a polymer of β-hydroxybutyric acid by Lemoigne, Delaporte & Croson (1944), can be demonstrated with Sudan black B (Hartman, 1940; Burdon, 1946) but not with ordinary stains. The lipid globules therefore appear as unstained holes or 'vacuoles' in the cytoplasm of stained bacteria (Guilliermond, 1908; Schaede, 1939). The chromatin bodies seem to be softer than the lipid globules and are moulded by them into a variety of different shapes (Pl. 2, figs. 10–13). In bacilli with many small lipid globules the chromatin bodies are compressed between them in the thin lamellae of the remaining cytoplasm and appear, but probably are not, fragmented. Bacilli in this condition have been described by Guilliermond (1908) as having dispersed or 'chromidial' nuclei. It is obvious from the literature and from the illustrations on Pl. 2 that the chromatin bodies of lipid-laden bacilli are not gathered in sets of regular numbers inside a nucleus, but lie separately and independently in the cytoplasm. After transfer to fresh nutrient medium each chromatin body divides directly and behaves as an independent unit body or 'nucleus'. A simple situation in which the new growth starts from cells containing one chromatin body compressed between a few large lipid globules is illustrated in Text-fig. 8, but bacilli with 'chromidial' nuclei are also fully viable and in subcultures their chromatin bodies, however distorted they may have been at the start, eventually revert to their normal size and appearance (Delaporte, 1950; Robinow & Hannay, unpublished).

Lipid is not the only material likely to modify the normal disposition of chromatin bodies in bacterial cells. Other examples have been discussed by Delaporte (1939, 1950).

(g) Induced abnormal arrangements of chromatin bodies

Visible accumulations of lipid droplets which affect the morphology of the chromatin bodies are not commonly seen in Gram-negative bacteria. But here, too, there is impressive evidence of great plasticity of the chromatin elements under different conditions of growth. This, as well as their ability to recover from the effects of treatments which thoroughly disrupt their normal structure and arrangement in the cell, has been clearly described by Johnson & Gray (1949), Kellenberger (1953) and Whitfield (1955), whose instructive studies should be consulted in the original.

Here must also be mentioned the weird networks of chromatin in certain abnormal but viable forms which arise spontaneously in Gram-negative bacteria (Stempen & Hutchinson, 1951) or which can be induced in them by low concentrations of LiCl or CsCl (Braun, Berg, Kessler & Mavroidi, 1954).

(h) The behaviour of chromatin bodies during spore formation

There is as yet no satisfactory systematic study of the behaviour of the chromatin bodies during spore formation. There is general agreement that only one of the several chromatin bodies originally present in a sporing bacillus is incorporated into the spore. But opinions differ about the nature of the events which lead to the segregation of one privileged chromatin body from others destined to disintegrate.

In *Clostridium oedematiens* and *Bacillus mycoides* (Badian, 1933; Klieneberger, 1945), *B. anthracis* (Flewett, 1948) and *C. tetani* (Bisset, 1950 b), the chromatin bodies have been found fused into a continuous axial core early in the process of spore formation and this has been con-considered as having genetical significance. There are now serious reasons for doubting this. The chromtain bodies of spore-forming as well as non-sporing species can at any time be aggregated into axial filaments by exposing them to cold, to antibiotics, to media of high pH or to a sudden increase in the salt concentration of the medium. These changes, all of them indirect salt effects according to Whitfield (1955), are readily reversible. The axial filaments of chromatin, for example, which are normally found in bacilli from relatively old but not yet spore-forming cultures of *B. cereus*, and which are so clearly shown in the ultra-thin sections of this *Bacillus* by Chapman & Hillier (1953), revert to chromatin patterns typical of very young growth within minutes of being transferred to fresh nutrient medium (personal communication from R. G. E. Murray).

In view of these observations it seems at present doubtful whether the formation of axial filaments in connexion with spore formation is anything more than an unspecific and reversible response to changes in the environment or of the cell's permeability or both. These doubts are enhanced by the demonstration that spores may be formed in bacilli whose chromatin bodies are normally arranged at random between numerous lipid globules and assume the form of an axial thread only rarely and probably because a space of that shape happens to be the only one available to them.

Spore formation under these conditions has been clearly described in *Bacillus cereus* by Delaporte (1950, p. 9). Her account, which corresponds closely to the writer's experience in *B. megaterium*, is worth quoting in full: 'If we observe stained cells from a 16-hour culture of *B. cereus*, for example, we see many cells in which several granules of nuclear substance [the "chromatin bodies" of the present article] are located between the lipid globules; that is, the nuclear substance is fragmented between the globules in two to six (occasionally more) main centres. Each of these nuclear granules of a cell seems to be completely separate from the others, but perhaps they are linked by non-apparent ties. A few cells have only one nuclear element in the form of an axial thread and many cells are just beginning to form their spores.... At first, all the nuclear granules inside the cell seem alike, but at the very beginning of spore formation, one granule situated nearest an end of the cell [Pl. 2, fig. 15 of the present article] appears a little larger. Then the cytoplasm around this granule becomes more homogeneous and denser, without globules, and stains pink with Giemsa.... This region which is to develop into the spore grows larger and becomes ovoid in shape....' Delaporte's findings agree with and explain the earlier studies of Guilliermond (1908).

Photomicrographs of sporulating cells of *Bacillus megaterium*, many of which resemble the illustrations of Delaporte (1950), have been published by DeLamater and Hunter (1952; figs. 4, 8, 9, 10, 12, 13 and 14). The authors state that 'at no time has there been evidence observed for the occurrence of a rod-like nucleus during the process of sporulation'; but their figs. 12 and 14 are clear examples of such nuclei. The divergence of opinion between Delaporte and the American authors regarding the nature of these shapes lies in this, that Delaporte, observing an axial thread (of nuclear material) compressed between fat droplets, refers to it as 'an axial thread', whereas DeLamater & Hunter, ignoring the fat, call it 'an elongated telophase divisional stage'.

A species like *Bacillus megaterium* whose cells invariably develop lipid is not the best choice for detailed studies of the behaviour of chromatin bodies during spore formation. In the disorderly array of chromatin bodies jostled by lipid globules it is impossible to trace the origin of the tiny terminal chromatin granules around which the spore is formed. *Bacillus* species which develop little or no lipid or where the formation of lipid can be controlled are more rewarding subjects for studies of spore formation than *B. megaterium*.

Flewett (1948) and Delamater & Hunter (1951) found that the minute spore primordium later widens into a delicate ring embedded in non-chromatinic material (Pl. 2, fig. 16). This is an early and fleeting appearance of the ring of chromatin which sectioning and shattering has now also revealed in mature, free, resting spores (Text-fig. 2).

It is a curious fact that the configuration of the chromatin in mature resting spores resembles *dividing* rather than 'resting' chromatin bodies of vegetative bacilli, and also resembles the *division* stages of *Plasmodium elongatum* (Text-fig. 3).

To summarize, much remains to be learned about the role of the chromatin bodies in spore formation. In *Bacillus megaterium* the spore arises at one end of the cell from a tiny hyperchromatinic granule whose origin has not been determined but which probably arises in continuity with preformed chromatin bodies. The dot-like initial stage of the spore chromatin later changes into a ring which persists through the resting phase and is still clearly visible early in germination. The observations of Klieneberger, Flewett and Bisset suggest that the behaviour of the chromatin bodies during spore formation is not everywhere the same as in *B. megaterium*.

(j) *Synchronization of spore formation*

The majority of the vegetative bacilli in confluent growth in plate cultures of *Bacillus cereus* and *B. megaterium* can be induced to begin spore formation simultaneously at a chosen time. When cultures of *B. megaterium* on plain potato extract agar are first incubated for 18 hr. at 16–20° and thereafter at 37° most of the bacilli will start forming spores 3–4 hr. later. To give an example: Pl. 2, fig. 16, is from a culture in which two-thirds of the bacilli were in the same early stage of spore formation 4 hr. after the temperature shift. Under constant conditions the moment of onset of spore formation is accurately predictable.

This method is helpful in cytological work, where it provides an objective basis for the interpretation of sequences of morphological changes. It may also have uses in physiological studies.

(k) General properties of chromatin bodies

Studies with the light microscope now permit the following general conclusions.

The multiple chromatin bodies in growing rod-shaped bacteria are replicas of a single unit and are homologous. The unit body is simple in the sense that its chromatinic material is in one piece. Beaded chromatin bodies, commonly seen during division, behave as continuous structures, not as sets of separate granules.

The shape of chromatin bodies and their disposition in the cell is liable to extreme variations from causes other than division movements. In bacilli with much lipid the number and behaviour of individual chromatin bodies may be impossible to determine. Bacilli in this condition are nevertheless fully viable.

In electron micrographs of sectioned bacteria the chromatin bodies are either finely granular (Chapman & Hillier, 1953) or filled with randomly crossing fibres of varying degrees of coarseness (Bradfield, 1954; Birch-Andersen et al. 1953; Tomlin & May, 1955; R. G. E. Murray, C. L. Hannay, unpublished). The coarseness of the fibres seems related to the salt content of the culture medium and the fixative. In any one specimen the chromatin bodies have the same fine structure between and during divisions. Methods of fixation and sectioning for electron microscopy which regularly reveal distinct membranes around the nuclei of cells of higher organisms and Protozoa have consistently failed to show a membrane at the surface of chromatin bodies. These entities must therefore be regarded as lying directly and separately in the cytoplasm.

In electron micrographs of vegetative bacilli chromatin bodies have never been found inside a nucleus. DeLamater (1954) believes that he has found a nucleus in the shape of 'a sharply delineated vesicle with an aggregation of what is thought to be chromosomal material' in the sections of Birch-Andersen et al. (1953), but this interpretation derives from a confusion of magnitudes. The vesicles in question measure in microns and are profiles of whole chromatin bodies or 'chromosomes' (of DeLamater) as comparison of Fig. 1 of Birch-Andersen et al. (1953) with DeLamater, (1953b, p. 174, figs. 6 and 18) will readily show. The constituent threads of the chromosomal material in the sectioned vesicles measure in millimicrons and Ångstroms, and would be invisible in the light microscope!

What still stands in the way of a complete description of chromatin bodies is uncertainty about the nature and configuration of peculiar non-chromatinic material which under certain conditions seems to be associated with them (Murray, 1953). This material is most conspicuous after fixation with methanol-formalin, less so, but still noticeable, after osmium fixation. Recently divided ('resting') chromatin bodies in Giemsa preparations appear to consist only of chromatinic matter, but division figures frequently appear to enclose a core of non-chromatinic matter more refractile than ordinary cytoplasm. The sudden emergence of this material during division makes one wonder whether it is not in the chromatin bodies at all times but usually invisible because we see them mostly in profile. The non-chromatinic centre of the 'small c'-type of 'resting' chromatin body, mentioned above, may well be the origin of the 'core' in division figures.

The following other examples of chromatin structures with a core of non-chromatinic matter have been observed: the chromatin body in resting spores, the reticulum or chromatin threads which Whitfield (1955) has described in *Shigella dysenteriae*, the disk-shaped bodies with marginal chromatin which Hoelling (1910) saw in *Fusiformis* and which resemble those later demonstrated in isolated cells of mechanically disrupted trichomes of *Caryophanon latum* by Peshkoff (1945), and in intact trichomes by Pringsheim & Robinow (1947), and lastly the chromatin bodies of *Bacteroides* (Dienes & Smith, 1944). In short, it seems quite possible that the rodlet or dumbbell aspect of chromatin bodies (Text-fig. 5), as mentioned above, is in reality the side view of a disk- or lens-shaped element with a non-chromatinic core and a thick chromatinic edge. A formal model of this hypothetical chromatin body, which should be regarded as an entirely open structure, is to hand in the shape of the nuclei of *Plasmodium elongatum* (Text-fig. 3), whose resemblance to the chromatin of resting spores has already been pointed out above.

Most of the information from thin sections cannot yet be directly related to observations on hydrolysed stained specimens, but as far as it goes it encourages the idea of a core in chromatin bodies. Small enclosures of dense material different from ordinary cytoplasm have been seen inside chromatin bodies of *Bacillus cereus* (Chapman & Hillier, 1953) and in four successive longitudinal sections through a cell of *B. thuringiensis* made by C. L. Hannay. In the latter sections, as well as in those of Tomlin & May (1955), it is possible to see that dense material which appears as a core at one level is in communication with the cytoplasm at another level. A 'core', as Chapman & Hillier had already suspected, should therefore perhaps be regarded as cytoplasm modified by close association with the chromatinic material.

The absence of a membrane around the chromatin and the continuity of the core with the cytoplasm accounts for the readiness with which separate chromatin bodies and their cores flow together to form the rings and chains of rings (Text-fig. 7) which have been demonstrated with great clarity in *Escherichia coli* K12 exposed to sublethal concentrations

1μ

Text-fig. 7. Aggregates of chromatin bodies (white shapes) in *Escherichia coli* K12 surviving in nutrient broth in the presence of 3μg/ml. of aureomycin. The chromatin bodies are seen to have 'cores' of a density intermediate between that of the chromatin and that of the cytoplasm. Drawn after an electron micrograph by Kellenberger (1953, fig. 15).

of aureomycin (Kellenberger, 1953) and which have also been produced in other bacteria in a variety of other ways (DeLamater, 1953; Whitfield, 1955). In Kellenberger's electron micrographs the non-chromatinic interior of the rings is not significantly different from the surrounding cytoplasm but it is so in the light microscope. In ordinary light the aureomycin artifact appears as a solid piece of chromatin. In red light it is a ring with a clear interior which is not chromatinic but more refractile than ordinary cytoplasm. These artifacts must be regarded as exaggerations of the normal structure of chromatin bodies but they are reversible and compatible with life, and it seems not unreasonable to see in them, as in the nuclei of *Plasmodium elongatum*, an approximation to the truth about structures whose true shape and construction cannot yet be described with certainty.

(*l*) *Affinities*

The simplicity of chromatin bodies gives them a character entirely their own, and one can sympathize with Geitler (1942), one of the most experienced cytologists of our time, when he hailed the discovery of the chromatin bodies as final proof that bacteria have no nuclei.

Morphological criteria of nuclei are at present based on information from light microscopy. The microscope cannot resolve the structure of the unit chromatin body, but it does convey the impression that, within the limits of its performance, the structure of chromatin bodies is the same between and during divisions. This fact and their mode of division are the characters which we have to use in trying to find affinities of chromatin bodies with known types of nuclei.

Light-optical and electron micrographs are in good agreement that the chromatin bodies of cocci divide directly (Dobell, 1911; Knaysi, 1942; Robinow, 1942; Bisset, 1954; Bradfield, 1954; and especially Wigand & Peters, 1954). In light-optical preparations of slender bacilli such as *Bacillus subtilis* one also finds nothing to suggest that the division of chromatin bodies involves anything more elaborate than simple constriction. The chromatin bodies in large bacteria also divide directly, but because they are optically better resolved, the term 'constriction' no longer adequately describes what one sees. As described above the division of a chromatin body of, say, *B. cereus* usually begins at one end, not in the middle, and proceeds to completion through a series of V- and U-shaped forms. The beaded appearance of some dividing chromatin bodies is another feature which makes 'constriction' inadequate as a description of division.

The direct division of chromatin bodies recalls the behaviour of macronuclei (Piekarski, 1949). Taken seriously this analogy would imply that chromatin bodies arise by repeated endomitoses of sets of chromosomes. This has not been demonstrated. Moreover, the facts of bacterial genetics do not support the idea that chromatin bodies are normally highly polyploid.

For affinities with known chromatin organs we must look elsewhere. The direction of our search is not in doubt. Unsolved questions of detail apart, there is frequently a striking general resemblance between the chromatin bodies of bacteria and those of the blue-green algae. It is impossible to study the splendid photographs of *Synechococcus* and *Gloecapsa*, of *Oscillatoria*, *Fremyella* and *Microcoleus* in Cassel & Hutchinson's (1954) recent memoir without becoming aware of this relationship. The study of similar preparations made by J. P. Truant in our own laboratory has strengthened this impression. The resemblance is strongest between phase-contrast pictures of living filamentous Myxophyceae and Bouin-thionin preparations of rod-shaped bacteria from very young cultures (Pl. 1, fig. 3). The chromatin organs of blue-green algae are, in most instances, more complex than those of bacteria. In some instances they appear to be constructed from many small and inter-connected chromatin bodies of the kind which, single and larger, are found in bacterial cells. The chromatin structures of both classes of organisms share the lack of a limiting membrane, divide in a simple way not involving spindles and recognizable chromosomes and have no distinct resting stages.

There is nothing very surprising in this resemblance. The blue-green algae have long been known to be more closely related to bacteria than to any other group of organisms. Both occur in the same range of basic shapes (cocci, rods, helices, chains), one colourless organism, *Caryophanon latum* Peshkoff, reckoned among the bacteria because of its peritrichous flagellation, has, in its native habitat, the cell structure and proportions of *Oscillatoria* species; and lastly it has been shown that bacteria and blue-green algae share the distinction of being the only micro-organisms which contain diaminopimelic acid (Work & Dewey 1953; Stanier, 1954).

It seems desirable that real morphological differences be recognized by the use of distinctive terms. The chromatin organs of the Myxophyceae and the bacteria, though different in detail, have in common that they lack most of the properties which cytologists consider charac-teristic of nuclei. Hence they should be called by some other name such as 'chromatin bodies'. They do not become less interesting for being so treated. In fact the only danger to the advancement of knowledge could come from describing these enigmatic structures in terms of unwarranted familiarity. It is differentiating rather than levelling terminologies that stimulate further work!

It seems quite possible that the activities of chromatin bodies corre-spond to those of nuclei, and geneticists have, in some instances, obtained results which are conveniently explained on this assumption (Witkin, 1951; Ryan & Wainwright, 1954). The constancy of the deoxyribonucleic acid content of bacterial cells growing under a wide variety of conditions (Caldwell & Hinshelwood, 1950) also suggests that the chromatin bodies are important. But on the whole, the link between morphology and physiology of these organelles is still a very slender one.

The writers' views on the protean chromatin bodies owe much to the experiences and the comment of his colleagues, Prof. R. G. E. Murray and Dr J. F. Whitfield, to whom he tenders sincere thanks.

* * *

ON THE ALLEGED EVIDENCE OF MITOSIS IN BACTERIA

What is wanted is not the will to believe, but the wish to find out, which is its exact opposite.

BERTRAND RUSSELL (*Free Thought and Official Propaganda*, 1922)

The observations discussed in the preceding pages suggest that the chromatin bodies of bacteria, though they may consist of several different materials, are morphologically simple structures, which divide directly. By contrast, DeLamater and his associates at the University of Pennsylvania are convinced that they have obtained 'evidence for the occurrence not only of a true mitotic process in *Bacillus megatherium* but also evidence for the occurrence of a nucleus, the intrinsic structure of which is essentially similar to that long known and accepted as occurring in larger forms' (DeLamater & Mudd, 1951).

Such wide differences in the interpretation of the same kind of observable facts should not be left unexplained.

DeLamater discovered mitosis first in vegetative forms of *Bacillus megaterium* (DeLamater & Hunter, 1951; DeLamater & Mudd, 1951; DeLamater, 1951 b; DeLamater, Hunter & Mudd, 1952). The experience of mitosis was then applied to show that spore formation and germination in *B. megaterium* were vegetative processes involving neither nuclear fusions nor reduction divisions (DeLamater & Hunter, 1952; Hunter & DeLamater, 1952). DeLamater and his associates later also examined other bacteria, but their first few publications are still representative of the group's outlook and method, and a discussion of their design will serve to illuminate the origin and extent of the disagreement between us.

The Problem

Vegetative rods of *Bacillus megaterium*, DeLamater's principal source of information, normally consist of two cells with at least two constellations of chromatin bodies in each. In a sample from logarithmically growing cultures all the bacilli and all their chromatin structures are in one phase or another of a ceaselessly repeated cycle of growth and division. In fact, it would be correct to say that every bacillus in such a culture consists of two *dividing* cells. The behaviour of the chromatin bodies in these bacilli is not immediately obvious. Before we can expect to see how different, simultaneously present, chromatin constellations are related in time, we have to find some non-nuclear character of the bacilli whose change with time can be objectively determined. *Growth in length* provides a useful character of this kind and objectively fixes the time coordinate of the unknown division process which we intend to explore.

The cytologist who is given a random sample of growing bacteria will therefore first arrange them according to length and will then look for recurrent changes of the shape and size of chromatin bodies which can be correlated with the growth of the bacteria.

It has been necessary to make these rather obvious statements in order to make clear at the start how differently the problem of the behaviour of the chromatin bodies has been approached by DeLamater & Mudd (1951). The cytologist of the previous paragraph did not know in advance how chromatin bodies divide and made an experiment to find out. Not so DeLamater & Mudd. They did know in advance! Before the presentation of any evidence the authors declare their belief that 'The process of mitosis, or its equivalent is as necessary to the biologic stability and activity of bacteria as to the same functions in larger organisms' (DeLamater & Mudd, 1951, p. 503). This *a priori* judgement has coloured all of DeLamater's writings up to the present day. There is no space to refute in detail the entirely unwarranted assumption of the universal necessity of mitosis as a means for the equitable distribution of chromosomes (and the authors mean 'true' mitosis, not one of its physiological equivalents), but the blue-green algae, near relatives of the bacteria, might perhaps be pointed out as an example of organisms, both stable and active, whose chromatin bodies have never been shown to divide by mitosis.

The material

A. *Concerning evidence of mitosis in vegetative bacilli*

It is claimed by DeLamater & Mudd (1951) that their photographs 'demonstrate the sequence of events in the mitotic process of *Bacillus megatherium*' (p. 505). This is an illusion. There are three main reasons why this claim cannot be accepted.

(1) *Absence of proof of genetic relationship of the morphological types composing the alleged division sequence.* The authors have presented their evidence in the form of two series of separate photographs of single bacilli or small groups of them. In each bacillus, one or two nuclei are pointed out and identified as being in prophase, metaphase and so forth. Something odd about this 'sequence' is immediately apparent. It is the curious fact that the length of the bacilli does not steadily increase but fluctuates randomly during the course of the alleged cycle of mitosis. The number of nuclei per bacillus also varies unpredictably but, on the

whole, remains surprisingly constant at 4. Thus the bacillus whose four nuclei are at 'metaphase' in DeLamater & Mudd (1951, pl. II, fig. 3) is considerably *longer* than the 'telophase' bacillus in fig. 13 on the same plate, which has only four of the eight nuclei one would expect to find in it.

It is obvious that individual nuclei have been identified as being in this or that phase of mitosis merely because they bear a fancied resemblance to stages of an abstract sequence of mitosis in the mind of the authors. No attempt has been made to test the aptness of this comparison by relating it to the growth of the bacteria! The authors' photographs form a series only in the sense that they bear consecutive numbers. The lack of any *objectively demonstrable* relationship between the illustrations makes it impossible to regard them as evidence of a real sequence of events.

(2) *Different stages of the alleged sequence of mitosis are illustrated with examples from cultures which are not comparable with each other* (De-Lamater & Mudd, 1951). It is characteristic of growing cultures of *Bacillus megaterium* that all their members have at any one time the same general appearance. It is especially true of very young cultures of the kind used by DeLamater & Mudd (1951) in their studies of mitosis. It is therefore surprising to find that the mitosis story is illustrated with photographs of at least two quite different kinds of bacilli. One kind is relatively large and has many small granular chromatin bodies in a foamy cytoplasm (pl. I, figs. 5, 6, 7, 8, 9, 11 and pl. II, fig. 1). These bacilli serve to illustrate all but one of the interphase and prophase nuclei. The other bacilli are slender and have a few compact chromatin bodies in clear cytoplasm (pl. II, figs. 3, 4, 8, 11, 12, 13). Bacilli of this kind are used to illustrate metaphases and telophases.

These same photographs, in different combinations, have been used in the four publications on mitosis quoted above and elsewhere. They cannot be passed over in favour of other ones. They are the evidence and deserve to be studied carefully. The difference between these two sets is so great as to make it virtually certain that they were in fact derived from cultures in different states of growth and were thus not directly comparable. One finds, for example, that all five bacilli in one illustration on pl. II are of the one kind and seven in another illustration are all of the other kind. Most probably each of these random samples is so uniform because it comes from a uniform culture.

It can be categorically stated that the chromatin bodies in normal vegetative bacilli in pure cultures of *Bacillus megaterium* never arrange themselves alternately in the 'large interphase nuclei' and dense 'metaphase plates' of DeLamater & Mudd (1951). Their true division changes are subtle and inconspicuous; see, for example, figs. 7 and 8 of Smith (1950) and Pl. 1, fig. 9, of the present paper. DeLamater & Mudd have succeeded in giving an illusion of a regular alternation of strikingly different chromatin patterns only by illustrating the different phases of mitosis with pictures of bacilli from different cultures, each homogeneous in respect of cell size, texture of cytoplasm and type of chromatin pattern. The twofold origin of the author's series of photographs further reduces its value as evidence of a true sequence of events.

(3) *The distribution of chromatin in the cells of the authors' starting material reveals that the 'interphase' and 'prophase nuclei' in the series of DeLamater & Mudd (1951) are open aggregates of several independent chromatin bodies.* The differences between the cultures from which DeLamater & Mudd (1951) chose their illustration can be explained when the history of their samples is taken into account. The authors (p. 504) state that their 'cytologic preparations for study were made from cultures grown on Morton and Engley medium, dextrose nutrient agar, and blood agar....Inocula were taken from 18–24 hour old cultures and incubated on the above media for two hours at 37° prior to the making of mounts.' What was the condition of the nuclei in the cells of the old cultures? There should be more 'interphase nuclei' in 18–24 hr. old cultures than in 2 hr. old cultures. But are there? The authors have not described the disposition of chromatin in their starting material (which is odd in an investigation of nuclear cycles), but it has been studied by the present writer and C. L. Hannay. The result is quite definite. There are no 'interphase' or 'prophase nuclei' with sets of tangled chromosomes in any of the cells of the three kinds of 18–20 hr. cultures which the authors say they have used as inoculum. There are only separate chromatin bodies (Pl. 2, figs. 10 a, b). After subculture the cells of the inoculum elongate and their chromatin bodies divide directly (Text-fig. 8), each one by itself, without either then or later going through a phase where they form interphase or prophase nuclei of the kind illustrated by DeLamater & Mudd (1951).

What then is the origin of those large granular bacilli with complex chromatin patterns which remind the authors of prophase nuclei? The most probable answer to this is to be found in the fact that the cells of the author's inocula contain large amounts of lipid (Pl. 2, figs. 10 b, 11 b). The chromatin bodies are compressed between large lipid globules and after transfer begin to grow and divide in that cramped position (Pl. 2, figs. 10 a, 11 a and 12). In other instances the chromatin of the cells of the inoculum is dispersed in many small pieces between many small lipid globules all over the cell. After subculture the separate, perhaps invisibly connected, pieces of chromatin proceed to enlarge, grow and divide on the spot, right among the lipid globules. Complicated constellations do thus arise until the lipid is lost from the bacilli in the third hour of incubation, when normal patterns are restored. A typical example of a mitosis-like aggregate of separate, independent chromatin bodies in a cell with foamy (i.e. lipid-encumbered) cytoplasm is shown in Pl. 2, fig. 13.

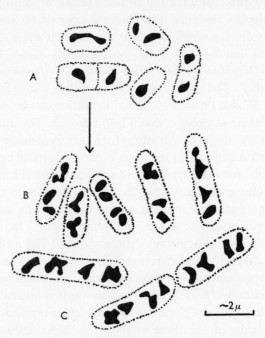

Text-fig. 8. A, *Bacillus megaterium*. 18 hr. on blood agar at 37°. The chromatin bodies should be imagined compressed by lipid globules in the manner of Pl. 2, figs. 10*a*, *b*, on which this diagram is based. B, C, successive stages in the direct division of the chromatin bodies of bacilli from A, after transfer to fresh blood agar. All drawn from photographs.

There are many shiny white clearings, which may be unstained lipid, between the chromatin bodies of the large granular bacilli which provided DeLamater & Mudd with illustrations of interphase nuclei. The appearance of these cells strongly suggests that they had not yet entirely rid themselves of their original lipid charge and that they owe their complex chromatin patterns to this fact.

It speaks for this interpretation that the present writer has been able to simulate interphase nuclei (Pl. 2, fig. 18*b*) by staining the chromatin of large heavily lipid-laden bacilli having the proportions of those in the authors' illustrations.

The authors' failure to study the history of the chromatin constellations which they describe as resting nuclei provides a further reason why their story cannot be accepted as evidence of a true sequence of events.

B. *Mitosis and spore formation*

DeLamater & Hunter (1952) claim to have observed mitosis during spore formation in *Bacillus megaterium*. A single bacillus with four evenly spaced clusters of chromatinic elements is presented, and quoted in later publications, as evidence that 'the last nuclear division prior to spore formation appears to be a typically mitotic one (fig. 1)'. But can a single step be evidence of a *process*? And by what token do we recognize this division as the last one before spore formation? Here as elsewhere the authors' standards of validity are obviously not the common ones.

Other illustrations purport to show 'typical and recognizable' 'supportive interphase nuclei' in the part of the bacillus not occupied by the developing spore. The author's photographs are quite representative of the distribution of chromatin in sporing *Bacillus megaterium*. But their interpretations of these starry patterns as interphase nuclei can only have been arrived at by a determined refusal to apply to their own case all pertinent information on spore formation in the literature of the last seventy years.

It has already been mentioned that *Bacillus megaterium* develops lipid globules in its cytoplasm after a few hours' cultivation on any medium on which it will grow at all. There is always much lipid at the time of spore formation. On the medium on which spore formation was studied by DeLamater & Hunter (1952) there is a great deal of it hours before spore formation begins (Pl. 2, fig. 17), and when the spore primordia are first clearly visible the bacilli are so choked with lipid globules that they appear almost black in preparations stained with Sudan (Pl. 2, fig. 14). The chromatin bodies have to find room between the lipid in the thin lamellae which are all that remains of the cytoplasm. It is this that causes them to disperse into starry patterns. If there were 'typical and recognizable' interphase nuclei among the lipid globules they should stand out as large clear unstained spaces, but such are never found.

A discussion of the behaviour of chromatin during spore formation in *Bacillus megaterium* that does not take into account the hosts of lipid globules in the vegetative portion of the cell has no scientific interest.

C. *Mitosis in germinating spores*

Hunter & DeLamater (1952) claim to have obtained evidence of mitosis in germinating spores of *Bacillus megaterium*. The events of the first division remain obscure in the authors' photographs, but the last five pictures in the first of the authors' two series form a sequence of comparable bacilli smoothly graded according to length. The essential features of this series are reproduced in Text-fig. 9. In *a* and *b* there are 'two condensed and separate daughter nuclei'. In *b*, *c*, and *d* we see them becoming larger and more complex, as if they were preparing for another division. After one more step the sequence breaks off. What is the nature of this last stage? Reason says it must represent one step further towards the completion of the second (direct) division. A longer series (Text-fig. 4) would have shown this to be true. But this is not the conclusion arrived at by Hunter & DeLamater. Disregarding all objective signs to the contrary the authors provide two different incompatible

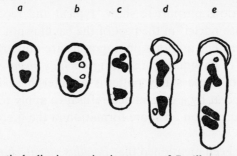

Text-fig. 9. Chromatin bodies in germinating spores of *Bacillus megaterium* after Hunter & DeLamater (1952, figs. 15–19). According to the authors there are in *a* 'two separate daughter nuclei'; *b* and *c* are 'binucleate stages with one nucleus commencing second mitosis' but *e* is again described as a binucleate stage representing the end of the *first* mitosis! Further explanation in the text.

and unwarranted interpretations of the chromatin constellations in the last member of their sequence (bacillus *e*). The *caption* reads: '...binucleate stage, chromosomes elongating in late telophase or early interphase.' If this interpretation were true it would turn the authors' linear sequence into a circular one in which the last and the first members are identical. However, the *text* says of the same figure that it represents compared with (*d*): '...a somewhat later stage in the mitotic division of the two daughter nuclei.' This comes nearer the truth but is later contradicted on the same page by the description of another bacillus in the same advanced stage of the second division as fig. 10*e*, which again declares in favour of the unreasonable 'interphase' interpretation.

Hunter & DeLamater's very short sequences lack the internal controls provided by longer series. Moreover, photographs of which their authors are uncertain whether they show resting or dividing nuclei can scarcely be regarded as compelling evidence for mitosis.

DeLamater has published many other papers on chromatin bodies in bacteria besides those here discussed.

They have enriched the literature with many, frequently excellent, pictures of chromatin bodies, but practically all these papers assume what remains to be proved and present agglomerations of observation and interpretation that are hard, if not impossible, to disentangle.

REFERENCES

ATWOOD, K. & ORINSTEIN, L. (1949). Exhibit A.A.A.S. New York City (abstract in programme).

BADIAN, J. (1933). Eine cytologische Untersuchung über das Chromatin und den Entwicklungszyklus der Bakterien. *Arch. Mikrobiol.* **4**, 409.

DE BARY, A. (1884). *Vergleichende Morphologie und Biologie der Pilze, Mycetozoen und Bacterien*, pp. 500 and 502. Leipzig.

BAYNE-JONES, S. & PETRILLI, A. (1933). Cytological changes during the formation of the endospore in *Bacillus megatherium*. *J. Bact.* **25**, 261.

BEALE, G. H. (1954). *The Genetics of* Paramaecium aurelia. Cambridge: University Press.

BIRCH-ANDERSEN, A., MAALØE, O. & SJÖSTRAND, F. (1953). High-resolution electron micrographs of sections of *E. coli*. *Biochim. biophys. Acta*, **12**, 395.

BISSET, K. A. (1950). The sporulation of *Cl. tetani*. *J. gen. Microbiol.* **4**, 1.

BISSET, K. A. (1953). Do bacteria have mitotic spindles, fusion tubes and mitochondria? *J. gen. Microbiol.* **8**, 50.

BISSET, K. A. (1954). The cytology of *Micrococcus cryophilus*. *J. Bact.* **67**, 41.

BRADFIELD, J. R. G. (1954). Electron microscopic observations on bacterial nuclei. *Nature, Lond.*, **173**, 184.

BRAUN, H., BERG, ST., KESSLER, S. & MAVROIDI, P. (1954). Über die Anormomorphogenese bei Bakterien. *Med. Mschr., Stuttgart*, **1**, 446.

BURDON, K. L. (1946). Fatty material in bacteria and fungi revealed by staining dried fixed slide preparations. *J. Bact.* **52**, 665.

CALDWELL, P. C. & HINSHELWOOD, C. (1950). The nucleic acid content of *Bact. lactis aerogenes*. *J. Chem. Soc.* p. 1415.

CASSEL, W. A. & HUTCHINSON, W. G. (1954). Nuclear studies on the smaller *Myxophyceae*. *Exp. Cell Res.* **6**, 134.

CASSEL, W. A. & HUTCHINSON, W. G. (1955). Fixation and staining of the bacterial nucleus. *Stain Tech.* **30**, 105.

CHAPMAN, G. B. & HILLIER, J. (1953). Electron microscopy of ultra-thin sections of bacteria. *J. Bact.* **66**, 362.

CHEN, T. T. (1944). The nuclei in avian malaria parasites. I. The structure of nuclei in *Plasmodium elongatum* with some considerations on technique. *Amer. J. Hyg.* **40**, 26.

CLIFTON, C. E. & ERHARD, H. (1952). Nuclear changes in living cells of a variant of *Bacillus anthracis*. *J. Bact.* **63**, 537.

DELAMATER, E. D. (1951a). A staining and dehydrating procedure for the handling of microorganisms. *Stain Tech.* **26**, 199.

DELAMATER, E. D. (1951b). A new cytological basis for bacterial genetics. *Cold Spr. Harb. Symp. quant. Biol.* **16**, 357.

DELAMATER, E. D. (1953a). Structure and Division of the Bacterial Nucleus. *Bacterial Cytology, Symp. 6th Congr. int. Microbiol., Rome*, p. 108.

210 C. F. ROBINOW

DeLamater, E. D. (1953b). Aspects of bacteria as cells and as organisms. Part II. *Int. Rev. Cytol.* **2**, 158.

DeLamater, E. D. (1954). Cytology of bacteria. Part II. The bacterial nucleus. *Ann. Rev. Microbiol.* **8**, 23.

DeLamater, E. D. & Hunter, M. E. (1951). Preliminary report of true mitosis in the vegetative cell of *Bacillus megatherium. Amer. J. Bot.* **38**, 659.

DeLamater, E. D. & Hunter, M. E. (1952). The nuclear cytology of sporulation in *Bacillus megaterium. J. Bact.* **63**, 13.

DeLamater, E. D., Hunter, M. E. & Mudd, S. (1952). Current status of the bacterial nucleus. *Exp. Cell Res.* Suppl. 2, p. 319.

DeLamater, E. D. & Mudd, S. (1951). The occurrence of mitosis in the vegetative phase of *Bacillus megatherium. Exp. Cell Res.* **2**, 449.

Delaporte, B. (1939). Recherches cytologiques sur les Bactéries et les Cyanophycées. *Rev. gén. Bot.* **51**, 615, 689 and 748.

Delaporte, B. (1950). Observations on the cytology of bacteria. *Advanc. Genet.* **3**, 1.

Dienes, L. & Smith, W. E. (1944). The significance of pleomorphism in *Bacteroides* strains. *J. Bact.* **48**, 125.

Dobell, C. (1911). Contributions to the cytology of the bacteria. *Quart. J. micr. Sci.* **56**, 395.

Douglas, S. R. & Distaso, A. (1912). Über den Kern der Bakterien. *Zbl. Bakt.,* Abt. I. Orig., **66**, 21.

Fitz-James, P. C. (1953). The structure of spores as revealed by mechanical disruption. *J. Bact.* **66**, 312.

Fitz-James, P. C. (1954). The duplication of bacterial chromatin. *J. Bact.* **68**, 464.

Flewett, T. H. (1948). Nuclear changes in *Bacillus anthracis* and their relation to variants. *J. gen. Microbiol.* **2**, 325.

Geitler, L. (1942). Kern- und Chromosomenbau bei Protisten im Vergleich mit dem höherer Pflanzen und Tiere. Ergebnisse und Problem. *Naturwissenschaften,* **30**, 162.

Geitler, L. (1953). Endomitose u. endomitotische Polyploidisierung. In *Protoplasmatologia,* **6**, C, edit. Heilbrunn, C. V. & Weber, F.

Grell, K. G. (1953a). Die Konjugation von *Ephelota gemmipara* R. Hertwig. *Arch. Protistenk.* **98**, 288.

Grell, K. G. (1953b). Der Stand unserer Kenntnisse ueber den Bau der Protistenkerne. *Verh. dtsch. zool. Ges. in Freiburg* 1952, pp. 212–251.

Guilliermond, A. (1908). Contribution à l'étude cytologique des bacilles endosporés. *Arch. Protistenk.* **12**, 9.

Hartman, T. L. (1940). The use of Sudan black B as a bacterial fat stain. *Stain Tech.* **15**, 23.

Hartman, P. E. & Payne, J. I. (1954). Direct staining of nucleoproteins in *E. coli. J. Bact.* **68**, 237.

Hedén, C.-G. (1951). Studies of the infection of *E. coli* B with the bacteriophage T2. *Acta path. microbiol. scand.* suppl. 88, 1.

Hoelling, A. (1910). Die Kernverhältnisse von *Fusiformis termitidis. Arch. Protistenk.* **19**, 239.

Huebschman, C. (1952). A method for varying the average number of nuclei in the conidia of *Neurospora crassa. Mycologia,* **44**, 599.

Hunter, M. E. & DeLamater, E. D. (1952). Observations on the nuclear cytology of spore germination in *Bacillus megaterium. J. Bact.* **63**, 23.

Jacobson, W. & Webb, M. (1952). The two types of nucleoproteins during mitosis. *Exp. Cell Res.* **3**, 163.

JOHNSON, F. H. & GRAY, D. H. (1949). Nuclei and large bodies of luminous bacteria in relation to salt concentration, osmotic pressure, temperature and urethane. *J. Bact.* **58**, 675.

KELLENBERGER, E. (1953). Les formes caractéristiques des nucleoides de *E. coli* et leurs transformations dues a l'action d'agents mutagènes-inducteurs et de bactériophages. *Bacterial Cytology, Symp. 6th Congr. int. Microbiol., Rome*, p. 45.

KLIENEBERGER-NOBEL, E. (1945). Changes in the nuclear structure of bacteria, particularly during spore formation. *J. Hyg., Camb.*, **44**, 99.

KNAYSI, G. (1942). The demonstration of a nucleus in the cell of a staphylococcus. *J. Bact.* **43**, 365.

KNOELL, H. (1944). Zur Anwendung der Phasenkontrastmikroskopie in der Bakteriologie. *Zeiss Nachr.* **5**, 38.

KNOELL, H. & ZAPF, K. (1951). Untersuchungen zum Problem des Bakterienzellkerns. *Zbl. Bakt.* Abt. I, Orig., **157**, 389.

LEMOIGNE, M., DELAPORTE, B. & CROSON, M. (1944). Contribution à l'étude botanique et biochimique des bactéries du genre *Bacillus*. *Ann. Inst. Pasteur*, **70**, 224.

LEWIS, I. M. (1934). Cell inclusions and endospore formation in *Bacillus mycoides*. *J. Bact.* **28**, 133.

LIEB, M., WEIGLE, J. J. & KELLENBERGER, E. (1955). A study of hybrids between two strains of *Escherichia coli*. *J. Bact.* **69**, 468.

MUDD, S. & SMITH, A. (1950). Electron and light microscopical studies of bacterial nuclei. *J. Bact.* **50**, 561.

MURRAY, R. G. E. (1953). The problem of fixation for studies of bacterial nuclei. *Bacterial Cytology, Symp. 6th Congr. int. Microbiol., Rome*.

MURRAY, R. G. E. (1955). In preparation.

MCINTOSH, D. L. (1954). A Feulgen-carmine technic for staining fungus chromosomes. *Stain Tech.* **29**, 29.

NEUMANN, F. (1941). Untersuchungen zur Erforschung der Kernverhältnisse bei den Bakterien. *Zbl. Bakt.*, Abt. II, Orig., **103**, 385.

OGINSKI, E. & UMBREIT, W. (1954). *An Introduction to Bacterial Physiology*, San Francisco: Freeman.

PESHKOFF, M. A. (1940). Phylogenesis of new microbes, *Caryophanon latum* and *Caryophanon tenue*, organisms which are intermediate between blue-green algae and the bacteria. (Summary in English.) *J. gen. Biol.* (Russ.), **1**, 598.

PETERS, D. & WIGAND, R. (1953). Enzymatisch-electronenoptische Analyse der Nucleinsäureverteilung, dargestellt an *E. coli* als Modell. *Z. NaturForsch* **8**b, 180.

PIEKARSKI, G. (1937). Zytologische Untersuchungen an Paratyphus- und Colibakterien. *Arch. Mikrobiol.* **8**, 428.

PIEKARSKI, G. (1949). Zum Problem des Bakterienzell-kerns. *Ergebn. Hyg. Bakt.* **26**, 334.

PIEKARSKI, G. (1952). Mikroskopische und chemische Organisation der Zelle. 2. *Colloq. Dtsch. Ges. Phys. Chemie*, p. 83. Berlin: Springer.

PRINGSHEIM, E. G. & ROBINOW, C. F. (1947). Observations on two very large bacteria *Caryophanon latum* Peshkoff and *Lineola longa* (nomen provisorium). *J. gen. Microbiol.* **1**, 267.

ROBINOW, C. F. (1942). A study of the nuclear apparatus of bacteria. *Proc. Roy. Soc.* B, 130.

ROBINOW, C. F. (1944). Cytological observations on *Bact. coli, Proteus vulgaris* and various aerobic spore-forming bacteria with special reference to the nuclear structures. *J. Hyg., Camb.*, **43**, 413.

ROBINOW, C. F. (1945). Addendum to *The Bacterial Cell*, by R. J. Dubos. Cambridge, Mass.: Harvard University Press.

ROBINOW, C. F. (1953). Spore structure as revealed by thin sections. *J. Bact.* **66**, 300.

RYAN, F. J. & WAINWRIGHT, L. K. (1954). Nuclear segregation and the growth of clones of spontaneous mutants of bacteria. *J. gen. Microbiol.* **11**, 364.

SCHAEDE, R. (1939). Zum Problem des Vorkommens von chromatischer Substanz bei Bakterien und Actinomyceten. *Arch. Mikrobiol.* **10**, 473.

SCHRADER, F. (1953). *Mitosis. The Movements of Chromosomes in Cell Division.* 2nd ed. New York: Columbia University Press.

SMITH, A. G. (1950). An improved staining technique for the nuclear chromatin of bacterial cells. *J. Bact.* **59**, 575.

SONNEBORN, T. M. (1947). Recent advances in the genetics of *Paramaecium* and *Euplotes*. *Advanc. Genet.* **1**, 263.

STANIER, R. Y. (1954). Singular features of bacteria as dynamic systems. In *Cellular Metabolism and Infections*, p. 3. New York: Academic Press.

STEMPEN, H. (1950). Demonstration of the chromatinic bodies of *E. coli* and *Proteus vulgaris* with the aid of the phase contrast microscope. *J. Bact.* **60**, 81.

STEMPEN, H. & HUTCHINSON, W. G. (1951). The formation and development of large bodies in *Proteus vulgaris* OX-19. *J. Bact.* **61**, 337.

STILLE, B. (1937). Zytologische Untersuchungen an Bakterien mit Hilfe der feulgenschen Nuclealreaktion. *Arch. Mikrobiol.* **8**, 125.

TOMLIN, S. G. & MAY, J. W. (1955). Electron microscopy of sectioned bacteria. A study of *Escherichia coli*. *Aust. J. exp. Biol.* **33**, 249.

TRUANT, J. P. (1954). Ph.D. thesis. University of Western Ontario, London, Canada.

TULASNE, R. (1949). Sur la cytologie des bactéries vivantes étudiées grâce au microscope à contraste de phase. *C.R. Soc. Biol., Paris*, **143**, 1390.

TULASNE, R. (1953). Le cycle L et les formes naines des bactéries. *Bacterial Cytology, Symp. 6th Congr. int. Microbiol., Rome*, p. 144.

TULASNE, R. & VENDRELY, R. (1947). Demonstration of bacterial nuclei with ribonuclease. *Nature, Lond.*, **160**, 225.

VENDRELY, R. & LIPARDY, J. (1946). Acides nucléiques et noyaux bactériens. *C.R. Acad. Sci., Paris*, **223**, 342.

WHITFIELD, J. F. (1955). Ph.D. thesis, University of Western Ontario, London, Canada.

WHITFIELD, J. F. & MURRAY, R. G. E. (1954). A cytological study of the lysogenization of *Shigella dysenteriae* with P1 and P2 bacteriophages. *Canad. J. Microbiol.* **1**, 216.

WHITFIELD, J. F. & MURRAY, R. G. E. (1955). In preparation.

WIGAND, R. & PETERS, D. (1954). Licht- und elektronenoptische Untersuchungen über den Abbau gram-negativer Kokken mit Nucleasen und Proteasen. *Z. NaturForsch* **9**b, 586.

WITKIN, E. (1951). Nuclear segregation and the delayed appearance of induced mutants in *Escherichia coli*. *Cold Spr. Harb. Symp. quant. Biol.* **16**, 357.

WORK, E. & DEWEY, D. L. (1953). The distribution of α,ϵ-diaminopimelic acid among various micro-organisms. *J. gen. Microbiol.* **9**, 394.

EXPLANATION OF PLATES

The writer regrets that limitations of space have made it necessary to keep some of the illustrations very small. With few exceptions, all figures are small segments of photographs of uniform groups of 50–300 bacilli. The photographs in turn were representative of entire preparations.

PLATE 1

Chromatin bodies in cells from 1–1½ hr. old cultures of *Bacillus cereus* and *B. megaterium* on Difco heart infusion or 2 % tryptose agar at 37°. The magnification is everywhere 3600 times, except in fig. 5, where it is 4500 times. With the exception of figs. 1 and 2, all photographs are from preparations mounted in water.

Fig. 1. *B. cereus*. Living bacilli photographed with phase-contrast illumination. One of them appears banded. Courtesy of Prof. R. G. E. Murray.

Fig. 2. *B. cereus*. OsO_4 vapour, mercuric chloride/alcohol, Feulgen, photographed mounted in aceto-carmine according to McIntosh (1954). Arrow at lower right points to a single chromatin body, the cross at the top of the figure is above a dividing chromatin body. The arrow on the left, continued across the first bacillus in its path, points to a single chromatin body with attached accessory granule.

Figs. 3, 3a. *B. cereus*. Transferred to glass *in situ* by Bouin fixation through the agar. Fig. 3 stained with thionine 0·01 %, 40 seconds; fig. 3a stained in the same way with toluidine blue. The chromatin bodies are not stained. Comparison with fig. 1 suggests that Bouin is a better fixative for chromatin bodies than the osmium used for fig. 2. Arrow on the left points towards a single chromatin body. There are division figures at either end of the central arrow. Oval chromatin bodies can be seen in two bacilli at the upper margin of fig. 3.

Figs. 4, 5. *B. cereus*. OsO_4 vapour, HCl, Giemsa. Just below the 4 there are two single, recently divided chromatin bodies. Immediately to their left are two bodies preparing to divide. Second from the top, on the left, in fig. 5, is an oval chromatin body, on its right a C-shaped one.

Figs. 6–9. *B. megaterium*. Successive divisions of the chromatin bodies during the development of germinating spores into the first generation of vegetative bacilli. OsO_4 vapour, HCl, Azure-A, SO_2; after DeLamater or Huebschman.

Fig. 6. Accessory granule ('centriole' of DeLamater) by the side of chromatin bodies separating after the first division. Other good examples of accessory granules are seen in a cell in the centre of fig. 7 and in the third cell from the right along the bottom margin.

Fig. 7. In the top left corner and elsewhere are ovoid cells with two compact separate chromatin bodies, products of the first division. The second division is under way in large cells immediately above and below the centre. It has been completed in the bacillus with four chromatin bars in the extension at the top right of the figure.

Fig. 8. The bacillus in this figure contains four separate chromatin bodies of a plumpness which suggests that the third division is about to begin. In the original photograph this cell lies close to the group shown in fig. 9 where the third division is well under way.

Fig. 9. The chromatin bodies in the two bacilli in the centre of the figure are undergoing the third division. Chromatin patterns are now becoming unintelligible through crowding (Smith, 1950). At the lower end of the first bacillus from the right, in the top row, is a common type of division figure which has sometimes been mistaken for a resting nucleus with three chromosomes.

PLATE 2

All figures are of *Bacillus megaterium*. Many are examples of what might be termed the 'Delaporte effect', namely, the behaviour of chromatin bodies in the presence of much lipid. Figs. 10 and 12–16 are magnified 3600 times, figs. 11, 17 and 18, 4500 times.

Fig. 10a. A group of bacilli from an 18 hr. 37°. slant culture on blood agar. OsO₄, HCl, Giemsa.

Fig. 10b. The same bacilli stained with Sudan black B after the Giemsa stain had first been removed with alcohol. As the example of the marked bacillus in the right top corner shows, the chromatin bodies are compressed between large masses of lipid. Note absence of 'interphase nuclei'.

Figs. 11a, b. A similar pair, lipid left, chromatin right. From a culture similar to that of fig. 10, fixed 1 hr. 40 min. after transfer to fresh blood agar.

Fig. 12. Chromatin bodies beginning to multiply between lipid globules represented here by white 'vacuoles'. Same material as in fig. 10a, fixed 1 hr. after transfer to fresh medium. Compare with Delaporte, 1950, plates III and IIIa.

Fig. 13. Irregular arrangement of chromatin bodies in the foamy cytoplasm of a bacillus from an originally fat-laden inoculum, fixed 2 hr. after transfer to fresh medium.

Fig. 14. Early stage of spore formation after 6 hr. on 0·1 % casamino acids agar. Air-dried impression film mounted in 0·3 % Sudan black B in equal parts of ethylene glycol and 70 % alcohol. The bacilli are filled with lipid except for the regions where spores are developing.

Fig. 15. OsO₄, HCl, Giemsa. Earliest detectable stage of spore formation on potato agar. Note solitary dark granules at the tip of the bacillus parallel with the lower margin, at the tip of the two bacilli in the inset, and elsewhere. The presence of many small lipid globules has transformed the cytoplasm into a system of thin lamellae in which the chromatin bodies appear randomly dispersed. These photographs resemble drawings of 'chromidial nuclei' by Guilliermond (1908). Fixed 3½ hr. after the temperature shift described in the text.

Fig. 16. A later stage of spore formation on potato agar fixed 5 hr. after the temperature shift. Above the centre and in the lower left corner ring-shaped chromatin bodies may be seen in developing spores.

Fig. 17. Lipid globules in vegetative bacilli from a heavily inoculated plate culture on 0·1 % casamino acids incubated for 4 hr. at 37°. Air-dried impression film mounted in Sudan black B in alcohol/ethylene-glycol.

Figs. 18a, 18b. Bacilli from the same culture as those in the previous figure. OsO₄ vapour, HCl, Azure-A, SO₂. Chromatin bodies randomly dispersed between many white 'vacuoles', i.e. unstained lipid globules. A fanciful observer, unaware of the presence of lipid, might detect a 'large interphase nucleus' at the right end of the bacillus in fig. 18b.

PLATE 1

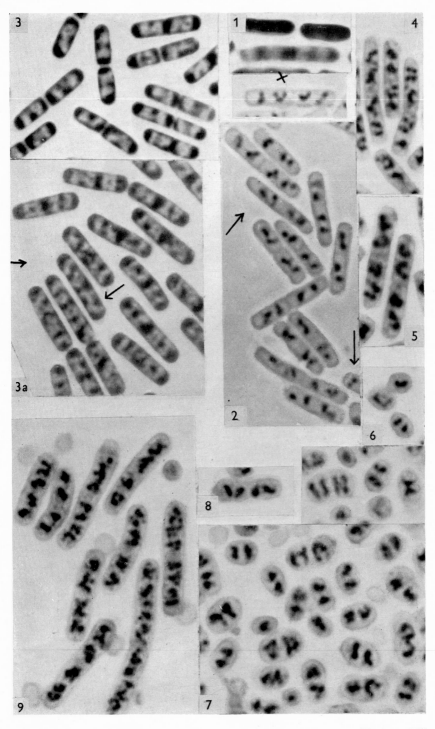

(Facing p. 214)

PLATE 2

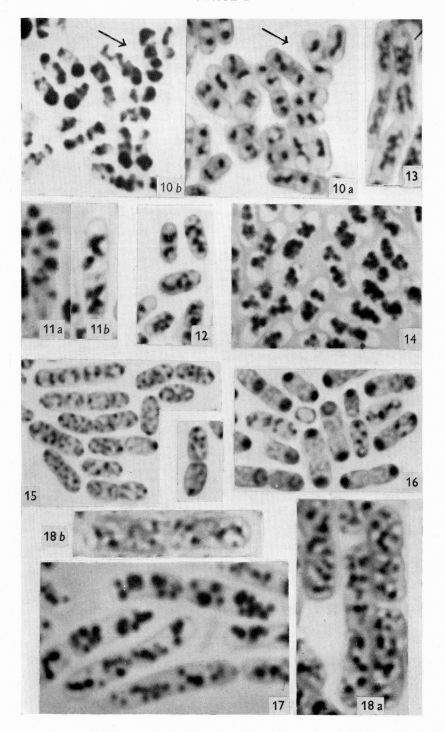

10 b   10 a   13

11 a   11 b   12   14

15   16

18 b

18 a

17

BACTERIAL CHROMOSOMES AND THEIR MECHANISM OF DIVISION*

E. D. DeLAMATER

Department of Physiology, School of Medicine, University of Pennsylvania, Philadelphia, U.S.A.

For many years the idea that bacteria constitute special and unique cells has pervaded the literature. This has been especially true when the organization of the bacterial nucleus has been considered. The reasons are many; some of them are obvious. The cells are for the most part small. In consequence what can be seen with ordinary methods has been thought to be limited. Chemically specific cytological techniques have become available and have been applied only relatively recently. Much of the residual confusion produced by the use of non-specific methods has not yet been clarified or eliminated (Knaysi, 1955; Chance, 1955). Appropriate new methods necessary to the proper application of the newer instruments now available are still in the process of evolution (Bradfield, 1954). The subject of bacterial cytology is not, however, 'frenetic' (Spiegelman & Landman, 1954), it is simply growing.

It appears to me that, as bacterial cytologists, we have tended to limit ourselves too closely to purely morphological concepts. In this we lag behind our colleagues in general cytology (de Robertis, Nowinski & Saez, 1954). Cytology should not be limited to structure alone, but should aim towards a definition of the chemical organization of the cell and point towards an understanding of the integrated functions of the various parts as well. If we conceive of the cell as a chemical machine which operates in the living state as an integrated whole, then it appears proper to attempt to analyse from a combined cytological and chemical point of view the activities of the cell in terms not only of chemically definable morphological units, but likewise in terms of the over-all organization. This, of necessity, will require the simultaneous application of techniques from other disciplines, such as biochemistry. This is admittedly a very large order, and one which I know I am not alone in wishing to see fulfilled. I believe, however, that this approach puts bacterial cytology into its proper perspective, relating it immediately to the disciplines like cytochemistry, biochemistry, immunochemistry and

* This article was submitted too late to allow complete editing of the text-figures.—Ed.

intracellular physiology, which can contribute to it. But even more important, I believe, it preserves *the cell* conceptually as a whole integrated system that must be studied as such, if we are ultimately to understand its total mechanism. This I deem to be the cytologist's arena, and since bacteria may now, without apology, be thought of as cells, it becomes likewise the bacterial cytologist's arena.

Much is being learned and much is to be learned by fractionation and by the study of the isolated morphological and chemical systems which are so produced. But this valuable information does not necessarily tell how, where, or what the functional relationships are which occur within the intact living cell. To attempt to approach these complex problems I believe to be the cytologists' avenue of progress.

This paper is divided into three parts. In the first we will consider the general organization of the bacterial cell as shown by selected cytochemical tests. In the second, the organization of the nucleus and its mechanism of division and the structure of the chromosomes will be considered. In the third part our recent efforts to approach the problems of synthesis of nuclear material and the dynamics of the nuclear mechanism will be presented.

CONSIDERATION OF INTRINSIC CHEMICAL STRUCTURE OF THE BACTERIAL CELL

Since confusion still persists even as to what constitutes a nucleus in the bacterial cell (Knaysi, 1955), it is necessary and proper to consider here what can be differentiated and defined within the bacterial cell by means of the cytochemical methods currently available. The concordance of the results obtained by these methods with the results obtained by chemical analyses is remarkably good, as will be obvious as the discussion proceeds. Because of space, however, comparisons with these data will not be made here. I will present in this section of the discussion a summary of the recent work of Dr Abraham Widra in my laboratory. Methods for this work will not be given in detail, since they can be found in standard reference texts (Pearse, 1953), and in Dr Widra's detailed paper (Widra, 1955) as he has applied them.

Before proceeding, it may be justifiable to point out that in using cytochemical procedures which are known to have specificity only for a particular chemical radical or grouping, no specific conclusion can usually be drawn as to the class of the cellular moiety one is dealing with until adjuvant tests are done. Thus, it is not usually permissible to identify a compound such as 'polysaccharide' with a reaction which only specifies the presence of a 1,2-glycol grouping, without having performed the necessary additional tests. Table 1 indicates the necessary procedures to identify specific types of substances.

Table 1 summarizes these studies. The methods used, with the chemical specificity of each, are indicated; the locus of each reaction and the cellular moiety reacting are shown comparatively for *Bacillus megaterium* and *Escherichia coli*. Text-fig. 1 summarizes graphically and comparatively the results obtained with *B. megaterium* and with *E. coli*. In both organisms the cell wall and the cell membrane have not been separ-

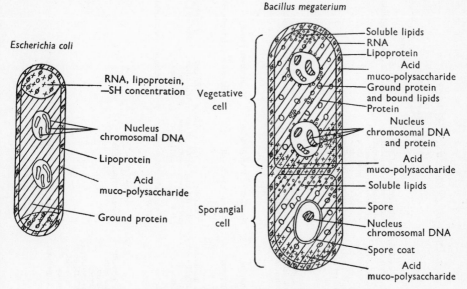

Text-fig. 1. Comparison of key structures, labelled as to chemical content, of *Bacillus megaterium* and *Escherichia coli*.

ated. They are shown in both organisms to contain lipoprotein and acid muco-polysaccharide. In *B. megaterium* the wall also contains RNA. RNA predominates in the wall of young cells, while the acid muco-polysaccharide predominates in older cells. In the vegetative cell of *B. megaterium* the protoplasm is shown to contain protein and bound lipids with concentrations of soluble lipids scattered throughout the cell. The nuclei are well-defined areas containing the chromosomes, which can be clearly demonstrated to contain DNA as well as a sulphhydryl-containing protein. The periodic-acid-Schiff positive areas (acid muco-polysaccharide) and free fat are mutually exclusive. In the sporangial cell of *B. megaterium* there is a marked bipolarity with the soluble lipids concentrated at one pole and the acid muco-polysaccharide at the other.

Table 1. *Summary of cytochemical studies*

Procedure	Chemical specificity	*Bacillus megaterium* Loci	*Bacillus megaterium* Moieties	*Escherichia coli* Loci	*Escherichia coli* Moieties
1. Periodic-acid-Schiff (PAS): Osmium vapour fixed cells—1% periodic acid, 3 min—wash—Schiff reagent—10 min.—SO_2 rinse (10% potassium metabisulphite, 5 ml.; N-HCl, 5 ml.; water, 90 ml.)—wash—Farrant's medium	1,2-Glycol grouping, its oxidation product, equivalent amino or alkylamino derivatives. Practically, this includes certain amino acids (serine, threonine, hydroxylysine), ATP, phospholipids, and unsaturated lipids, as well as various classes of polysaccharides	Cell wall of vegetative cell; localized concentrations along wall and septa; granules within cell. Old degenerate cells show fainter even staining throughout cytoplasm	Lipoprotein. Acid muco-polysaccharide	Cell wall; polar granules. Cell wall	Lipoprotein Acid muco-polysaccharide
1 a. Controls No free aldehydes present (cells plus Schiff reagent—negative) No plasmalogens present in *B. megaterium* (cells plus $HgCl_2$—Schiff—negative) No unsaturated lipids present in *B. megaterium* (cells plus peracetic acid oxidation—Schiff—negative)					
2. Hyaluronidase extraction: Stock 'Wydase' (150 TR units/ml., same as 500 viscosity units/ml) diluted 1:5 with water at pH 6.0. Incubate smears in this solution for 3 hr. at 37°. Run water control. Wash. Stain in 0.5% aq. toluidine blue 10 min. Wash. Mount wet under Vaspar seal	Abolishes hyaluronic acid and chondroitin sulphuric acid; acid muco-polysaccharides are usually fast	No diminution of staining with basic dye after hyaluronidase treatment	No hyaluronic acid or chondroitin sulphuric acid	No effect	—
3. α-Amylase (as ptyalin in saliva): Extract osmium-fixed smears for 30 min. at room temperature	Abolishes glycogen staining	No effect on PAS-positive	No glycogen present	No effect	—
4. Alcian blue staining: Place osmium-fixed smears in 1% aq. solution of dye for 5 min. Wash. Mount in Farrant's medium	Acid muco-polysaccharides, rarely mucoprotein	Cell and spore wall	Acid muco-polysaccharide	Cell walls. Slime layer of mucoid strain	Acid muco-polysaccharide
5. Methylene-blue extinction (MBE): 0.0005 M concentrations of methylene blue (final concentration) in veronal-acetate buffer solutions ranging from pH 2.62 to 8.18 are used to stain osmium-fixed smears for 24 hr. at room temp. Smears are then washed and mounted with a Vaspar seal	If presence of nucleic acids can be excluded, MBE at pH 4 or below indicates acid muco-polysaccharides	Old cells: Cell walls and septa below pH 4. Young cells: Walls do not stain below pH 4. Sporangial extrasporal granule	Old cell: Acid muco-polysaccharide. Young cell: Mainly RNA. Acid muco-polysaccharide	Polar granules; stain at pH 2.6; abolished by ribonuclease	RNA
5 a. Control: Ribonuclease followed by MBE; run with MBE and water control (for ribonuclease)					
6. Metachromasy: Osmium-fixed smears are stained in 0.5% aq. solution of toluidine blue. Wash. Seal while wet with Vaspar	Not specific; positive for acid muco-polysaccharides with glucuronic, sulphuric or phosphoric acid moieties; positive for large carbohydrate molecules with —COOH end groups, other large molecules with anionic end-groups	No metachromatic loci	—	None	—
7. Sudan black B: Osmium or formalin-fixed smears are stained in a 0.25% solution of acetylated Sudan black B in ethylene glycol for 2 hr., rinsed in 70% ethanol, washed in water, then mounted in Farrant's medium	Stains soluble lipids, sometimes phospholipids	Small granules in young cell; large central and polar areas in mature cell; polar area in sporangial cell	Soluble lipids	None	—

No.	Technique					
8.	Oil red 0: Identical with Sudan black B stain, except that a saturated solution of oil red 0 in ethylene glycol is used	Soluble in neutral lipids	Small granules in young cell; large central and polar areas in mature cell; polar area in sporangial cell	Soluble neutral lipids	None	—
9.	Sakaguchi reaction (Baker modification): Osmium-fixed smears are immersed in α-naphthol hypochlorite solution for 15 min., drained, blotted, placed in dry pyridine; chloroform (1:1), then mounted in dry pyridine	In practice, specific for arginine; used to demonstrate histones	Coincides with PAS-positive areas	Protein	Cell wall and poles	Protein
10.	—SH technique of Barnett: Fix in 1% TCA in 80% ethanol—70% ethanol wash—water wash—1 hr. at 50° in solution of 25 mg. DDD in 15 ml. ethanol plus 35 ml. 0·1 M-veronal-acetate buffer at pH 8·5. Cool 10 min.—wash. Rinse 4 times (2 min. each rinse) in water acidified with acetic acid (pH 4). Wash. Dehydrate to ether. Rehydrate. Place in fresh 0·1% tetradiorthodianisidine in 0·1 M-phosphate buffer at pH 7·4 for 2 min. Wash and mount in Farrant's medium	—SH groups	Coincides with PAS-positive areas; additional sites within nuclear vesicle. Also, sporangial extra-sporal granule	Protein	Faintly throughout cell. Marked at the poles	Protein —SH groups
11.	Coupled tetrazonium: Osmium-fixed smears are placed in freshly prepared tetrazotized benzidine (0·1%) in pH 9·2 veronal-acetate buffer for 15 min. at 4°. Wash in water and in several changes of pH 9·2 buffer. Immerse in a saturated solution of β-naphthol in veronal buffer (pH 9·2) for 15 min. Mount in Farrant's medium	Specific for histidine, tryptophane, tyrosine	Spore wall; PAS-positive areas	Protein	Throughout cell. Marked at the poles	Protein
12.	Ninhydrin-Schiff: Incubate osmium-fixed smears in 0·5% ninhydrin solution for 24 hr. at 37°. Wash well. Place in Schiff reagent 10 min.—SO_2 rinse—water rinse—Farrant's medium	Specific for proteins with reactive —NH$_2$ groups	Coincides with PAS-positive areas; additional sites within nuclear vesicle. Also, sporangial extra-sporal granule	Protein	Cell wall and polar granules	Protein
13.	Hale dialysed iron technique: Osmium-fixed smears—10 min. in dialysed iron: 2 M-acetic acid (1:1)—Wash—10 min. in 0·02 M-potassium ferrocyanide: 0·14 M-HCl (1:1)—Wash—Farrant's medium	Low specificity for acid muco-polysaccharides	Spore wall; vegetative cell wall	Acid muco-polysaccharide	Cell wall; diffusely in cytoplasm. Poles unstained	Acid muco-polysaccharide
14.	Citric-Sudan black B: Fix in 40% formalin: 10% calcium chloride (anhyd.): 2% cobalt nitrate: water (1:1:1:7) for 12 hr.—Wash—5% citric acid: Sudan black B in ethylene glycol (sat. soln.) (1:1) for 2 hr. at 60°. Differentiate in 70% ethanol—Wash—Farrant's medium	Reveals bound ('masked') lipids	Spore wall; throughout cytoplasm of young and mature cell. None in old degenerate cell	Combined lipids	Faintly in cell wall. Very marked at poles	Combined lipids
15.	Fat stain (for neutral and acidic lipids) (Cain): Osmium or formalin-fixed cells—5 min. in 1% aqueous Nile blue at 60°—Wash in 60° water—Differentiate in 1% acetic acid—Wash—Farrant's medium. Parallel smear is re-stained at 60° in 0·02% Nile blue—Wash in 60° water—Differentiate in 1% acetic acid—Wash—Farrant's medium	For lipids (Sudan stainable and pyridine extractable). Neutral lipids (pink); acidic lipids, fatty acids (blue)	Blue stain coincides with Sudan stainable areas	Acidic lipids (the presence of neutral lipid is not excluded by this test)	Test not applicable in absence of purely lipid inclusions	—

Within the spore the nucleus is more concentrated than in the vegetative cell, and in the spore nucleus only chromosomal DNA could be demonstrated.

Escherichia coli appears to be differently organized in terms of what can be defined cytochemically. At each pole there is a concentration of lipoprotein and sulphhydryl-containing protein and RNA. The nucleus of *E. coli* contains chromosomes in which only DNA could be demonstrated; no sulphhydryl-containing protein could be demonstrated by the methods used. The protoplasm contains a ground protein. Lipoprotein and acid muco-polysaccharide both appear in the cell wall and cell membrane.

In *Escherichia coli* the evidence gives further definition of mitochondrial areas of activity. These areas contain bound lipids and RNA as well as a considerable quantity of sulphhydryl-containing protein, which is in accordance with the presence of the enzyme succinic dehydrogenase.

Widra believes that the criteria for mitochondria in higher cells and bacteria should include the following: that they are particulate and visible with a light microscope, at least in the aggregate; that they contain sulphhydryl-containing proteins, RNA, and bound lipids of the phosphorus- and nitrogen-containing types; but that no DNA is present.

Such criteria separate the nuclei and chromosomes from the mitochondria, and should, if properly applied, end dispute as to what constitutes a nucleus on the one hand, and what constitutes the mitochondrial area on the other. For comparison, it should be pointed out that the chromosomes in the nuclei are visible with the light microscope both singly and in the aggregate. They contain no bound lipids, little RNA, much DNA, and, in the case of *Bacillus megaterium* at least, can be shown to contain sulphhydryl-containing protein.

In *Escherichia coli* and other Gram-negative organisms it is not surprising to find different types of biologically different material accumulating about these active chemical centres, i.e. the mitochondria. RNA has been demonstrated by Hartman & Payne (1954). Acid muco-polysaccharides have been demonstrated by Bisset (1951) and Bergerson (1953). It has also been demonstrated that they contain alkaline phosphatase (Schaechter, Treece & DeLamater, 1954). They may contain metaphosphate, as suggested by Mudd (1954) and Davis & Mudd (1955).

Claims as to the occurrence of clearly defined mitochondrial areas in *Bacillus megaterium*, presented by Mudd, Brodie, Winterscheid, Hartman, Beutner & McLean (1951), should be re-evaluated in the light of the work by Hartman & Liu (1954), Weibull (1953), Schaechter *et al.* (1954), Novikoff (1955) and Gonse & Yotsuyanagi (1955).

The work of Widra obviously confirms the definition of the nuclei and areas of mitochondrial activity that have been given by other authors (Mudd, 1954), and should aid in the elimination of confusion of these two morphologically and chemically distinct areas of cellular activity. His work leaves to the future the definition of the 'centrioles' as discrete physiological and structural entities, and likewise the possibility of the presence of nucleoli in these small nuclei. As shown in figs. 26 and 27 of Pl. 2, not only the chromosomes but the centrioles and spindles also contain sulphhydryl-containing protein.

It is worth special emphasis here that the simultaneous demonstration of nuclear components, cell walls and septa by chemically specific methods invalidates the arguments of Bisset (see DeLamater, 1954a) that DeLamater has confused these structures in the past. Likewise Robinow's claim (Robinow & Hannay, 1953) that fat produces the nuclear configurations visualized by DeLamater is also invalidated. The nuclear configurations described occur in fat-free cells, including Gram-negative organisms, such as *Escherichia coli* and *Salmonella*, as well as in spores and young cells of *Bacillus megaterium*, which contain no fat. They also occur in older cells of *B. megaterium* from which the fat has been removed. Widra has also attempted simultaneous double stains to demonstrate both nucleus and fat in the same cell. Cytochemically the fat and the chromosomes are mutually exclusive. Chapman & Hillier (1953) and Dawson & Stern (1954), in addition to myself (DeLamater, 1953a, b), have shown that the cross-walls form by the centripetal growth of the cell wall. Both the electron microscope and histochemical methods refute Bisset's contention (see Discussion in DeLamater's paper (1951b)), that the cross-walls could be confused with the nuclear apparatus (Delamater, 1954a).

The presence of sulphhydryl-containing protein in the chromosomes of *Bacillus megaterium*, but not in the chromosomes of *Escherichia coli*, suggests that the organization of the nucleus of *B. megaterium* is more complex than that of *E. coli*, and this degree of complexity may be reflected in the genetic mechanisms that are being studied in each (Hayes, 1953).

A final point should perhaps be made before proceeding to the next phase of the discussion. Widra, studying cultures in different stages of growth, has been struck by the dramatic changes that occur in the cyto-chemical reactions during the growth of the organism. These reflect the dynamics of the integrated intracellular machine, and may, with further study and a further clarification of the specific chemical conditions of growth which produce them, lead to interesting biochemical and physiological knowledge. It is as yet too early to attempt to draw too much from the data now at hand.

RÉSUMÉ OF EVIDENCE SUPPORTING THE VIEW OF A COMPLEX MECHANISM OF NUCLEAR DIVISION IN BACTERIA

The belief in and the evidence supporting the occurrence of a mitotic mechanism in a variety of bacteria have been presented extensively elsewhere by the author (DeLamater and his various associates, 1951-5; Hunter & DeLamater, 1952, 1955). In the reports of these studies the accepted terminology used with larger organisms has been deliberately applied. In this past work and in the present paper these terms have been used in the following way: 'prophase', to indicate the nuclear stage in which the chromosomes are shortening and becoming denser, in preparation for the coming division; 'prometaphase' (unipolar metaphase), to indicate the stage at which the single centriole appears at one side of the condensed chromosomes; 'metaphase', to indicate the stage at which the two centrioles derived from the single one of 'prometaphase' have migrated to the poles and the condensed chromosomes have come to lie on the 'metaphase plate' between them; 'anaphase', to indicate the stage of separation of the sister chromosomes; 'telophase' to indicate the stage of complete separation and early reorganization of the sister nuclei produced in the division; 'interphase', to indicate the vegetative phase of the nucleus in which the chromosomes have elongated and the nucleus has greatly enlarged. These stages are demonstrated in figs. 1-8, Pl. 1, and in fig. 1-10, Pl. 2, which have been previously published. For details see the legends to the figures (DeLamater, 1951b).

The methods that have been used in this work have been dealt with extensively elsewhere (DeLamater, 1951b, c, 1953b). These have consisted, in essence, of a modified Feulgen reaction and a method of freezing-dehydration, which produces permanent preparations with a minimum of distortion. Squash techniques have also been used to separate the chromosomes, the better to permit their individual analyses (DeLamater 1953a, b).

The studies up to the present have consisted of direct cytological analysis of preparations made from actively growing organisms in various stages of growth. The organisms studied to date have included *Bacillus megaterium* (DeLamater, 1951a, b, 1953a; DeLamater & Hunter, 1951; DeLamater, Hunter & Mudd, 1951), *Escherichia coli* (strains K12 and B) (DeLamater, 1953a, c), *Micrococcus cryophilus* (DeLamater, 1952a; DeLamater & Woodburn, 1952), *Caryophanon latum* (DeLamater, 1952b), and *Salmonella* (Minsavage & DeLamater, 1955a, b), among others (DeLamater, 1951b). In these studies on these various organisms extensive photographic evidence has been presented which we believe supports the view that a mitotic apparatus exists in all of the organisms studied. In *B. megaterium* (DeLamater, 1951*b*, 1953*a*), *E. coli* (De-Lamater, 1953*c*), and in *Salmonella* (Minsavage & DeLamater, 1955*a*) the chromosome number has been shown in each case to be 3. In *C. latum* (DeLamater, 1952*b*), and in *M. cryophilus* (DeLamater, 1952*a*; DeLamater & Woodburn, 1952) the chromosome number has been found to be 2. In the case of *M. cryophilus* confirmation of the chromosome number has been given by Hunter (1955) in a study of 'large cells', which suggest a diploid phase. In these the chromosomes undergo a sequence of events which suggests meiosis.

In *Bacillus megaterium* the three chromosomes have been most clearly characterized (DeLamater, 1953*a*); there is one large chromosome with what appears to be a satellite structure at one end (DeLamater, 1953*a*, pl. IV, fig. 11); there is a middle-sized chromosome, and a short chromosome. On the long chromosome the centromere has been seen and appears to be about in the middle (DeLamater, 1953*a*, pl. XIII, fig. 5), while in the middle-sized chromosome the centromere appears to be terminal or subterminal (DeLamater, 1953*a*, pl. XIII, fig. 6). The centromere has not been seen on the short chromosome. The centromeres of all three chromosomes have, however, been seen in the fully contracted state of the chromosomes when they appear as paired granules at pro-metaphase and metaphase in crushed preparations (DeLamater, 1953*a*, pl. III, fig. 3). In *Escherichia coli* the three chromosomes have again been characterized as one long and two shorter chromosomes (DeLamater, 1953*a*). No satellite has been observed on any of the chromosomes of this organism. It is interesting to note that the cytological evidence for three chromosomes in *E. coli* is in accord with the genetical evidence given by Hayes (1953) for the presence of three linkage groups in this organism. The three chromosomes in *Salmonella*, as worked out by Minsavage and the author (1955*a*), appear to be similar to those seen in *E. coli*.

In *Bacillus megaterium* during prophase in crushed preparations the longitudinal split of the chromatids to two has been clearly delineated and photographed (DeLamater, 1953*a*, pl. II, figs. 5–12; pl. III, figs. 1–6), and the evidence supports the view that this longitudinal separation of the chromatids occurs simultaneously in all three chromosomes. This evidence does not support the views of Fitz-James and was not cited by him in his recent article (Fitz-James, 1954), in which he suggested the asynchronous growth and division of the chromosomes in *B. megaterium* and *B. cereus*. Further, his interpretations are not consistent with the observations of Hunter & DeLamater (1952) on the nuclear activities of spore germination.

Photographic evidence on all of the organisms studied to date has been presented which indicates the presence of centrioles and the spindle element in these organisms. This is especially well shown in Pl. V, figs. 1, 2, 7, 8, 10, 12, 13, 16, 17, 18 of an earlier publication by the author (DeLamater, 1953 a). As indicated earlier, there has been considerable discussion whether these centriolar structures were not being confused with other elements within the cell, i.e. septa, cross-walls, etc. (Bisset, 1951 and subsequent papers; see DeLamater, 1954 a). The evidence of Widra (1955), summarized here, clearly suggests that this is not the case.

In collaboration with Minsavage, Bryson and the Szybalskis (De-Lamater, 1953 a, 1954 c; DeLamater, Hunter, Minsavage, Szybalski & Bryson, 1953; Minsavage & DeLamater, 1955 b) the author has studied the effects of various bacteriostatic agents on the cytology of the bacterial nucleus. In these studies nuclear arrest in prometaphase and metaphase was demonstrated, with the concomitant arrest of the division and migration of the centrioles and with their tremendous enlargement with increasing time of exposure to the drugs. This evidence alone strongly suggests that these structures are discrete and different from those with which Bisset claims they are being confused.

In the earlier publications the presence of the spindle element is clearly defined and photographed. Since these structures consistently and repeatedly occur, and since, as has been shown in the studies on the influence of drugs as well as of cold, these structures are modifiable by the physiological state of the cell, it appears to the author that they must be considered as real. These various configurations are demonstrated in Pl. 2, figs. 1–25 (see description of plate for details). In the study of the effects of these various drugs, including terramycin, aureomycin, strepto-mycin and *para*-aminosalicylic acid, among others, it was also possible to differentiate the effects of different drugs at the cytological and cyto-chemical level. An additional observation of some interest was the demonstration of the occurrence of what have been called 'transient polyploid nuclei' (DeLamater, 1953 a, 1954 c; DeLamater, Hunter, Minsavage, Szybalski & Bryson, 1953). The chromosomes continue to multiply and divide, but they remain clustered within a single nuclear membrane. In such nuclei the centrioles were found to multiply indepen-dently in the cytoplasm as this 'polyploidy' developed (DeLamater, 1953 a, pl. IX, figs. 6, 7, 12 and 14). When the organism was released from the influence of the drug, either by chemical degradation of the drug or by its removal, the normally organized nuclei were reinstituted by a process of segregation of the chromosomes into separate nuclei (De-Lamater, 1953 a, pl. X, figs. 1–11).

The use of cold shock in an effort to produce synchronization of bacterial nuclei has likewise been studied in this laboratory by the author and his assistant, M. E. Hunter. Detailed studies of synchronization experiments will be discussed in detail below. It is desired here to emphasize that cold, like certain of the antibiotics (i.e. aureomycin and terramycin), produces nuclear figures which are very similar to those already described and demonstrated in Pl. 2. Here again the nuclei are arrested predominantly in prometaphase and metaphase, and on continued exposure to cold produce configurations suggesting 'transient' polyploidy when the arresting temperature is 15° or when the organism is grown on agar and chilled in the refrigerator. The synthesis of the chromosomes does not appear to be affected, but the kinetics of the divisional mechanism appear to be arrested. The centrioles appear and then stagnate. They become much enlarged and they may undergo independent division without nuclear division. These observations are demonstrated in Pl. 1, figs. 14–20. See explanation of plate for details.

The current evidence indicates that the 'centriole' is real, and that it should not be confused with other structures within the cell; it is affected by cold; it is also affected by certain drugs, indicating that it is susceptible to modifications of the physiological state of the organism. This structure has been referred to as the 'centriole' by the author; has been called a 'secondary nucleus' or 'nuclear bud' by Knaysi (1955); a 'cross wall', 'growth centre', etc., by Bisset (see DeLamater, 1954 a); and ignored by Fitz-James (1954), among others.

Studies on the action of fixing agents (Murray, 1953; and unpublished observations of the author) have demonstrated a thickening of the nuclear membrane with the production of patterns suggesting that the nuclear membrane persists throughout the divisional cycle. This interpretation was suggested at the Rome International Microbiological Congress in 1953. Similar responses were produced in cells under the influence of certain of the drugs studied (DeLamater, 1953 a, pls. 7 and 8).

In consequence of the impact of these accumulated studies, supported by numerous photographs, a concept of the bacterial nucleus has been formulated. This is demonstrated in Text-fig. 2, and is as follows (DeLamater, 1954 a, b). The cell of the rod-like bacteria is considered to be multinuclear, although the diagram shows only a single nucleus for purposes of clarity. The divisional activities are thought to occur within a membrane which persists throughout the cycle, as in certain Protozoa, but not as is usually found in higher forms where the membrane disappears in prophase and re-forms in telophase. The chromosomes are threadlike, beaded structures in interphase, which contract and split longitudinally during prophase. With further contraction the chromatids separate but remain attached to the undivided centromere, appearing at this stage, prometaphase, as paired granules. At this time the centriole appears in the cytoplasm in juxtaposition to the membrane. It then divides and the two resulting centrioles migrate to opposite sides of the nucleus, producing the metaphase stage.

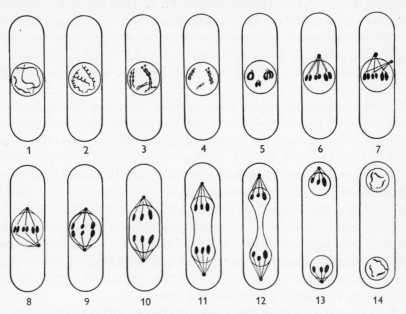

Text-fig. 2. Division of the bacterial nucleus.

The spindle element is thought to attach both to the nuclear membrane and through it to the centromeres of the chromosomes. As anaphase occurs, the centromeres divide and separate with their respective daughter chromosomes to each pole, being drawn apart by the spindle apparatus which likewise draws out the nuclear membrane. The membrane pinches off, producing separate daughter nuclei in telophase. In interphase the centrioles disappear, the nucleus swells, and the chromosomes again elongate.

In closing this section of the discussion, it is perhaps germane to re-emphasize the following points. The chromosomes can be counted, characterized and identified with relative ease and clarity, especially in *Bacillus megaterium*. Their activities can be followed during the course of the mitotic cycle. On the larger two chromosomes during the elongated stages the centromeres have been identified in prophase. The centrioles and spindle appear to be real structures, since they can be stained, observed and photographed in normal cells, and also can be made to enlarge greatly and increase their stainability under the influence of both cold and drugs. The centrioles can likewise be shown to multiply independently of nuclear division. The polyploidy so far observed appears to be 'transient', and the nuclei recover when the stimulus is removed. The recognition of the stages of division, as seen in the figures, is not difficult.

SYNCHRONIZATION OF BACTERIAL NUCLEI AND ITS SIGNIFICANCE

Hotchkiss (1954) reawakened interest in the problems of synchronization of bacterial nuclei with his studies on *Pneumococcus* and the transforming principle. In this work he used cold shock to bring the nuclei into phase. He then followed the susceptibility of the organism to the transforming principle at intervals after release from cold. He found that there was a lack of susceptibility to the transforming principle during the divisional stages. Maaløe & Lark (1954) and Lark & Maaløe (1954), working with *Salmonella*, used repeated exposure to 25° in order to synchronize their cultures. They studied the susceptibility of such synchronized systems to lysogenization, and found that the susceptibility doubled when the nuclei per organism doubled. Scherbaum & Zeuthen (1954) and Zeuthen & Scherbaum (1954) used cold to synchronize the nuclei in cultures of the protozoan *Tetrahymena*. Adams (1954), in an editorial, reviewed the problems of synchronization in *Tetrahymena* and in *Pneumococcus*. Adams also suggested that the study of synchronized bacterial cultures might clarify problems in bacterial cytology. Scott (personal communication), in unpublished studies on *Escherichia coli*, has used cold to synchronize the nuclear activity in this organism. She has been interested in studying the phenomena relating to DNA and RNA synthesis during synchronized cellular division. Her work will appear in the near future. In important early studies Hegarty & Weeks (1940), Adolph & Bayne-Jones (1932), Sherman & Cameron (1934) and Rogers & Greenbank (1930) appear to have recognized the occurrence of synchronization in bacterial cultures.

Fitz-James (1954) claimed to have produced synchronization of nuclear division in *Bacillus megaterium* and *B. cereus* by using spore germination as his method of synchronization. This author likewise states that he followed DNA synthesis in cultures synchronized by this method, and claimed that the curve produced suggested that the synthesis of DNA in the chromosomes was a continuous process. To use such evidence as the basis for an elaborate and cytologically unsupported hypothesis for the continuous formation of chromosomes appears to me to have been premature, especially since the chemical methods were not presented.

In numerous experiments the author has tried to repeat the work of Fitz-James, by attempting to produce nuclear synchrony by spore germination. To date there has been no evidence that nuclear synchrony is produced by this method. It does not appear likely that spore germination can be used for this purpose, since it can easily be demonstrated, not only with *Bacillus megaterium* but with a variety of diverse organisms, that there is a wide range in time between the germination of the first spore and the germination of the last in any given suspension. Since the nuclear cycle in an actively growing bacterial culture in nutrient medium would be in the neighbourhood of 30 min., it would be impossible to synchronize the nuclei in spores germinating over a period of an hour or more. In such a culture germinated from spores, which for the reason given above alone would be asynchronous, one would expect to find that DNA synthesis occurred in such a way that log of concentration plotted against time gave a straight line. The experiments done in this laboratory support this view.

During the summer of 1954, M. E. Hunter, working as my assistant, attempted to synchronize *Bacillus megaterium* by means of cold shock, and to study the nuclear apparatus during and after the influence of cold. Subsequent studies on fluid cultures were carried out both in this laboratory, and in New Brunswick by Hunter and Szybalski.

In these studies (Hunter-Szybalska, Szybalski & DeLamater, 1955) synchronization was produced by bringing an active culture of *Bacillus megaterium*, growing at 34°, suddenly to 15°, and maintaining this temperature for 30 min. Cytological preparations were made during the process of chilling and at intervals following the re-establishment of growth temperatures. The authors of this work have observed and correlated the nuclear cytological findings with the cellular activities in cultures so synchronized. In untreated cultures growing at normal growth temperature prior to the chilling period, the cytological picture is continuously essentially the same, and is as previously described by DeLamater (see Pl. 1, figs. 1–8). The relative rarity of meta- and anaphase stages in such actively growing cultures suggests both the short duration of these stages and the reason why other workers, such as Bisset, have been unable to accept them.

During the chilling period in broth cultures at 15° and on nutrient agar cultures chilled at 6°, the nuclei become larger, the centrioles increase in size, and may even multiply independently of nuclear division (Pl. 2, fig. 18), and the numbers of nuclei in early and late metaphase (prometa- and metaphase) increase. At lower temperatures, 3–10°, the cytological picture is more like that found in untreated cells, although synchroni- zation is produced at these temperatures, as will be demonstrated.

Upon re-establishment of growth by raising the temperature from 15 to 34°, nuclear division takes place in the succeeding 10–15 min., and interphase nuclei are established in which the chromosomes re-elongate. With prolonged chilling, a change which has been described as 'transient polyploidy' and which is very similar to that produced by the action of terramycin or aureomycin is produced. The data presented by these authors document the synchronizing effects of cold as recently reported by Hotchkiss (1954). The clear demonstration of the mitotic apparatus produced by the cold shock further confirms the presence of a mitotic cycle in this organism. The results likewise re-emphasize the centriole as a distinct structure. The stages of division are not difficult to recognize.

It is apparent that chilling inhibits only certain phases of division, especially those which have to do with the separation of the chromo- somes, that is to say, this phase of the cycle is very sensitive to tempera- ture. This suggests that these phases have a high energy of activation. The synthesis of nuclear material (DNA) does not appear to be pre- dominantly affected and does not appear to constitute the essence of the action at this synchronizing temperature. The same may be said for the similar responses produced by the bacteriostatic agents previously mentioned.

Cellular multiplication and nuclear division proceed in parallel. The nuclear duplication appears to occur a full cycle ahead of the cellular division. The cyclical nature of the nuclear division disappears in the theory of continuous growth of nuclear material produced by Fitz-James. The present author (DeLamater) concludes that the nuclei of *Bacillus megaterium* are analogous to those of higher forms, and that this evi- dence supports the view that bacterial nuclei divide by mitosis.

Barner & Cohen (1955), using a thymine-deficient strain of *Escherichia coli*, were able to produce synchronization of the nuclear materials in this organism by depriving the culture of the required thymine and subsequently adding it. The addition then started a nuclear cycle which was essentially synchronous in all cells, and behaved in a characteristi- cally stepwise manner. DNA synthesis was shown to occur in a stepwise fashion, thus further refuting Fitz-James's thesis. These authors likewise attempted cytological analysis, but were limited unfortunately in what they could see by the small size of the cells.

The author believes that the production of synchronization of nuclear division alone is not proof of the occurrence of mitosis, but when correlated with cytological observations, the results are most impressive and important evidence for the occurrence of mitosis in these organisms. When the results are correlated further with statistical analyses of the nuclei in the various phases of mitosis and with simultaneous chemical analyses of DNA and RNA synthesis, glucose utilization, etc., an approach is then gained to what might be called physiological cytology.

CHEMICAL STUDIES ON SYNCHRONIZED SYSTEMS
Methods for synchronization in the present experiments

In the experiments to be described here, *Bacillus megaterium*, Robinow strain, and *Escherichia coli*, strain B, were grown in M9 salt-glucose medium with continuous aeration and agitation. The length of the reproductive cycle is, as expected, much longer under these conditions than when nutrient broth is used (Hunter-Syzbalska *et al.* 1955). Initial Klett density was in the neighbourhood of 120 units, and the cell count was approximately $2 \cdot 2 \times 10^8$ bacterial/ml. Cell counts were made directly in a Petroff-Hausser bacterial counting chamber and by plating. Cold shock was produced by transferring the actively growing culture to a water-bath at the desired temperature, or colder, and bringing the culture to the desired temperature. A flask of the same volume and containing the same medium with a thermometer attached was chilled in parallel with the culture. A curve of the temperature changes thus obtained provided a graphic means of comparing the conditions of temperature occurring in different experiments. The cultures were re-established at growth temperature in the same manner.

The cytology was handled as previously described in other studies (DeLamater, 1951*c*; Blank, McCarthy & DeLamater, 1951), except that from the liquid cultures aliquots of 0·5 ml. to 1 ml. were put either on dried agar blocks or on 'Millipore' filters and were then quickly transferred to cover-slips following fixation with osmium vapour (2 %). The 'Millipore' filter technique proved to be more rapid and gave somewhat better results (Hunter-Szybalska *et al.* 1955), but is not a *sine qua non* for good preparations. The cells were hydrolysed in 1 N-HCl for 6 min., and were stained by the azure A-SO$_2$ technique. They were subsequently dehydrated in freezing alcohol and mounted in one of the mounting resins.

Samples were taken for cytological and statistical analyses after 6, 15, 30 and 60 min. chilling and at 6- or 8-minute intervals during the subsequent growth period at 34° for 2–5 hr.

At intervals during each experiment samples were taken for DNA analysis, RNA analysis, cell count, absorption studies for purines and pyrimidines (technique to be described below), and on special occasions for cytochemical analyses for fat and —SH protein.

Chemical procedures

RNA. Chemical determinations for RNA were done by the Bial-Miller test (Miller, Miller & Golder, 1950).

DNA. The Dische reaction (Seibert, 1940) was used for DNA analysis. The modification finally arrived at was as follows. 8 ml. of culture was removed and placed in a tube containing 0·1 ml. of 1 N-HCl to acidify the material and to stop growth. The sample was then placed in an ice-salt-water bath. All samples were held in this manner until the end of the experimental run. The samples were subsequently spun down; the concentrated cells were resuspended in 0·7 ml. of distilled water; then 0·5 ml. of this suspension was removed and placed in a separate tube for DNA analysis. The 0·2 ml. remaining was used, as below, for the Bial-Miller test for RNA. To the 0·5 ml. aliquot for DNA analysis, 1·5 ml of the Dische reagent was added. The tubes were then placed in a boiling water-bath for 1 hr.; the tubes were stoppered with glass marbles. Following the boiling period, the tubes were rapidly chilled in ice water and were read in a 'Beckman' spectrophotometer at 600 mμ.

The standard procedure using 10 min. of heating for the Dische reaction was found to be too short for *Bacillus megaterium*. The cells did not dissolve, nor was all of the DNA removed from the cells in this short period. It was found that the reaction was increased approximately 50–60% by adequate boiling, and that the cells dissolved only after about 20 min. exposure to the hot reagent. Incidentally, it was found that even with commercial DNA there was approximately 30% increase in the intensity of the reaction after 1 hr. of boiling instead of the usual 10 min. For *Escherichia coli* the 10 min. heating period was found to be adequate. This is the method used by D. B. McNair Scott (personal communication) and Barner & Cohen (1955) for this organism. By this technique it was found that the DNA per cell in *B. megaterium* was approximately ten times that to be demonstrated in *E. coli*. This ratio is in accord with the relative size of the cells. Complete details of these studies, along with the strictly biochemical data, are being presented elsewhere.

In an effort to remove DNA, as demonstrated by the Dische reagent, from *Bacillus megaterium* by boiling in 5% perchloric acid, it was found that the largest amount was removed in the first 10 min., with a large amount remaining in the cells. With continued boiling, the demonstrable DNA in the supernate decreased, and less could be extracted from the treated cells. It was, therefore, concluded that boiling 5% perchloric acid broke down the deoxyribose for which the Dische tests were being made, and hence this procedure could not be used.

In consequence of these difficulties, the Webb & Levy (1955) technique was attempted with perfectly usable results. The difficulty with this procedure is that the colour reaction is very transient; in consequence, accurate readings are difficult to obtain. In the experiments where this procedure was used, however, the same pattern of DNA synthesis observed in other experiments was demonstrated.

Because of the difficulties that were encountered in obtaining what might be considered quantitative results by the established chemical techniques or modifications of them, an effort was made to produce a method which would permit an analysis of the total nucleic acid in whole cells, and the remaining DNA in cells which had been treated with cold 5% perchloric acid in order to remove the RNA. From the work of Barer (1955), it was thought that it might be possible to use a suspending medium which would have a refractive index essentially similar to that of the bacteria, but which would not have a characteristic absorption in the region of the spectrum in which we were interested (230–350 mμ). The test would depend upon the characteristic absorption spectra of purines and pyrimidines. For this purpose, 96% glycerine was found to be suitable; 1 ml. samples of culture were spun down and resuspended in 4 ml. of 96% glycerine.

Fig. 3 shows the absorption spectrum of untreated *Bacillus megaterium* in 96% glycerine. The upper curve demonstrates a dilution of 1/1, which means that 1 ml. of culture was spun down and resuspended in 1 ml. of 96% glycerine, thus re-establishing the same cell concentration as in the original culture. In the lower curve the dilution was 1/2. The proportionality between these curves is apparent. In Text-fig. 4 whole cells suspended in 96% glycerine, and a corresponding sample extracted with cold perchloric acid for 20 hr. to remove the RNA, are compared. The unextracted cells gave essentially the same curve as shown in Text-fig. 3. In the RNA-extracted cells suspended in the same concentration there is a rise in the 280-290 mμ region. The appearance of this shoulder has been consistently produced by the extraction of RNA, and may depend upon (*a*) the change in the pH of the cells; (*b*) an unmasking of protein, giving an absorption in this range; or (*c*) an unmasking of selected nucleo-tides present in the remaining DNA having relatively greater absorption in this region. Text-fig. 5 demonstrates a corresponding absorption curve of unextracted and of 5% cold perchloric-acid-extracted cells of *Escherichia coli* likewise mounted in 96% glycerine. Again one sees the rise of the shoulder of the curve in the 280–290 mμ region. The peak at 230 mμ is a characteristic feature of the absorption curves obtained on

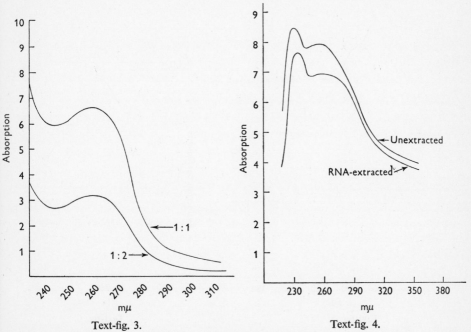

Text-fig. 3.   Text-fig. 4.

Text-fig. 3. Absorption spectrum of untreated *Bacillus megaterium* cells in 96% glycerine. 1:1, undiluted suspension. 1:2, suspension diluted 1 in 2.

Text-fig. 4. Absorption spectra, in 96% glycerine, of untreated *Bacillus megaterium* cells and of cells extracted with cold perchloric acid for 20 hr., to remove RNA.

both the whole cells and the extracted cells of both *E. coli* and *B. mega-terium*. It is interesting to note that this has also been observed by Caspersson (1950) in his absorption curves taken from areas of chromo-somes of *Tradescantia* pollen mother cells, as shown in Text-fig. 6. In Text-fig. 7 the three curves represent the absorption spectra obtained by treating an aliquot of *B. megaterium* cells with cold perchloric acid to remove RNA and then with boiling perchloric acid to remove DNA. The adsorption curve for the extracted RNA in 96% glycerine is shown at the bottom of the graph. The height of the curve reflects dilution and should not be construed as representing the quantity extracted. The peak

is at 260 mμ. The cells were then treated with boiling 5 % perchloric acid
for 20 min. to remove DNA. The extract of DNA was put into 96 %
glycerine and was then analysed; the curve obtained is shown by the
black line. It is characteristic of the DNA absorption pattern, as shown
by comparison with Text-fig. 8 for commercial DNA in glycerine. The
upper dotted line was taken from the cells from which both the DNA and

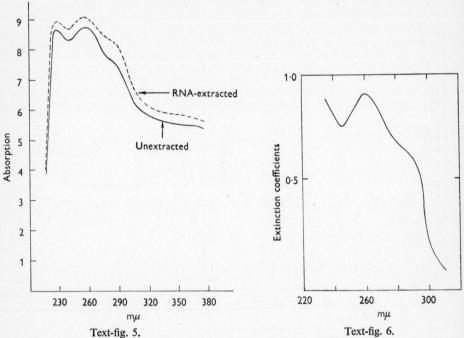

Text-fig. 5.   Text-fig. 6.

Text-fig. 5. Absorption spectra, in 96 % glycerine, of untreated *Escherichia coli* cells and of cells
extracted with cold perchloric acid for 20 hr., to remove RNA.

Text-fig. 6. Extinction coefficients for a point on a chromosome of a *Tradescantia* pollen mother
cell (Caspersson, 1950, p. 66.)

the RNA had been extracted, as described. These cells were suspended in
96 % glycerine. The resulting curve shows that the peak at 230 mμ
persists; that there is a broad flattening of the curve between 250 and
290 mμ with a slight peak which persists at 260 mμ. The persistent
shoulder at 280–290 mμ remains. This probably represents protein. The
peak at 230 mμ indicates that there is some substance in the cells responsible for it which persists despite the removal of the DNA and the RNA.
This curve also indicates that 20 hr. extraction with cold perchloric acid
followed by 20 min. of boiling in hot 5 % perchloric acid is not sufficient
to remove all of the nucleic acids from the cells.

It would appear, however, that the absorption spectra taken on perchloric-acid-extracted bacteria with this technique gives some measure of the DNA of the cells, but so far it has not been possible to make this procedure entirely quantitative. It is also unlikely that all of the RNA is removed by the cold perchloric acid extraction and, therefore, the reading for DNA on the RNA-extracted cells probably includes absorption due to some RNA.

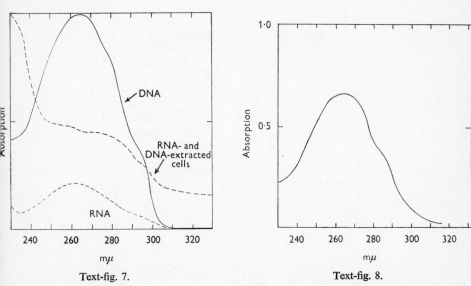

Text-fig. 7.   Text-fig. 8.

Text-fig. 7. Absorption spectra, in 96 % glycerine, of RNA extracted from *Bacillus megaterium* cells by cold perchloric acid; of DNA extracted from the same cells by 20 min. treatment with boiling 5 % perchloric acid; of the cells from which RNA and DNA had been thus extracted.

Text-fig. 8. Absorption spectrum, in 96 % glycerine, of commercial DNA.

An additional peculiarity has been found. When the total nucleic acids are assayed by this method, giving, let us say, a value of one, and a parallel aliquot is extracted for RNA, the assay for RNA likewise gives a value of approximately one. If the DNA which remains in the RNA-extracted cells is then assayed, it also gives a value of approximately one. The reasons for this are not yet clear, but it is most likely due to an unmasking effect. It is felt, however, that despite the unsolved difficulties and lack of absolute measurement here, the correlations observed are valid, interesting and provocative, and worth presenting as preliminary at this time.

Experiments on synchrony

In the synchrony experiments to be described different conditions of chilling have been used, ranging from 15° for 30 min. to 2° for 1 hr. Of the numerous experiments made, the results that are deemed pertinent to our discussion are presented in the accompanying graphs. In Text-fig. 9

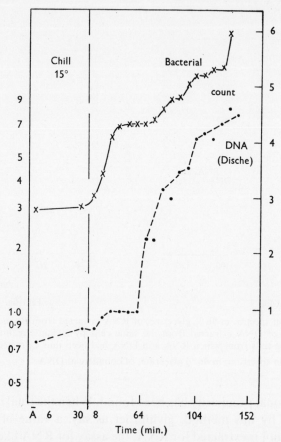

Text-fig. 9. *Bacillus megaterium* culture, partial synchronization by chilling at 15° for 30 min. followed by restoration of growth temperature. Bacterial counts and DNA content (Dische).

a partial synchronization was produced with *Bacillus megaterium* chilled 30 min. at 15°. The bacterial count, following release from the chilling, is shown to rise steeply during the course of the succeeding 24 min., then to level off, and subsequently at 72 min. to taper off in an asynchronous slope. The DNA is found to remain constant until the 64th minute following release from the cold, and then to undergo a marked steplike rise, which also tapers off out of synchrony. The parallel relationship between the stepwise increase of the bacterial count, indicating cell division, and the DNA synthesis, is clearly defined. This parallel relationship between cell division, as indicated by the cell count, and the DNA synthesis is likewise shown in

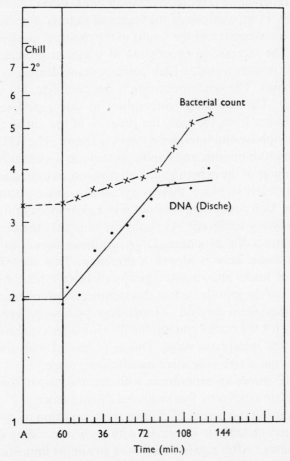

Text-fig. 10. *Bacillus megaterium* culture, partial synchronization by chilling at 2° for 60 min. followed by restoration of growth temperature. Bacterial count and DNA content (Dische).

Text-fig. 10, in which the degree of synchrony was much less than that shown in the previous experiment. The abruptness of the step in DNA synthesis will be discussed more fully below. It would seem that in experiments where only partial synchrony is produced, significant interpretations are still possible. Here the chilling temperature was 2° for a period of 60 min., and the relationship of DNA synthesis to the cell division suggests that this temperature interferes with DNA synthesis as well as with cell division. Chilling at 15°, on the other hand, does not appear to have arrested DNA synthesis. In these two experiments no cytological examinations were made. However, in other experiments where the cytology has been examined, the nuclear division also shows a separate parallel curve (Hunter-Syzbalska *et al.* 1955).

In Text-fig. 11 an analysis of the stages of mitosis is presented along with the bacterial count and the results of the chemical analysis for DNA and RNA. The increase in proportion of nuclei in prometaphase and metaphase is demonstrated, with a corresponding decrease of nuclei in the other phases. The synchronization is not complete, but is nearly so (about 80%). The shocking temperature in this experiment was 8°. Following release from the cold, the progress of the nuclei through the anaphase, telophase and interphase stages is shown. The RNA begins to rise about the 30th minute, and continues to do so with minor variations during the course of the experiment. Cell division, as indicated by the cell count, is not clearly stepwise; there is a gradual increase with a slight step in the centre. Cell count here does not give a clear index of the degree of nuclear synchrony achieved. At about the time that the chromosomes begin to contract for prophase, DNA synthesis occurs as an abrupt step. The increase here is almost a doubling. This accords with the proportion of nuclei shown cytologically to be in synchrony ($\pm 80\%$). The duration of the mitotic cycle in this instance is approximately 68 min. following release from the cold. From this graph it is apparent that there is a tendency for the nuclei undergoing division after synchronization to build up in the interphase stage. This is in accord with the idea that interphase is the active vegetative metabolizing stage.

Text-fig. 12 shows an experiment with *Bacillus megaterium* in which almost complete synchrony was produced by cold shock at 3° for 60 min. Here again during the period of chilling the proportion of nuclei in pro-metaphase and metaphase increases, with a corresponding decrease of the other phases. After release, there was an almost immediate impulse to complete the division, with a marked build-up in the interphase stage which persisted in this experiment for a period of nearly 1 hr. Again, at the time the chromosomes begin the contraction for prophase, the DNA synthesis occurs as a sharp step, and here the DNA doubles in amount. The cellular division has occurred in the early minutes following release from the cold, and the bacterial count has remained constant for the succeeding 130 min. before a second step begins at the end of the experiment. As shown by Hunter-Szybalska *et al.* (1955), this relationship between cell division and nuclear division appears to be parallel, and appears to be independent of the mechanism of DNA synthesis. DNA synthesis also, however, appears to occur in a parallel manner. It may be suggested that the temperature coefficient for each of these reactions

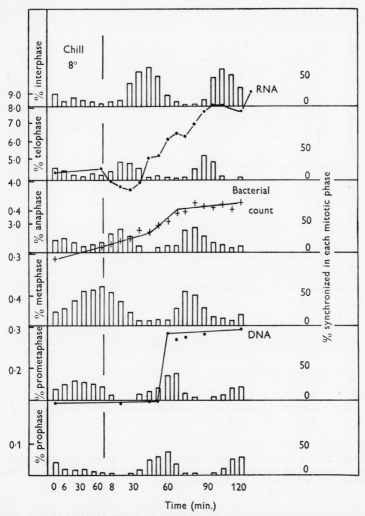

Text-fig. 11. *Bacillus megaterium*, culture chilled at 8° for 60 min.; bacterial count, RNA and DNA content and proportion of nuclei in various stages of mitosis during chilling and after restoration to growth temperature.

is distinctive. Bentzon, Maaløe & Rasch (1952) have already shown the temperature coefficient of DNA (phage) synthesis is approximately twice that for cell division. Incomplete analysis of additional data suggests that cell division, nuclear division, deoxyribose synthesis, and purine and pyrimidine synthesis (ring closure) may have distinctive temperature coefficients. This should prove to be an interesting and fruitful avenue to pursue.

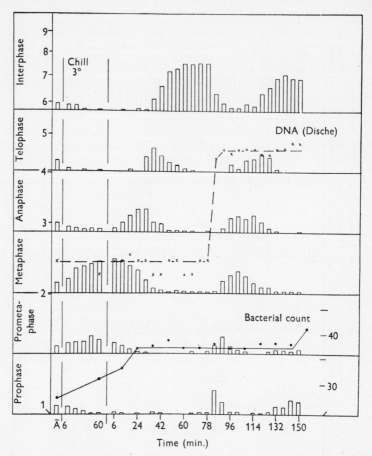

Text-fig. 12. *Bacillus megaterium*, culture chilled at 3° for 60 min.; bacterial count, DNA content and proportion of nuclei in various stages of mitosis during chilling and after restoration to growth temperature synchrony.

It became apparent during the course of these studies that it was not possible to anticipate precisely what the results of a given experiment would be, even though the same temperature and, so far as could be controlled, the same conditions of inoculum, growth, etc., were maintained. Text-fig. 13 demonstrates an experiment identical with that shown in Text-fig. 12, in which DNA synthesis was not completely synchronized. The factors which cause these variations are difficult to ascertain; additional studies are in progress.

An experiment in which only partial synchrony was produced is presented in Text-fig. 14. In this case the chilling temperature was 10° for 40 min. Chilling was accomplished in the icebox, the culture being

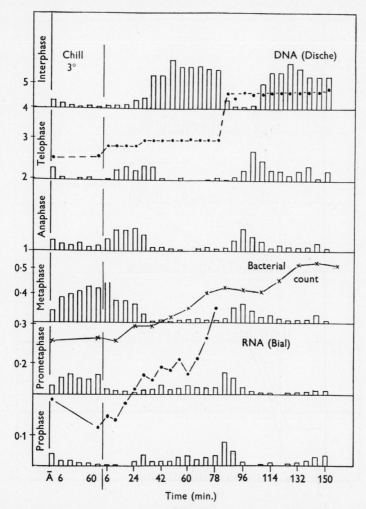

Text-fig. 13. *Bacillus megaterium*, culture chilled at 3° for 60 min.; bacterial count, RNA and DNA content and proportion of nuclei in various stages of mitosis during chilling and after restoration of growth temperature. Partial synchrony of nuclei and of DNA synthesis.

surrounded by air, not ice water. The chilling was, therefore, much slower than in other experiments. Here the nuclei accumulated almost equally in the prometaphase and metaphase stages. After release, a relatively small number proceeded to interphase. The bacterial count rose in a sharp sloping step and then levelled off in a second discrete phase. It is felt that the slope of this curve also indicates the degree of asynchrony present. The DNA rose in a staircase-like series of steps, again suggesting that the synchrony produced was only partial, and that the nuclei may

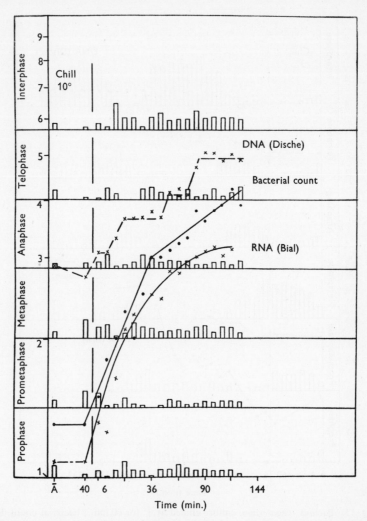

Text-fig. 14. *Bacillus megaterium*, culture held in air at 10° for 40 min.; bacterial count, RNA and DNA content and proportion of nuclei in various stages of mitosis during chilling and after restoration of growth temperature. Partial synchrony.

have been only partially arrested and in more than one phase at this temperature, or that the chilling was too slow and incomplete. The distribution of the nuclei through the different phases of the mitotic cycle after the first sweep into interphase also indicates the asynchronous nature of this culture. The most obvious cause of the asynchrony in this experiment was the slowness of the chilling to 10°.

In Text-fig. 15 is shown an interesting experiment in which *Bacillus*

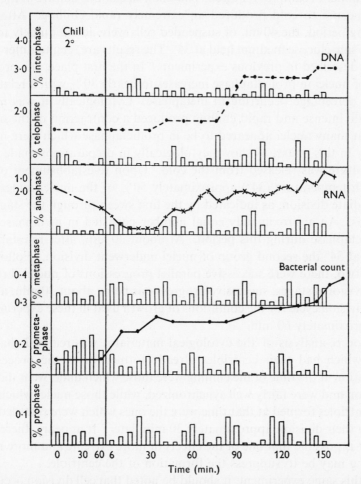

Text-fig. 15. *Bacillus megaterium*, culture chilled rapidly to 2°; bacterial count, RNA and DNA content and proportion of nuclei in various stages of mitosis during chilling and after restoration of growth temperature. Partial synchrony and depression of centrioles.

megaterium was chilled very rapidly to 2° in a salt-water-ice bath. In a sense this is the opposite situation to that in the previous experiment, and caused asynchrony for different and understandable reasons. In this case the cells were grown in the active state for a period of several hours, transferred to fresh salt-glucose medium, and grown again at 34° for one additional hour. They were then rapidly spun down, and resuspended in

40 ml. of fresh salt-glucose medium. This 40 ml. suspension was very rapidly chilled in a salt-ice bath. In other experiments the size of the culture being chilled ranged between 240 and 450 ml., depending upon the number of samples required. The small size of this culture at the time of exposure to cold produced an extremely rapid chilling. After the chilling period, the 40 ml. of suspended cells were added quickly to 200 ml. of salt-glucose medium held at 34°. The results are seen to differ from those described in previous experiments. In the first place, the proportion of nuclei in prometaphase increases to nearly 80% with a relatively small percentage occurring in metaphase. Cytologically it was found that the intense and rapid chilling produced a contraction of the nuclei so that many nuclei appeared to be in prometaphase which were not in reality in this phase, as shown cytologically in preparations made after the culture was released from the cold. Upon re-establishment of the growth temperature (34°) approximately 50% of the nuclei underwent immediate division, as indicated by the first sweep through the stages of mitosis. An approximately equal number persisted in metaphase and prometaphase during this period. At about 30 min. after re-establishment at 34° the second group of nuclei underwent division. Following these two, there were successive parallel progressions of nuclei through the divisional stages, successive progressions being about 30 min. apart. The division cycle for the conditions of growth used in these experiments is approximately 60 min.

Upon re-analysis of the cytological material it was realized that the cells which had their centrioles already formed or in the process of formation at the time of the chilling were those which underwent the first division and were fairly well synchronized, while those nuclei which had no centrioles formed at that time were the ones which were retarded and began their division approximately 30 min. later. It appears, therefore, that it is possible that one of the effects of more extreme and more rapid chilling may be to suppress the formation of the centriole.

In this same experiment, it should be noted that cell division occurred immediately after release from arrest, and did not occur again for a period of approximately 150 min. The RNA fell and remained low for about 36 min. After release, it rose in a progressive manner. The DNA rose in three successive steps, and never attained a complete doubling during the course of the experiment. It is difficult to correlate these episodes of DNA synthesis with the nuclear divisions.

Asynchrony, therefore, appears to be a product, in the two experiments just described, of at least two different sets of conditions: in the first, inadequate chilling, and in the second, too rapid chilling. Where the volume of the culture is sufficient to slow down the chilling process, even to a very low temperature (3°), the synchronization, as demonstrated in Text-fig. 12, may be excellent. The nuclei have had time to come into phase. This also occurs at the higher temperatures, such as 15°, but if the chilling is too rapid the nuclei accumulate in late prophase without centrioles if these have not yet formed, or if the centrioles have begun to form they are arrested in prometaphase. This suggests that centriole formation may have a distinctive temperature coefficient.

Text-fig. 16 shows an experiment in which a special situation again appears to obtain. The chilling temperature of 10° was achieved in a salt-ice-water bath and was maintained for a period of 40 min. The nuclei again accumulated in both prometaphase and metaphase during the course of the chilling period. After release from the cold there is a sweep of division through the stages of mitosis, but the nuclei do not persist in interphase as in previous experiments (see Text-fig. 12), but immediately proceed into prophase and a second division. Here the division cycle is much shorter. At the time, however, of the progress from interphase to prophase there is only about a 50% step synthesis of DNA. The DNA curve is then flat for a period of about 80 min. before it begins to rise in a gradual slope. During this period when there is no demonstrable DNA synthesis, beginning at about 72 min. after the chilling period, there is a third wave of nuclear division in the culture. This does not appear to be related to any DNA synthesis. At the same time cell size is reduced to about one-half. This peculiar result suggests one of two possible inter-pretations: (1) that the necessary synthesis for this division occurred prior to the chilling period, or (2) that nuclear division may occur as a consequence of the polytene nature of the chromosomes, and that once the chromatids have multiplied they may separate under certain un-known physiological conditions. The results of this experiment suggest the possible occurrence of polyteny in bacterial chromosomes, along with the possibility of the progressive separation of the strands without further synthesis of DNA. Such an interpretation, if proved true, could support the view that the granular filterable phase of bacteria produced from 'large bodies' may result from a progressive segregation of the strands of polytene chromosomes. This is admittedly speculative, but it is likewise enticing. Some such mechanism must operate to maintain the integrity and continuity of the genetic material during the filterable phase.

In the experiments discussed so far the DNA analyses have been done by means of the Dische procedure, as described. In the following experiments the absorption method described previously was used alone or in parallel with the chemical procedures. In Text-fig. 17 an experiment is presented in which *Bacillus megaterium* was chilled to 9°. Here the absorption method only was used to demonstrate the DNA. It is considered that partial synchrony only (about 60%) was obtained. As

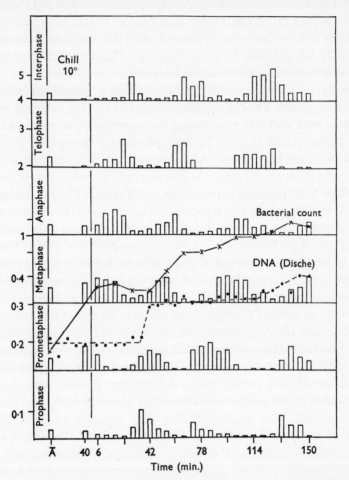

Text-fig. 16. *Bacillus megaterium*, culture chilled at 10° for 40 min.; bacterial count, DNA content and proportion of nuclei in various stages of mitosis during chilling and after restoration of growth temperature. Partial synchrony; nuclear division without DNA synthesis.

indicated, the nuclei accumulate during the chilling period in prometaphase and metaphase, predominantly in the latter. After release from chilling, the nuclei proceed through division to the interphase stage. This interphase stage constitutes about 60% of the nuclei counted. Sixteen minutes after release from the cold an abrupt synthesis of purines and pyrimidines occurs. This analysis is based upon absorption at 260 and

290 mμ in samples taken at the indicated intervals. The curve represents the readings taken on RNA-extracted cells, and represents predominantly the purines and pyrimidines of the DNA remaining in the chromosomes. A second step in purine and pyrimidine synthesis occurs nearly 140 min. later, as shown. The total increase in the two steps is in the

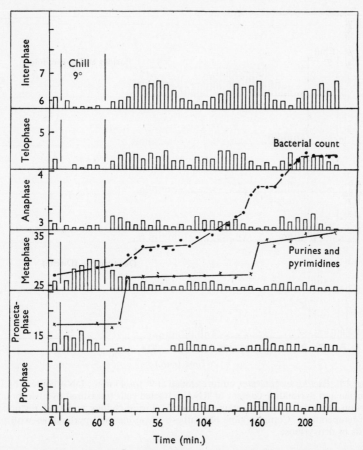

Text-fig. 17. *Bacillus megaterium*, culture chilled to 9° for 60 min.; bacterial count, purine and pyrimidine content of RNA-extracted cells (measured by absorption) and proportion of nuclei in various stages of mitosis during chilling and after restoration of growth temperature. Partial synchrony; stepwise synthesis of DNA purines and pyrimidines.

neighbourhood of one complete doubling, again suggesting that the degree of synchrony in this experiment was in the neighbourhood of 50–60%, which correlates with the percentage of nuclei found to be in synchrony cytologically. It is interesting to note that the amount of synchronization, as indicated by the bacterial count, is rather low, since the increase in the bacterial count here is progressive and slow. The increase in bacterial count, however, is somewhat less than a single doubling in the total course of this experiment. It should be noted that the first step in purine and pyrimidine synthesis occurs very early in the telophase-interphase stage of the first division cycle, while the second step in the purine-pyrimidine synthesis occurs late in the interphase

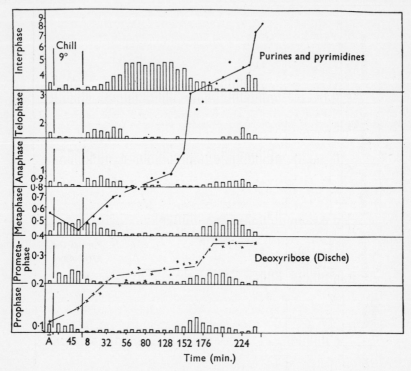

Text-fig. 18. *Bacillus megaterium*, culture chilled at 9° for 45 min.; DNA content by Dische test, purine and pyrimidine content of RNA-extracted cells (measured by absorption) and proportion of nuclei in various stages of mitosis during chilling and after restoration of growth temperature. Compare time of synthesis of purines and pyrimidines with time of synthesis of deoxyribose.

stage but before the chromosomes have begun to go over to prophase in any great numbers. In other words, there is a suggestion that this step would have preceded the step indicated by analysis of the deoxyribose had the Dische test been carried out in this experiment.

As a consequence of this result, and in an effort to ascertain whether the chemical readings for deoxyribose and the absorption readings for the purines and pyrimidines gave the same picture, experiments were set up in which both tests were made simultaneously on the same experimental system. In this experiment (Text-fig. 18) *Bacillus megaterium* was again the test organism, and chilling was produced at 9° for a period of 45 min. The nuclei are demonstrated to have accumulated in prometaphase and metaphase and, after release from the cold, to have undergone immediate division and passed into interphase. The number persisting in interphase is between 80 and 90%. After release from the cold, the

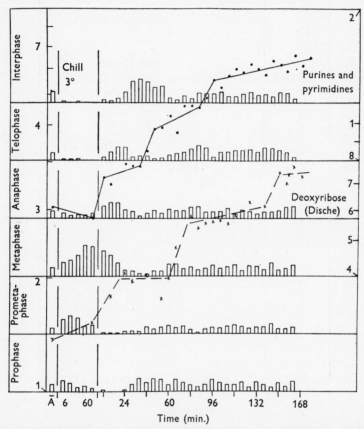

Text-fig. 19. *Bacillus megaterium*, culture chilled at 3° for 60 min.; DNA content by Dische test, purine and pyrimidine content of RNA-extracted cells (measured by absorption) and proportion of nuclei in various stages of mitosis during chilling and after restoration of growth temperature. Partial synchrony. Compare time of synthesis of purines and pyrimidines with time of synthesis of deoxyribose.

purines and pyrimidines show a rise over a period of 8–152 min.; at this time there is a sharp step in which there is almost a complete doubling of these materials, as indicated in Text-fig. 18. This step occurs towards the end of the interphase period, as shown. The deoxyribose curve demonstrates a slow rise from 8 to 40 min., after which there is a flattening of the curve and relatively little synthesis for the next 120 min. There is

then a half step before the curve again flattens out. It is interesting that
there is a 16 min. interval between the step in the purine and pyrimidine
synthesis and the step in deoxyribose synthesis. This result was not
expected and was most provocative, suggesting that it is possible to

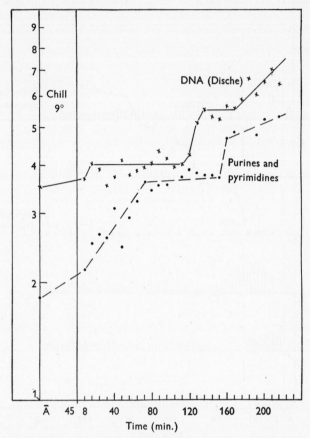

Text-fig. 20. *Escherichia coli*, culture chilled at 9° for 45 min.; DNA content by Dische
test and purine and pyrimidine content of RNA-extracted cells (measured by absorption)
after restoration of growth temperature. Compare time of synthesis of purines and
pyrimidines with time of synthesis of deoxyribose.

separate in time the synthesis of the purines and pyrimidines of the
chromosomes on the one hand, from the synthesis of deoxyribose on the
other. This experimental result with the same relationships has been
repeatedly obtained, as shown in Text-fig. 19. Here the shocking temperature was 3° for 60 min.; synchronization was about 60–70%.

The result just described for *Bacillus megaterium* was not expected on
the basis of the biochemical studies on ribonucleic acid synthesis which

have been done with pigeon-liver homogenate and *Escherichia coli*, in which it has been shown that the ribose is attached first to the carboxamide, and that the ring closure forming the purines occurs subsequently (Reichard, 1955; Schlenk, 1955; Brown & Roll, 1955).

Experiments were set up with *Escherichia coli* in the same manner as described for *Bacillus megaterium*. Here, interestingly, as shown in Text-fig. 20, the sugar as measured by the Dische reaction was essentially constant until the 114th to the 120th minute, at which time there was a

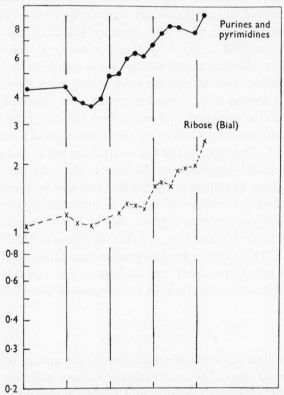

Text-fig. 21. *Bacillus megaterium*, synchronized culture. Increase of ribose (Bial test) and of RNA purines and pyrimidines (measured by absorption).

sharp step in the synthesis of this moiety. The curve subsequently flattened out for a period of 32 min., and then again turned upwards at a rather sharp slope, indicating the development of asynchrony in the system. The purines and pyrimidines, as indicated by the absorption readings at 260 mμ of the RNA-extracted cells mounted in 96% glycerine, showed a progressive rise from 8 to 72 min., at which time the curve levelled off. After an additional 80 min. there was a sharp step in the purine-pyrimidine synthesis, and the curve again sloped off as the system went out of synchrony. The present interpretation of this result accepts the view that the two sharp steps of synthesis of the two moieties are related, though this may be subject to revision. Thus, in accordance with the biochemical evidence for ribonucleic synthesis in *E. coli*, the deoxyribose moiety appears to be synthesized first in a stepwise manner, while the purines and pyrimidines appear to be synthesized about 40 min. later, likewise in a sharp stepwise manner. These results support the idea that the deoxyribose moiety may be linked to the carboxamide and that the ring closure of the purine occurs secondarily to this ribolization of the carboxamide. Since there is no extant evidence on the mechanisms or pathways involved in DNA synthesis in either *E. coli* or *B. megaterium*, these results may constitute the first evidence on the subject, and justify speculation, even though the work is little more than preliminary.

Since what appear to be opposing results were obtained on *Bacillus megaterium* on the one hand, and on *Escherichia coli* on the other, it was felt desirable to ascertain whether the ribose moiety had a similar pattern of synthesis. Unfortunately, the ribose data for the *E. coli* experiments were not more than suggestive at this stage of the work, but the data for ribose formation, as indicated by the Bial test and by the formation of the purines and pyrimidines of RNA, as indicated by the absorption data, again suggest, but only suggest, that in *B. megaterium* the purines and pyrimidines are formed first, and that the ribose is added secondarily (Text-fig. 21). These curves are less precise than those shown for DNA synthesis. It may be pertinent that our strain of *E. coli* B is sensitive to sulphonamides, while our strain of *B. megaterium* is very resistant.

DISCUSSION

The evidence that has been presented has led the author to support the following broad ideas. The cytochemical evidence indicates clearly that the nucleus is a distinct structure and is clearly separable, both cytochemically and optically, from other cellular structures, including the mitochondrial areas, the septa, etc. This cytochemical evidence further suggests that from the chemical point of view *Bacillus megaterium* is organized quite differently from *Escherichia coli*. It contains not only soluble lipids and bound lipids, but with age and during sporulation acid polysaccharide tends to accumulate at one pole, while lipid accumulates at the other. These substances remain discrete. In *E. coli* the bipolar material characteristically includes both lipoprotein and RNA as well as sulphhydryl-containing protein. The presence of both lipoprotein and

RNA at the poles of this organism precludes exact definition of any polysaccharide material which may be present and demonstrable by the PAS technique. In *E. coli* these polar areas correspond to mitochondria, and are discrete from the nuclei. The chromosomes of *B. megaterium* contain not only DNA, but likewise can be demonstrated to contain sulphhydryl-containing protein, at least in the vegetative cells. The nuclei of *E. coli*, on the other hand, can be demonstrated to contain only DNA by the present techniques. This suggests a different degree of complexity of the chromosomes in these two organisms, which may have a relative importance in terms of the genetic findings in *E. coli*. The cytochemical evidence also indicates that the centriole and spindle contain —SH protein.

Both *Escherichia coli* and *Bacillus megaterium* appear to have three haploid chromosomes which can be characterized with considerable accuracy, those in *B. megaterium* being so large that the satellite can be seen on the large chromosome. The centromere attachment on the large and middle-sized chromosomes can also be seen.

The accumulated evidence on the action of certain drugs, including terramycin, aureomycin and *para*-aminosalicylic acid, as well as cytological studies on the influence of cold on the bacterial nucleus, suggests that the divisional apparatus of the bacterial nucleus includes a centriole and spindle element. The centrioles have been shown not only to increase in size at the higher shock temperatures and under the influence of these drugs, but also to be capable of independent division. The cytological patterns observed in cells exposed to cold shock further support the view that we are dealing with a mitotic mechanism, and support the concept of nuclear structure and organization summarized in Text-fig. 2.

Using synchronized or partially synchronized systems, it has been possible to demonstrate the parallelism between nuclear division and cellular division. It has also been possible to demonstrate what appears to be the independent parallelism of the mechanism for both deoxyribose and purine and pyrimidine synthesis and to separate these from the kinetics of nuclear division.

The biochemical evidence produced as a consequence of these studies suggests in *Escherichia coli* a possible projection of the biochemical data to include DNA (Reichard, 1955; Schlenk, 1955; Brown & Roll, 1955), which indicate that in ribonucleic acid synthesis the ribose is formed first, and that subsequently the purine and pyrimidine rings are closed through the carboxamide. The opposite result obtained with *Bacillus megaterium*, both with DNA and RNA, strongly suggests that the synthetic pathways for the nucleic acids in this organism are different from those in

E. coli. This difference may represent a fundamental one between Gram-positive and Gram-negative bacteria. This hypothesis or speculation is, fortunately, easily susceptible of experimental test. If it is permitted to speculate further, such a difference might represent the basis for the difference between Gram-negative organisms and Gram-positive organisms in susceptibility to different antibiotics and antibacterial agents. It is perhaps pertinent that *E. coli* is sensitive to sulphonamides, whereas this strain of *B. megaterium* is resistant. The evidence that has been obtained by studying the synchronization at different temperatures suggests that the temperature coefficients of cell division may, when more fully analysed, be found to be different from the temperature coefficients of nuclear division and of deoxyribose and purine and pyrimidine synthesis, and should be approachable experimentally. The evidence further suggests the possibility that the centriole, which gives one set of reactions at 15°, becoming much enlarged, and even dividing independently, does not form at all at 2°, when chilling is sufficiently rapid. This structure with distinctive physiological activities and susceptibilities appears to be a crucial part of the machinery of the dividing nucleus.

The abruptness of the steps in the synthesis of both the deoxyribose and the purines and pyrimidines suggests that synthesis occurs extremely rapidly once the requisite preparations (i.e. the formation of a pool, perhaps, of the necessary building blocks) have been made by the cell. What the precise factors are which stimulate the sudden spurts of synthesis are not clear. It seems most significant, however, that these spurts of synthesis occur so suddenly and are complete within such short periods of time. Space does not permit description of the numerous interesting speculations which these topics provoke and deserve.

Quite obviously the studies which have been carried out to date represent only a beginning on a very complex and difficult set of problems. It appears entirely possible, however, that the kinetics of mitosis can be approached and separated from the problems concerned with the synthesis of nuclear materials that are involved in cellular reproduction.

It is obvious that the bacteria offer a unique opportunity for the combined simultaneous application of different scientific disciplines. The study of the cell as a whole from the combined point of view of the biochemist, cytochemist and cytologist is now feasible. It appears likely that with the combined application of these disciplines a real knowledge of the cell as an integrated system will eventually be forthcoming.

SUMMARY

Cytochemical evidence for the organization of *Bacillus megaterium* and *Escherichia coli* is presented and compared. The evidence indicates that *E. coli* possesses differentiated areas of mitochondrial activity, while *B. megaterium* does not. It further suggests that the chromosomes of *E. coli* contain little or no —SH protein, while *B. megaterium* contains —SH protein not only in the chromosomes but in the centriole and spindle as well.

Cytological evidence on the nuclear organization demonstrates three chromosomes in the vegetative cells of both organisms, and further shows that these can be identified and characterized with relative clarity. Evidence for their simultaneous longitudinal division is also recapitulated. The cytological evidence further supports the concept of a complex mitotic mechanism in both types of bacteria. It is suggested that this is essentially an intranuclear process and that the nuclear membrane persists throughout the nuclear cycle.

Selected drugs and cold cause mitotic arrest of very similar types, producing enlargement and arrest of division, and migration of the centrioles. Simultaneous cytological, chemical and statistical studies on synchronized bacterial cultures in which cellular and nuclear division have been brought into phase have shown that cellular division, nuclear division, deoxyribose synthesis and the synthesis of purine and pyrimidine of DNA proceed in parallel. The evidence suggests that the chemical reactions for these cellular activities have each a characteristic temperature coefficient. The formation of the centriole appears to have a distinctive temperature coefficient, different from that of the division and subsequent movement of this structure.

Deoxyribose synthesis and DNA purine and pyrimidine synthesis are shown to be separable in time in synchronized systems. In *Bacillus megaterium* the DNA purine and pyrimidine synthesis appears to occur prior to the formation of the deoxyribose, while in *Escherichia coli* the deoxyribose is demonstrably prior to the formation of the DNA purines and pyrimidines.

The significance of these results is discussed.

The author wishes to acknowledge the assistance of those who have contributed to the work described above, in particular Dr A. Widra, Dr E. J. Minsavage, Mrs C. G. Tosteson, Miss A. Phillips and Miss E. Chu.

This study was supported in part by grants from the Atomic Energy Commission (contract no. AT (30–1)–1341), and from the National Institutes of Health, Public Health Service (PHS no. C-2189).

256   E. D. DeLAMATER

REFERENCES

ADAMS, M. H. (1954). Synchronization of cell division in microorganisms. *Science*, **120**, 793.

ADOLPH, E. F. & BAYNE-JONES, S. (1932). Growth in size of microorganisms measured from motion pictures. II. *Bacillus megatherium. J. cell. comp. Physiol.* **1**, 409.

BARER, R. (1955). Spectrophotometry of clarified cell suspensions. *Science*, **121**, 709.

BARNER, H. D. & COHEN, S. S. (1955). Synchronization of division of a thymineless mutant of *Escherichia coli. Fed. Proc.* **14** (1, pt. 1), 177.

BENTZON, M. W., MAALØE, O. & RASCH, G. (1952). An analysis of increase in number of intracellular phage particles at different temperatures. *Acta path. microbiol. scand.* **30**, 243.

BERGERSON, F. J. (1953). A probable growth cycle in *Bacillus megaterium. J. gen. Microbiol.* **9**, 26.

BISSET, K. A. (1951). Morphology and cytology of bacteria. *Ann. Rev. Microbiol.* **5**, 1.

BLANK, H., McCARTHY, P. & DeLAMATER, E. D. (1951). A non-vacuum freezing-dehydrating technic for histology, autoradiography and microbial cytology. *Stain Tech.* **26**, 193.

BRADFIELD, J. R. G. (1954). Electron microscopic observations on bacterial nuclei. *Nature, Lond.* **173**, 184.

BROWN, G. B. & ROLL, P. M. (1955). Biosynthesis of nucleic acids. *The Nucleic Acids*, vol. 2, chapter 25, p. 341. Editors, E. Chargaff and J. Davidson. New York: Academic Press.

CASPERSSON, T. O. (1950). *Cell Growth and Cell Function.* New York: W. W. Norton.

CHANCE, H. L. (1955). Hydrogen chloride gas for effecting staining of internal structures in *Escherichia coli. Stain Tech.* **30**, 53.

CHAPMAN, G. B. & HILLIER, J. (1953). Electron microscopy of ultrathin sections of bacteria. I. Cellular division in *Bacillus cereus. J. Bact.* **66**, 362.

DAVIS, J. & MUDD, S. (1955). Cytology of a strain of *C. diphtheriae. J. Bact.* **69**, 372.

DAWSON, I. M. & STERN, H. (1954). Structure in the bacterial cell walls during cell division. *Biochim. biophys. Acta*, **13**, 31.

DeLAMATER, E. D. (1951a). Evidence for the occurrence of true mitosis in bacteria. *Science*, **113**, 477.

DeLAMATER, E. D. (1951b). A new cytological basis for bacterial genetics. *Cold Spr. Harb. Symp. quant. Biol.* **16**, 381.

DeLAMATER, E. D. (1951c). A staining and dehydrating procedure for the handling of microorganisms. *Stain Tech.* **26**, 199.

DeLAMATER, E. D. (1952a). Preliminary observation on the occurrence of a typical mitotic process in micrococci. *Bull. Torrey bot. Cl.* **79**, 1.

DeLAMATER, E. D. (1952b). Preliminary observations on the occurrence of mitosis in *Caryophanon latum. Mycologia*, **44**, 203.

DeLAMATER, E. D. (1952c). A consideration of the newer methods for the demonstration of nuclear structure in bacteria and other microorganisms. *Mikroskopie*, **7**, 358.

DeLAMATER, E. D. (1953a). Structure and division of the bacterial nucleus. *Bacterial Cytology, Symp. 6th Congr. int. Microbiol.*, Rome, p. 108.

DeLAMATER, E. D. (1953b). Aspects of bacteria as cells and as organisms, Part II. Nuclei and chromosomes. *Int. Rev. Cytology*, **2**, 158.

DeLamater, E. D. (1953c). The mitotic mechanism in bacteria. *Cold Spr. Harb. Symp. quant. Biol.* **18**, 99.

DeLamater, E. D. (1954a). Cytology of bacteria, Part II. The bacterial nucleus. *Ann. Rev. Microbiol.* **8**, 23.

DeLamater, E. D. (1954b). A conceptual formulation of the structure and divisional mechanism of the bacterial nucleus. *Trans. N.Y. Acad. Sci.* **16**, 366.

DeLamater, E. D. (1954c). A demonstration of the antimitotic nature of the inhibition produced in bacteria by antibiotics and other drugs. *Amer. J. Syph.* **38**, 593.

DeLamater, E. D. & Hunter, M. E. (1951). Preliminary report of true mitosis in the vegetative cell of *Bacillus megaterium*. *Amer. J. Bot.* **38**, 659.

DeLamater, E. D. & Hunter, M. E. (1952). The nuclear cytology of sporulation in *Bacillus megaterium*. *J. Bact.* **63**, 13.

DeLamater, E. D. & Hunter, M. E. (1953). Preliminary studies into the conditions controlling cellular fusion and secondary colony formation in *Bacillus megaterium*. *J. Bact.* **65**, 739.

DeLamater, E. D., Hunter, M. E., Minsavage, E. J., Szybalski, W. & Bryson, V. (1953). Observations on the influence of various inhibitors including colchicine, camphor, benzimidazole, formaldehyde, isoniazid, sodium *p*-aminosalicylate, and antibiotics of the tetracycline, erythromycin and streptomycin groups, on the bacterial nucleus. *Proc. 6th Congr. int. Microbiol.* **1**, 83.

DeLamater, E. D., Hunter, M. E. & Mudd, S. (1951). Current status of the bacterial nucleus. *Exp. Cell Res.* **2**, 319.

DeLamater, E. D., Hunter, M. E., Szybalski, W. & Bryson, V. (1955). Chemically induced aberrations of mitosis in bacteria. *J. gen. Microbiol.* **12**, 203.

DeLamater, E. D. & Mudd, S. (1951). The occurrence of mitosis in the vegetative phase of *Bacillus megaterium*. *Exp. Cell Res.* **2**, 499.

DeLamater, E. D., Schaechter, M. & Hunter, M. E. (1955). A chemically specific double-staining technique for desoxyribonucleic acid and other aldehyde-yielding or aldehyde-containing substances. *J. Histochem. Cytochem.* **3**, 16.

DeLamater, E. D. & Woodburn, M. (1952). Evidence for the occurrence of mitosis in the micrococci. *J. Bact.* **64**, 793.

de Robertis, E. D. P., Nowinski, W. W. & Saez, F. A. (1954). *General Cytology.* Philadelphia: W. B. Saunders.

Fitz-James, P. C. (1954). The duplication of bacterial chromatin. Interpretations of some cytological and chemical studies of the germinating spores of *Bacillus cereus* and *Bacillus megaterium*. *J. Bact.* **68**, 464.

Gonse, P. H. & Yotsuyanagi, Y. (1955). Note sur la réduction intracellulaire du triphényltétrazolium dans les œufs d'oursin. *Exp. Cell Res.* **8**, 500.

Hartman, P. E. & Liu, C. (1954). Comparative cytology of wild type *Saccharomyces* and a respirationally deficient mutant. *J. Bact.* **67**, 77.

Hartman, P. E. & Payne, J. I. (1954). Direct staining of two types of nucleoproteins in *Escherichia coli*. *J. Bact.* **68**, 237.

Hayes, W. (1953). The mechanism of genetic recombination in *Escherichia coli*. *Cold Spr. Harb. Symp. quant. Biol.* **18**, 75.

Hegarty, B. P. & Weeks, O. B. (1940). Sensitivity of *Escherichia coli* to cold shock during the logarithmic growth phase. *J. Bact.* **39**, 475.

Hotchkiss, R. D. (1954). Cyclical behavior in pneumococcal growth and transformability occasioned by environmental changes. *Proc. nat. Acad. Sci., Wash.*, **40**, 49.

Hunter, M. E. (1955). Studies on the nucleus of giant cells of *Micrococcus cryophilus*. *Exp. Cell Res.* (in the Press).

HUNTER, M. E. & DeLAMATER, E. D. (1952). Observations on the nuclear cytology of spore germination in *Bacillus megaterium. J. Bact.* **63**, 23.

HUNTER, M. E. & DeLAMATER, E. D. (1955). Further observations on the bacterial spore nucleus. *J. Bact.* **69**, 108.

HUNTER-SZYBALSKA, M. E., SZYBALSKI, W. & DeLAMATER, E. D. (1955). Temperature synchronization of nuclear and cellular division in *Bacillus megaterium. J. Bact.* (in the Press).

KNAYSI, G. (1955). The structure, composition and behavior of the nucleus in *Bacillus cereus. J. Bact.* **29**, 117.

LARK, K. G. & MAALØE, O. (1954). The induction of cellular and nuclear division in *Salmonella typhimurium* by means of temperature shifts. *Biochim. biophys. Acta,* **15**, 345.

MAALØE, O. & LARK, K. G. (1954). A study of bacterial populations with induced nuclear and cellular division. In *Recent Developments in Cell Physiology.* Editor, J. A. Kitching. London: Butterworths.

MILLER, G. L., MILLER, E. E. & GOLDER, R. H. (1950). Studies on the orcinal method for determining pentoses. *Fed. Proc.* **9**, 206.

MINSAVAGE, E. J. & DeLAMATER, E. D. (1955 a). The nuclear cytology of *Salmonella typhosa. J. Bact.* **70**, 482.

MINSAVAGE, E. J. & DeLAMATER, E. D. (1955 b). Some observations on the effect of colchicine upon *Salmonella typhosa. J. Bact.* **70**, 501.

MUDD, S. (1954). Cytology of bacteria. Part I. The bacterial cell. *Ann. Rev. Microbiol.* **8**, 1.

MUDD, S., BRODIE, A. F., WINTERSCHEID, L. C., HARTMAN, P. E., BEUTNER, E. H. & McLEAN, R. A. (1951). Further evidence of the existence of mitochondria in bacteria. *J. Bact.* **62**, 729.

MURRAY, R. G. E. (1953). The problems of fixation for studies of bacterial nuclei. *Bacterial Cytology, Symp. 6th Congr. int. Microbiol., Rome* p. 136.

NOVIKOFF, A. B. (1955). Histochemical and cytochemical staining methods. In *Analytical Cytology.* Editor, R. C. Mellors. New York: McGraw-Hill.

PEARSE, A. G. E. (1953). *Histochemistry, Theoretical and Applied.* Boston: Little, Brown & Company.

REICHARD, P. (1955). Biosynthesis of purines and pyrimidines. In *The Nucleic Acids,* vol. 2, chapter 23, p. 277. Editors, E. Chargaff and J. Davidson. New York: Academic Press.

ROBINOW, C. F. & HANNAY, C. L. (1953). The nuclear structures of *Bacillus megaterium. 6th Congr. int. Microbiol.,* Abstracts, vol. 1, Abstract no. 44, p. 76.

ROGERS, L. A. & GREENBANK, G. R. (1930). The intermittent growth of bacterial cultures. *J. Bact.* **19**, 181.

SCHAECHTER, M., TREECE, E. L. & DeLAMATER, E. D. (1954). Studies on the cytochemistry of alkaline phosphatase in various bacteria. *Exp. Cell Res.* **6**, 361.

SCHERBAUM, O. & ZEUTHEN, E. (1954). Induction of synchronized cell division in mass cultures of *Tetrahymena pyriformis. Exp. Cell Res.* **6**, 221.

SCHLENK, F. (1955). Biosynthesis of nucleosides and nucleotides. In *The Nucleic Acids,* vol. 2, chapter 24, p. 309. Editors, E. Chargaff and J. Davidson. New York: Academic Press.

SEIBERT, F. B. (1940). Removal of the impurities, nucleic acid and polysaccharide, from tuberculin protein. *J. biol. Chem.* **133**, 593.

SHERMAN, J. M. & CAMERON, G. M. (1934). Lethal environmental factors within the natural range of growth. *J. Bact.* **27**, 341.

SPIEGELMAN, S. & LANDMAN, O. E. (1954). Genetics of microorganisms. *Ann. Rev. Microbiol.* **8**, 181.

WEBB, J. M. & LEVY, H. B. (1955). A sensitive method for the determination of desoxyribose nucleic acid in tissues and microorganisms. *J. biol. Chem.* **213**, 107.

WEIBULL, C. (1953). Characterization of the protoplasmic constituents of *Bacillus megaterium*. *J. Bact.* **66**, 696.

WIDRA, A. (1955). Studies on the cytochemistry of bacteria. *J. Bact.* (in the Press).

ZEUTHEN, E. & SCHERBAUM, O. (1954). Synchronous divisions in mass cultures of the ciliate protozoan *Tetrahymena pyriformis*, as induced by temperature changes. In *Recent Developments in Cell Physiology*. Editor, J. A. Kitching. London: Butterworth.

EXPLANATION OF PLATES

PLATE 1. *Bacillus megaterium*

Figs. 1–8 and 14–20. Stained with azure A-SO₂. Figs. 1–8. Magnification, × 3200; Figs. 9–20. Magnification, × 4500. Figs. 1–8 demonstrate the stages in mitosis in untreated cells.

Fig. 1. Prophase. Third nucleus from the top shows three contracting rod-like chromosomes.

Fig. 2. Prometaphase. Upper nucleus shows densely clustered chromosomes lying opposite a single centriole. The area of the spindle is suggested.

Fig. 3. Metaphase. Upper nucleus shows the three chromosomes in a polar view of the metaphase plate. The adjacent nucleus shows a lateral view of a metaphase spindle with the chromosomes lying between the two polar centrioles.

Fig. 4. Anaphase. Second nucleus from the bottom shows daughter chromosomes separating to the poles. The centrioles are visible. The chromosomes are about one-half the size seen at metaphase.

Fig. 5. Telophase. The daughter nuclei have completely separated and are beginning to reorganize. In the second nucleus from the top the three chromosomes can be seen.

Figs. 6, 7. Interphase. The nuclei are swelling. The chromosomes are re-elongating. The nuclear membrane can be seen.

Fig. 8. Interphase. Chromosomes appear as long beaded threads.

Figs. 9, 10. *B. megaterium* showing periodic-acid-Schiff (PAS) reaction for acid muco-polysaccharide (see Table 1 for details). Fig. 9. Young cell. Area of cross walls stains sharply. Fig. 10. Cell 4 hr. old, showing dense polar masses of PAS-staining material in two adjacent cells.

Figs. 11–13. Cells stained for soluble fat (Sudan B). Fig. 11 shows young cells still attached to spore coat. They contain no fat. Fig. 12. One-hour-old cells with sparse droplets of fat.

Fig. 13. Five-hour-old cells showing dense accumulations of sudanophilic material.

Figs. 14–20 show effects on the nucleus of chilling active cells. These cells were grown on nutrient agar and chilled in icebox.

Fig. 14. Upper nucleus in lower cell shows mid-prophase with three chromosomes as bars.

Fig. 15. Second nucleus from top shows prometaphase with chromosomes densely clumped opposite a single centriole.

Fig. 16. Arrested metaphase with four centrioles visible.

Fig. 17. Uppermost nuclei in each figure in metaphase. Clumped chromosomes lie between centrioles.

Fig. 18. Arrested anaphases. Four of the nuclei show doubling of the centrioles at one pole.

Fig. 19. Arrested late anaphases showing membrane stretched, suggesting its continuity through the mitotic cycle.

Fig. 20. Two nuclei in right-hand cell in anaphase. Upper shows pulled-out membrane.

PLATE 2. *Bacillus megaterium*

Figs. 1–25. Stained with azure A-SO₂. Figs. 1–10 show normal stages in mitotic cycle.

Fig. 1. Early prophase; contracting chromosomes within distinct membrane.

Fig. 2. Later prophase chromosomes, dense contracting rods.

Figs. 3, 4. Shows three discrete rod-like chromosomes. The satellite is shown on the long right-hand chromosome in fig. 4.

Fig. 5. Prometaphase. Chromosomes clumped opposite single centriole with single spindle element.

Fig. 6. Metaphase. Two of three chromosomes in focus between two centrioles.

Figs. 7–9. Early and middle anaphase stages. Centrioles and spindles clearly shown.

Fig. 10. Telophase reorganization.

Figs. 11–25 demonstrate the effects of terramycin, aureomycin, neomycin and para-amino-salicylic acid. Figs. 11–20 show the effects of terramycin.

Fig. 11. Upper nucleus in prometaphase with dense chromosomes opposite a single centriole. Lower nucleus shows arrested metaphase.

Figs. 12–14 demonstrate arrest of migration of centrioles to the poles.

Figs. 15 and 16 show arrested metaphase stages. Centrioles much enlarged and dense. Dense masses of chromosomes lie between.

Figs. 17–20. Arrested anaphase stages.

Fig. 17. In left-hand cells are shown continued multiplication of chromosomes and persistence of nuclear membrane.

Fig. 20 shows division of centriole at the lower pole.

Fig. 21. Demonstrates similar effects produced by neomycin. Arrested anaphase stages. Left-hand nucleus shows centrioles, the upper with a clear area between it and the dense chromosomes. The middle nucleus shows the division of the lower centriole and the much enlarged upper centriole.

Fig. 22. Arrested anaphase. Both centrioles have divided, but remain connected by a delicate filament.

Figs. 23–25 show effect of *para*-aminosalicyclic acid.

Figs. 23 and 24 demonstrate the characteristic arrest of the centriole in prometaphase, producing the characteristic unipolar figures. The centrioles appear to be attached to the nuclear membrane.

Fig. 25 shows the division of the centriole into two and their attachment to the nuclear membrane.

Figs. 26 and 27 show *B. megaterium* stained for —SH protein. The delicate but definite staining of the chromosomes, the centrioles and the spindle can be seen in each figure.

(Some of these illustrations are reprinted with permission from the *American Journal of Syphilis, Gonorrhea and Venereal Diseases*, 1954, **38**, 593.)

PLATE 1

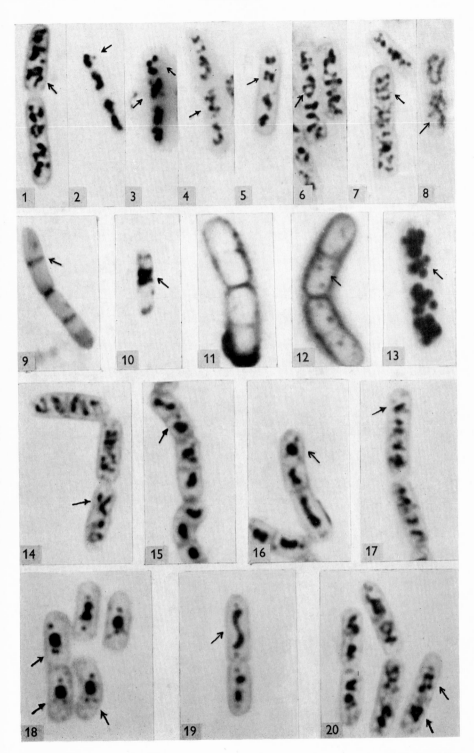

(*Facing p.* 260)

PLATE 2

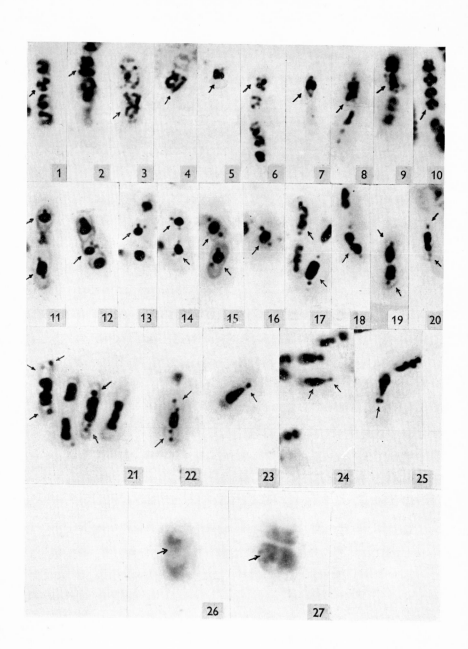

ON THE ORGANIZATION OF THE 'NUCLEAR MATERIAL' IN *SALMONELLA TYPHIMURIUM*

O. MAALØE AND A. BIRCH-ANDERSEN

Statens Seruminstitut, Copenhagen

Few biologists, if any, seriously doubt that bacteria, despite their small size, possess organs which function more or less as do the nuclei of cells of higher organisms. Several ingenious staining methods have been devised in order to reveal the number and the shape of the 'nuclear sites' in bacteria, which of course are small and difficult objects to study by means of the light microscope. At this Symposium cytologists with great experience in this province of bacteriology will present new developments in this direction.

It would seem that recent discoveries, especially in the fields of bacterial genetics and virology, call for an attempt to study the structure and organization of the nuclear apparatus of the bacterial cell in more detail than can be done by light microscopy. First, the rapid development of bacterial genetics during the past ten years has made it clear that the 'nuclear material' in bacteria behaves in several ways like the chromosomes of higher organisms (Lederberg, 1947). Secondly, it has been learned that, in addition to a more or less conventional genetic exchange mechanism which requires direct contact or pairing between bacterial cells, at least two unorthodox 'mechanisms', known as transformation and transduction, operate in bacteria (Griffith, 1928; Zinder & Lederberg, 1952). In these studies cytologists have been left far behind, as evidenced by the fact that very little is known about the size and shape of the structures which are involved in nuclear division and in genetic exchange in bacteria.

This lack of cytological information is, of course, due chiefly to technical difficulties, and it is not easy to foresee just how far cytological studies of the submicroscopic structures in bacteria can be pushed. It may be worth while, however, to recall that cytology proved an extremely useful tool for the advancement of genetic concepts in higher organisms. In *Drosophila* and in maize microscopic differentiation of the chromosomes has been successfully correlated with genetic evidence. This agreement between cytological and genetic data is most often made use of to support certain interpretations of genetic experiments; at the same time, however, it should be taken as evidence that cells can be fixed and stained in such a manner as to preserve the organization of the genetic material of the nucleus. In fact, only if this condition is fulfilled *and* if the genetic concepts are correct, can the close agreement between cytological and genetic observations be explained.

The experiments in bacterial genetics cited above have yielded very important information about the chemical nature of the material which carries and transfers the genetic determinants. Thus work on the transforming principle and on bacteriophages indicates that pure deoxyribose nucleic acid (DNA) can function in this way, and that the genetic differentiation of the DNA molecule is linear; i.e. that the essential element of the 'bacterial chromosome' may be considered to be a long thread-like DNA molecule carrying the genetic code in much the same way as an inscription on a tape. This suggestive picture has led to intensive studies of the structure of the DNA molecule by physical means, and it is now believed that this molecule consists of a cylindrical double-helix with a diameter of about 25A. (Watson & Crick, 1953). Clearly, most of this knowledge about the nuclear material of bacteria has been obtained by inference rather than by direct observation on the cell, and it may legitimately be asked whether cytology can be expected to contribute anything new at this level of investigation. It is evident that questions concerning the function or duplication of individual DNA threads cannot now be tackled by cytologists. However, the amount of DNA in, for example, a *Salmonella typhimurium* cell (Lark & Maaløe, 1956) corresponds to a thread almost one thousand times the length of the cell, and it is therefore reasonable to expect some kind of spatial organization of this material. If one or a few DNA threads of considerable length are coiled up in a regular manner within the nuclear site of a cell they should be quite easy to observe on electron micrographs of thin sections.

It is obvious that a search for nuclear structures in an *Escherichia coli* or *Salmonella typhimurium* cell is much more difficult than is a study of the large chromosomes of, for example, *Drosophila* and maize, which, individually, are much bigger than our bacteria. However, these bacteria have certain advantages from the experimental point of view; such events as the uptake by a bacterial nucleus of genetic material donated by another cell, or carried by a phage particle, can be brought about in a controlled manner, as can nuclear division. Despite the technical difficulties one may therefore try by means of electron microscopy to identify the structures in the bacterial cell which are involved in these processes.

This paper does not pretend to furnish much of the evidence on which a correspondence between bacterial cytology and genetics may eventually be established. It should be considered an early progress report, and it may be convenient, therefore, first to define the problems involved in a study of the organization of the nuclear material in bacteria.

(I) The first problem obviously is to obtain high resolution which means that at least part of the study must be done by means of electron microscopy of thin sections of cells. Several workers have described how these techniques may be adapted to work with bacteria (Birch-Andersen, Maaløe & Sjöstrand, 1953; Chapman & Hillier, 1953; Bradfield, 1954; Brieger & Glauert, 1954).

(II) The second problem is that of detecting artifacts produced during fixation, dehydration and embedding of biological material for sectioning and microscopy.

(III) The third and final problem to be dealt with is the identification, functional as well as chemical, of the structures revealed by the electron microscope.

In the following we shall discuss these different aspects in separate sections.

I. PROBLEMS CONNECTED WITH ELECTRON MICROSCOPY OF PREPARATIONS OF ORGANIC MATERIAL

The technique adopted for obtaining high-resolution electron micrographs of sections of bacteria has been described in detail by Birch-Andersen *et al.* (1953). Unless otherwise stated that technique has been used throughout this work, except that electron microscopy has been carried out with a Philips EM 100 electron microscope equipped with the new 25 A. lens.

The interpretation of the electron micrographs obtained will be discussed in § III of this paper. However, a few remarks on the difference between micrographs obtained with the light and the electron microscope respectively will be made here. Hillier (1950) has described the essential differences between the two microscopes, and Low (1953) has discussed in detail the difficulties met with when comparing light and electron micrographs of sections of tissue. For details and references the reader is referred to Low's paper, only some essential points being discussed below.

In electron microscopy the depth of field is generally about 1μ (Zworykin *et al.* 1945; Cosslett, 1951) compared with 0.2μ in the light microscope. The practical limit of resolution for ultra-thin sections with the embedding medium left in is at present 20–50 A. (Sjöstrand, 1953a;

Sjöstrand & Rhodin, 1953; Rhodin, 1954; and others), whereas the limit for light microscopy is about 2000A. The problems created by the relatively enormous depth of field in the electron microscope are aptly described by Low: 'A light micrograph is best interpreted as a plane surface without discernible thickness. But an electron micrograph may conveniently be compared to an X-ray photograph in which structures are superimposed on one another in mixed degrees of silhouette and translucency.'

The possibility of obtaining high-resolution electron micrographs is thus linked to the construction of microtomes producing extremely thin sections in which the superposition effect does not blur the picture (Sjöstrand, 1953b; Porter & Blum, 1953; and others). This means that only a very restricted part of a bacterial cell is viewed in any single section, and the integrated picture of the cell is lost. With sections 200–400A. in thickness only about 2% of the total volume of a *Salmonella typhimurium* or *Escherichia coli* cell is observed at once. Thus the size and shape of, for example, the nuclear vacuoles of the cells are found to vary considerably from section to section depending both on the position of the sections within the cell and the angle at which the cell has been sectioned. The only manner in which these difficulties can be overcome is by studying serial sections of the cells. Gay & Anderson (1954) have presented a series of 18–19 individual sections of *Drosophila* salivary gland cells, and by means of serial sections and a special composite picture technique we have recently shown that the 'vacuoles' seen in sections of *S. typhimurium* cells correspond closely to the dark regions in cells stained for DNA (Birch-Andersen, 1955).

The Palade technique, introducing buffered osmic acid solutions as fixing and staining agents for electron microscopy of sectioned material, has been generally accepted as giving excellent preservation of ultra-structures (Palade, 1952; Sjöstrand, 1953a; Rhodin, 1954; and others). The fixation of biological material has been discussed by Porter & Kallman (1953) and further studied by Bahr (1954). The electron-scattering power of osmium atoms (atomic number 76) is very much greater than that of the atoms of the biological material and the embedding substance (according to Bahr (1954) the average atomic number for the latter substances is 18). These figures led Bahr to assume that in thin sections the distribution of osmium taken up by the biological material is solely responsible for the contrast obtained, and he demonstrated that proteins and fats reduce OsO_4, whereas carbohydrates and pure preparations of nucleic acids are inert towards this agent. Contrary to Bahr's assumption we find that reasonably good contrast is obtained in thin sections of formaldehyde-fixed bacteria which have *not* subsequently been stained with OsO_4 (Pl. 1, fig. 2). Considering that the embedding material used contains no atoms heavier than oxygen, we must conclude that phosphorus and sulphur atoms, and perhaps the ions of the common metals, produce most of the contrast obtained in electron micrographs of sections of bacteria.

This observation is in accordance with data presented by Afzelius (personal communication), who studied the effects of different fixatives on the structures observed by electron microscopy of sections of sea-urchin eggs. Using OsO_4, formaldehyde, uranyl nitrate and methyl mercurichloride (according to Bahr & Moberger (1954) the latter compound specifically stains SH-groups) he obtained good contrast; moreover, the structures observed in the different cases were alike. A discussion of the chemical nature of some of the structures observed in sections of *Salmonella typhimurium* cells follows in § III of this paper.

II. PROBLEMS CONNECTED WITH FIXATION, DEHYDRATION AND EMBEDDING

Cytological work carried out by means of the light microscope permits comparison to be made between observations on living cells and those made by means of selective staining methods. In electron microscopy of bacteria this important control is almost completely lost. All we can do is to ascertain that the large 'vacuoles' regularly observed on electron micrographs correspond roughly in size and location to the light areas which can be seen in living bacteria by means of the phase-contrast microscope (Hillier, Mudd & Smith, 1949; Murray, 1953). When dealing with the smaller elements disclosed by the electron microscope we have no direct means by which to ensure that the structures we observe are not artifacts. The importance of this limitation cannot be stressed too strongly, and we shall devote the main section of this paper to a presentation of work done recently to detect and eliminate some sources of artifacts.

Preparation of bacteria for sectioning is usually carried out in three steps: viz. fixation with OsO_4, dehydration in ethanol and embedding in methacrylate (MET). In our laboratory this method gave fairly good results from the point of view of preserving the cells and demonstrating vacuoles containing dense structures which were interpreted as DNA masses (Birch-Andersen *et al.* 1953). In an effort to control this method we have now varied these conditions. (Our routine procedure was to add OsO_4, dissolved in buffered saline, directly to the broth culture to a concentration of 0·2%, centrifuge, and resuspend the cells in one-tenth the original volume of a 1·0% OsO_4 solution and incubate this suspension for 2 hr. at 37°. After careful washing the cells were dehydrated in 70, 96 and 100% ethanol and passed through three changes of a mixture of 1 part methyl and 9 parts N-butyl-methacrylate containing 1% benzoyl-peroxide.) With the light microscope the cells were examined at all stages between logarithmic growth in broth and the final suspension in liquid MET and, irrespective of the method of fixation (OsO_4 in concentrations between 0·1 and 1·0%, formalin in concentrations between 0·5 and 4%, or ethanol 70%), the cells were found to be unchanged up to this stage. It soon became clear, however, that the fixation procedure was of decisive importance for the fate of these cells during polymerization of the MET. From the polymerized block of MET a small piece was cut, placed in a drop of chloroform, to dissolve the MET, and stained with methyl violet (dissolved in chloroform). The liberated cells stain well, and in this way it was easy to observe whether the fixed cells had suffered gross damage during the polymerization process.

It was found that fixation for 2 hr. in broth with a low concentration of OsO_4 (0·1 or 0·2%) or for short times at a higher concentration (1% OsO_4 for about 10 min.), gave cells the majority of which were blown up to large ghost-like bodies and badly torn (see Pl. 1, fig. 1), while some cells had obviously collapsed. More intense fixation with OsO_4 or formaldehyde prevents the gross distortions, but many cells show a characteristic swelling of the vacuole regions with the result that the whole cell looks like a dumbbell (see Pl. 1, fig. 2). Our routine two-step fixation procedure preserves the cells relatively well, presumably because the broth is removed before the main fixation period (see summary on p. 270). Prepolymerization of the MET as described, for example, by Borysko & Sapranauskas (1954) likewise helps a great deal to prevent the distortions, without, however, eliminating them altogether. Fixation with formaldehyde gives similar results; using a high concentration of formaldehyde (2–4%) and embedding in prepolymerized MET the cells are relatively well preserved, but some obviously misshaped cells are seen. On the whole the fixation conditions can be classified according to their efficiency in making the cells resistant to the stresses they are exposed to during the polymerization of the MET; fixation with 1% OsO_4 for very long times at 37° (10–12 hr.) is most efficient, but such prolonged fixation causes shrinkage of the cells (see summary on p. 269).

When sections of cells fixed in these different ways are examined in the electron microscope it becomes clear that even cells that look normal in the stained preparations may show slight but obvious damage. The signs of damage are looseness of the outer cell membrane (which in extreme cases 'flutters' away from the cell remaining attached only in spots; Maaløe, Birch-Andersen & Sjöstrand, 1954) and irregular fissures in the otherwise regular pattern of the cytoplasm.

It is not a new observation that the polymerization process may cause disorganization of MET-embedded material. Borysko & Sapranauskas (1954) thus report that certain tissue preparations are completely disrupted if embedding is started in liquid rather than prepolymerized and highly viscous MET; and Chapman & Hillier (1953) found it necessary to fix bacteria very intensively (1 % OsO_4 for about 20 hr.) to prevent laceration of the cells. The significant part of our observations on MET-embedded cells is that a gradual transition between gross distortions and the slighter anomalies has been registered. By extension, this indicates that the finer cell structures cannot be considered *not* to have been disorganized even where no obvious signs of damage are seen. This reasoning applies in particular to the dark elements found inside the vacuoles, which we have described as irregularly coiled, solid strings, built, in part at least, of DNA (Birch-Andersen *et al.* 1953). In torn or in ghost-like cells these inner structures may look like solid strings, but more often they appear as an irregular web of thinner threads. This pattern is sometimes seen in cells with none of the obvious signs of damage, which indicates that the organization of these inner structures may be very sensitive to disturbances during preparation.

The reasons why polymerizing MET may cause disruption or collapse of embedded cells are to be sought in the great sensitivity of the catalytic process of hardening to impurities and in the fact that polymerization is accompanied by a considerable shrinkage (10–20 % reduction of the volume, depending on the composition of the mixture of methyl and butyl esters). The polymerization process is probably initiated in many different centres, thereby producing both mechanical and osmotic stresses. The very cells which we want to embed may accelerate or inhibit the polymerization process locally and thus contribute to the heterogeneity of the process.

From what has been said about the results obtained by sectioning bacteria embedded in MET and about the properties of this material it seems obvious that a different substance should be tried. Ideally this substance should have the low viscosity of the monomers of methyl- and butyl-methacrylate and the low electron-scattering capacity of the polymers, and at the same time it should harden in a homogeneous manner and without changing its volume. The material we have tried only satisfies the latter requirements; it is a highly viscous epoxy compound (EPO) which on addition of diethylene triamine and heating to about 60° hardens, without changing its volume, to form a light yellow resin-like block (Birch-Andersen, Maaløe & Sundien, unpublished). The hardening process is a homogeneous chemical reaction between the EPO and the amine, which is not influenced by impurities (as indicated by the fact that the reaction always proceeds in the same manner, whereas MET polymerization frequently fails completely in one or more of a series of apparently identical tubes). Since EPO seems not to have been tried before, a description of our embedding procedure follows.

The *Salmonella typhimurium* cells are fixed directly in the growth medium, washed and dehydrated in ethanol as usual. The final suspension in ethanol is centrifuged and the pellet suspended in a mixture of 2 parts of EPO and 1 part of ethanol. These two phases do not mix readily on shaking, but by means of a stirring rod a homogeneous mixture of relatively low viscosity is easily obtained. After about 30 min. the amine is added (the volume ratio between EPO and the amine always being 10:1), and the suspension centrifuged for about 15 min. at 8000 r.p.m. in a Servall angle centrifuge. The supernatant is carefully removed by siphoning and the pellet stirred up in a small volume of EPO + ethanol + amine (in the ratios 10:2·5:1). This rather viscous suspension is transferred to small gelatine capsules which are immediately spun for 20–30 min. in a horizontal centrifuge. Again the supernatant is siphoned off and the capsules are refilled with EPO + amine and incubated at 60° for at least 3–4 hr. It is important that the pellets in the capsules be not more than 1–2 mm. thick, otherwise the ethanol remaining with the sedimented bacteria will prevent fusion of the two layers and the tip of the block will be too soft. It may be added that microscopy of bacteria suspended in EPO is very difficult because the refractive index of this compound is very close to that of the cells. Also, the hardened EPO is hardly soluble in chloroform, ethanol or acetone, which makes it difficult to control on the embedded cells microscopically as described above.

Electron micrographs of sections of cells embedded in EPO show less contrast between the cells and the background than is found in MET preparations. The electron-scattering capacity of the EPO is somewhat greater than that of MET, although both compounds contain carbon, hydrogen and oxygen atoms only. This difference may be due to the presence in EPO of benzene rings. However, the loss of contrast does not affect the resolution perceptibly. In good micrographs of thin sections the resolution is between 25 and 50 A., whether embedding is carried out in MET or in EPO (compare Pl. 1, fig. 3 and Pl. 2, fig. 6).

Sections of cells embedded in EPO first of all show that the cells retain their size and shape, almost independently of the fixation procedure. This does not mean that the change from MET to EPO is a miracle, in the sense that the cells now present the same detailed picture under all conditions of fixation; the change is, however, a definite improvement in that *cells fixed with an appropriate concentration of* OsO_4 *and embedded in EPO are consistently free of any of the obvious signs of damage described above.* In particular, the outer membrane always remains uniformly and smoothly attached and the cytoplasm is free of fissures.

In the EPO-embedded specimens the 'nuclear' structures inside the vacuoles show very characteristic features; instead of the usual picture of long, solid strings or web-like structures, *a regular organization of this 'nuclear material' into round, winding tubes is observed in all the cells* (see Pl. 2, fig. 6). This orderly configuration has been observed occasionally in MET-embedded specimens as well; but only once, in a preparation fixed with 1% OsO_4 for 2 hr. at 37°, did many of the cells show this configuration (Pl. 1, fig. 3). In the fixed and dehydrated state the tubes are hollow and relatively impermeable structures, as shown by the fact that the viscous EPO often fails to diffuse into a tube (see Pl. 2, fig. 6).

We may now, by comparing results obtained with MET and with EPO respectively, estimate to what extent different methods of preparation preserve the size and shape of the cells and the smooth attachment of the outer membrane. In the following summary, in all cases fixation was initiated by mixing broth cultures of exponentially growing *Salmonella typhimurium* cells with the fixing agent:

A. *Fixation with constant concentrations of* OsO_4 *at* 37°

1. 1% *for c.* 20 *hr.*; *MET-embedding.* All cells considerably, and uniformly, shrunk. Membranes folded accordingly. Precipitation of intensely scattering grains (metallic osmium?) on the membranes and inside the cells.

2. i. 1% *for* 2 *hr.*; *MET-embedding.* Varying proportions of cells of normal size and regular shape (some batches of MET have yielded better results than others); always some grossly misshaped cells. Membranes sometimes folded or loose. (Occasionally tubular structures in the vacuoles (see Pl. 1, fig. 3), but mostly solid strings or webs.)

2. ii. 1% *for* 2 *hr.*; *EPO-embedding.* The optimal combination of fixation and embedding (see Pl. 2, fig. 6).

3. 1% *for* 10–15 *min.*; *MET-embedding.* All cells moderately or greatly enlarged and torn (see Pl. 1, fig. 1).

4. i. *0·2% for 2 hr.; MET-embedding*. All cells greatly enlarged and torn.

4. ii. *0·2% for 2 hr.; EPO-embedding*. Strikingly different from 4. i; all cells whole but uniformly shrunk, membranes folded accordingly. (Cytoplasm and vacuole contents irregular, thready—as if partly dissolved.)

B. *Initial fixation with* OsO_4, *broth removed by centrifugation before continued fixation with* OsO_4 *at* 37°.

1. i. *0·2% for 10–15 min. at room temperature→1% for 2 hr. at 37°; MET-embedding*. The early removal of the broth tends to prevent damage during embedding; the improvement is noticeable even using 1% OsO_4 in both fixation steps. Always some puffed-up cells and loose membranes. (Tubular structures in vacuoles rare.)

1. ii. *Same fixation; EPO-embedding*. Whole cells of normal size with smoothly attached membranes. (Tubular structures present but less regular than in A. 2. ii; compare Pl. 2, figs. 5 and 6.)

2. *0·2% for 2 hr. at 37°→1% for 2 hr. at 37°; EPO-embedding*. Whole cells of normal size with smoothly attached membranes. (Most cells contain irregular threads instead of tubular structures in the vacuoles; see Pl. 2, fig. 4.)

C. *Fixation with formaldehyde at* 37°

1. *0·5% for 2 hr.; MET-embedding*. Faint shadows of shrunken cells. Membranes invisible.

2. *0·5% for 2 hr., after-fixation for 2 hr. with 1% OsO_4 at 37°; MET-embedding*. Most cells puffed up, but cellular elements much better preserved than in C. 1. Membranes almost completely loosened.

3. i. *2 or 4% formaldehyde for 2 hr.; MET-embedding*. Many dumbbell cells, some further enlarged. Membranes almost completely loosened (see Pl. 1, fig. 2).

3. ii. *Same fixation; EPO-embedding*. No swelling of cells. Membranes loose.

Note. In cases A.2.i, A.4.i, C.3.i, the cells were embedded in liquid as well as in prepolymerized MET (Borysko & Sapranauskas, 1954); prepolymerization always improved results, but without eliminating distortions. In case C formaldehyde fixation (concentrations ⩾ 2%) gave almost as good contrast as did OsO_4 fixation (compare Pl. 1, figs. 2, 3); the degree of preservation, as judged by the regularity of cytoplasmic and 'nuclear' patterns and the attachment of the outer membrane, was always less than in the best OsO_4-fixed preparations.

In a discussion of these findings we may consider separately the three phases of the process by which the cells are prepared for sectioning, viz. the fixation proper, the dehydration and the embedding.

Fixation may be obviously insufficient from the point of view of preserving the maximum degree of orderly organization of the different cell elements. Thus low concentrations of OsO_4 or of formaldehyde (A. 4, B. 2 and C. 1) yield disorganized pictures irrespective of subsequent treatment. In this connexion it may be mentioned that the efficiency of OsO_4 fixation is very dependent on the ionic environment. If a culture grown in broth diluted 1:5 with distilled water is fixed with OsO_4 dissolved in distilled water, the result is poorer than if fixation occurs in undiluted broth (viz. loosely fitting membranes, fissures in the cytoplasm and, when embedding in EPO, less regular tubular structures). Fixation at low salt concentration is probably poor because the reaction between OsO_4 and organic matter is very slow, as may be inferred from the observation that the usual dark colouring of the broth upon addition of OsO_4 is faint and occurs late when the ionic strength of the solution is reduced. A more thorough study of this reaction is now being carried out by Murray & Whitfield (personal communication). As will appear from sections A and B of the above summary, it is only after rather long exposures to high concentrations of OsO_4 that the cells can be carried through to sectioning and microscopy without obvious signs of disorganization.

Concerning dehydration, our data show that this process, like MET-embedding, is tolerated only after relatively intense fixation. Thus a comparison between A. 2. ii and B. 2 shows that after fixation for 2 hr. with 0.2% OsO_4, some disorganization had occurred. On the other hand, if cells fixed for 2 hr. at 0.2% OsO_4 were exposed directly to ethanol, *without* after-fixation with 1% OsO_4, disorganization proceeded further, to the A. 4. ii stage. The same was observed after fixation with a low concentration of formaldehyde as may be seen by comparing C. 1 with C. 2.

Finally, with respect to the embedding process, we may refer to the detailed discussion on pp. 269–71 of the results obtained with MET and EPO respectively.

The situation as it appears after these pilot experiments is not encouraging. Clearly it is difficult to steer a bacterial cell all the way from the culture to the embedded state without incurring obvious damage. The worst is, however, that we cannot judge whether the finer detail, such as the nuclear structures, about which no *a priori* judgement can be made, are faithfully reproduced. As already mentioned we have no means by which to study structures of this dimension in the living cell.

When it is considered that embedding in EPO gives micrographs in which the cells show no recognizable signs of damage, it may be safe to assume that the tubular structures seen in such preparations represent the state of the nuclear material *after* fixation with OsO_4. It is easy to visualize how these structures may collapse to form solid strings or be torn to form the irregular webs often found in sections of MET-embedded cells. On the other hand, from the micrographs it is impossible to decide whether fixation with OsO_4 may have caused dispersed elements to coil up to form the tubular structures. We shall return to this question in the last section when discussing ways in which a decision may eventually be reached.

III. INTERPRETATION OF THE STRUCTURES REVEALED BY THE ELECTRON MICROSCOPE

To make good electron micrographs of bacteria, as of all other biological specimens, remains a technical achievement with merits of its own, until the structures seen in the pictures have been interpreted biologically. Ideally, this interpretation should lead to chemical as well as functional identification of the cell structures.

In the present study we have focused attention on the organization of the dark structures seen in the 'vacuoles', and we have freely referred to these structures as 'nuclear material'. The justification for this interpretation is chiefly derived from cyto-chemical observations. First, studies of the nuclei of higher organisms have led to the identification of 'nuclear material' with structures containing DNA (see, for example, Ris & Mirsky, 1949); secondly, we know that bacteria stained selectively for DNA take stain in the areas which correspond to the light areas, or vacuoles, observed in the living cells (Hillier *et al.* 1949; Murray, 1953). Thus it seems that most of the DNA is to be found somewhere in these areas. Next we want to know what DNA will look like in an electron micrograph. We have sought an answer to this question by sectioning purified bacteriophage (the coli-phage T4) after fixation and embedding in MET (Maaløe *et al.* 1954). These phage particles consist of protein shells enclosing large amounts of DNA, which makes them an ideal object for the cytological characterization of this material. Sections of the OsO_4-fixed T4 particles showed a very electron-dense hexagonal core which corresponded to the inner zone of the phage particle, the size and shape of which may be estimated from electron micrographs of whole phage particles prepared by means of the critical point method (Anderson, 1951). It can therefore be concluded that aggregates of DNA are objects which appear dark in electron micrographs. In bacteria fixed by OsO_4 or by formaldehyde the vacuoles contain dark structures and we believe that they represent the DNA which, by selective staining methods, has been located to these regions. (In this connexion it is unimportant that the dark material shows different degrees of organization according to the fixation and embedding procedures employed.)

Further support for this assumption can be derived from experiments in which *Escherichia coli* cells were infected with T4 bacteriophage (Maaløe *et al.* 1954). In sections of cells fixed 8 min. after infection it was found that most of the compact dark material was distributed in small peripheral vacuoles; this distribution of the material which we assume is DNA agrees with observations on selectively stained cells (Murray, Gillen & Heagy, 1950; Luria & Human, 1950). Thus under various conditions and in various bacteria, material which, in part at least, may be DNA is found inside seemingly 'empty' regions, or vacuoles, the overall density of which is less than that of the surrounding structures (Birch-Andersen *et al.* 1953; Chapman & Hillier, 1953; Bradfield, 1954; Kellenberger & Ryter, personal communication). As pointed out earlier no well-defined membrane is seen separating the vacuoles from the cytoplasm (Birch-Andersen *et al.* 1953); the improved embedding technique described in this paper has not changed this situation, and it still looks as if the bacterial vacuoles lack one of the most characteristic features of the nuclei of higher organisms.

The conclusion that accumulations of DNA appear dark in electron micrographs should be considered in conjunction with previous statements about the electron-scattering properties of organic material (see pp. 264, 265). Since fixation with formaldehyde provides relatively good contrast it is obvious that the uptake by the cells of osmium atoms during fixation with OsO_4 is *not* a prerequisite for obtaining contrast between the cell structure and the embedding material. Indeed, the difference between the contrast obtained after fixation with formaldehyde and OsO_4 respectively is so slight that we may conclude that very little Os remains fixed in the cells (see Pl. 1, figs. 1, 2). If so, it is natural that DNA *per se* should give strong contrast, since it contains a high proportion of the relatively heavy phosphorus atoms (and possibly salt-bound metal ions) which, together with sulphur atoms, seem to produce most of the contrast found in organic material.

It should be recalled in this connexion that the reaction between OsO_4 and the main cell constituent seems to inhibit the bacterial enzymes completely without causing profound denaturation. This has been demonstrated by subjecting *Escherichia coli* cells, labelled with ^{32}P or ^{35}S, to enzymic treatment (Birch-Andersen *et al.* 1953). First it was found that after washing the cells free of medium activity and fixing with OsO_4 no activity was lost during further washing at room temperature, carried out to remove the OsO_4. Secondly, it was seen that samples treated with highly purified preparations of trypsin, deoxyribonuclease or ribonuclease liberated large amounts of ^{35}S and ^{32}P respectively. In a qualitative way this experiment shows that fixation with OsO_4 effectively prevents autolysis without destroying the proteins and the nucleic acids to such an extent that they cannot serve as substrates for the respective enzymes. Following the activity of the cells through the subsequent stages of preparation it was found that during treatment with 70% ethanol some 6–8 % of the ^{32}P activity was lost. This loss is probably due to phospholipids being dissolved in the ethanol. No further loss was observed during continued dehydration and treatment with the monomers of MET.

In the introduction it was mentioned that the amount of DNA in a *Salmonella typhimurium* cell (Lark & Maaløe, 1956) would make up a DNA molecule about one thousand times the length of the cell, and it was suggested that some kind of orderly arrangement of this material inside the cell might be expected. As a working hypothesis we suggest that the tubular structures observed in the vacuoles of OsO_4-fixed and EPO-embedded cells represent such an arrangement in which the thin, thread-like DNA molecule, itself helical in structure, is coiled up to form a second-order helix.* On this hypothesis the structure forming the tube must, of course, exhibit regular periodicity. However, the dimensions of the tubes and of the thread of which it may be composed are such that the required periodicity will be very difficult to observe. First, the elementary thread must have a diameter of 25–50A. (the DNA may be combined with protein, the diameter of the thread thus being more than the 25A. of the naked DNA helix), which means that the contrast will be very poor when the beam penetrates at a right angle to the axis of the thread. Secondly, when the beam passes tangentially through the tube good contrast is obtained but adjacent threads will only be separated if the angle between the axis of the tube and the beam is

---

* To avoid misunderstanding it may be mentioned that this 'second-order helix' is submicroscopic and therefore of a different order of magnitude from the coiled-up chromosomes in higher organisms (Ris & Mirsky, 1949). These large bodies might be imagined to be 'third-order helices'.

such that there is a free path for the beam between the threads. Thus, for steric reasons, periodicity in a structure of this kind can be expected to reveal itself only when a sectioned tube is viewed at a favourable angle. It remains to be seen to what extent the build of the tubes can be analysed.

In the micrographs the tubes present themselves sectioned at all angles. Their diameter, as measured on more or less circular cross-sections, is about 500A. and the thickness of the wall is of the order of 50A. A longitudinally sectioned tube sometimes presents a very uniform width over 4000–5000A. (see Pl. 2, fig. 6), which suggests that the tubes are all of the same dimension. The more irregular patterns frequently observed might be due to compression or ruptures during preparation. It should be mentioned that Bradfield (1954) has presented a section of a *Staphylococcus aureus* cell which shows structures very similar to our 'tubes'.

The last paragraphs of the preceding section stressed the difficulties encountered when trying to interpret the finer details observed in micrographs of sectioned bacteria. It was emphasized that a micrograph can at best reproduce, for example, the nuclear structures as they exist after fixation; the state of these structures in the living cell remains unknown. An obvious way out of this difficulty is to study cells in which a defined sequence of physiological or genetic events takes place in a synchronous manner, and to see if corresponding cytological changes can be observed. If so, we would know that the preparation of the cells for electron microscopy had not destroyed the *true* cytological pattern beyond recognition.

To achieve such experimental conditions we have recently developed a technique for inducing synchronous nuclear division in *Salmonella typhimurium* (Maaløe & Lark, 1954; Lark & Maaløe, 1954), and some cytological work, chiefly with staining methods, has been done on this system (Lark, Maaløe & Rostock, 1955). Attempts were made to carry out parallel studies by means of electron microscopy of serial sections of MET-embedded preparations. With our present knowledge it would seem to be a waste of time, however, to look for systematic changes in the rather disorganized nuclear structures which the micrographs of these preparations represent. All that these preliminary studies tell is that the shape of the nuclear vacuoles, as reconstructed from serial sections, may lead to an identification of the state of the nucleus with respect to division (Birch-Andersen, 1955).

New preparations will be made using the improved fixation and embedding methods, and we hope to decide whether the tubular structures

18-2

behave during nuclear division in a manner compatible with our assumption that they represent the bacterial chromosomes.

Bacteriophage experiments are another line of study which may yield information about the functional significance of these structures. In *Salmonella typhimurium* as in *Escherichia coli* the genetic aspects of lysogenization and transduction have been worked out very carefully, and it is well established that in both cases the material donated to the cell by the infecting phage particle becomes intimately associated with the bacterial nucleus (Lederberg & Lederberg, 1953; Appleyard, 1953; Stocker, Zinder & Lederberg, 1953; Bertani, personal communication). It may be possible to establish correspondence between these genetic events and cytological observations.

We wish to thank Mrs H. Ravn who has performed most of the sectioning. We are grateful also to Miss A.-G. Overgaard and to Mr O. Rostock for valuable assistance in carrying out the photographic and experimental parts of the work, respectively.

REFERENCES

ANDERSON, T. F. (1951). Technique for the preservation of three-dimensional structure in preparing specimens for the electron microscope. *Trans. N.Y. Acad. Sci.*, Series II, **13**, 130.

APPLEYARD, R. K. (1953). Segregation of Lambda lysogenicity during bacterial recombination in *E. coli*, K-12. *Cold Spr. Harb. Symp. quant. Biol.* **18**, 95.

BAHR, G. F. (1954). Osmium tetroxide and ruthenium tetroxide and their reactions with biologically important substances. *Exp. Cell Res.* **7**, 457.

BAHR, G. F. & MOBERGER, G. (1954). Methyl-mercuri-chloride as a specific reagent for sulphydryl groups. *Exp. Cell Res.* **6**, 506.

BIRCH-ANDERSEN, A. (1955). Reconstruction of the nuclear sites of *Salmonella typhimurium* from electron micrographs of serial sections. *J. gen. Microbiol.* **13**, 327.

BIRCH-ANDERSEN, A., MAALØE, O. & SJÖSTRAND, F. S. (1953). High resolution electron micrographs of sections of *E. coli*. *Biochim. biophys. Acta*, **12**, 395.

BORYSKO, E. & SAPRANAUSKAS, P. (1954). A new technique for comparative phase-contrast and electron microscope studies of cells grown in tissue culture with an evaluation of the technique by means of time-lapse cinemicrography. *Johns Hopk. Hosp. Bull.* **95**, 68.

BRADFIELD, J. R. G. (1954). Electron microscopic observations on bacterial nuclei. *Nature, Lond.*, **173**, 184.

BRIEGER, E. M. & GLAUERT, A. M. (1954). The demonstration of tubercle bacilli in ultra-thin sections of infected tissues by electron microscopy. *Tubercle, Chicago*, **35**, 80.

CHAPMAN, G. B. & HILLIER, J. (1953). Electron microscopy of ultra-thin sections of bacteria. I. Cellular division in *Bacillus cereus*. *J. Bact.* **66**, 362.

COSSLETT, V. E. (1951). *Practical electron microscopy*. New York: Academic Press.

GAY, H. & ANDERSON, T. F. (1954). Serial sections for electron microscopy. *Science*, **120**, 1071.

GRIFFITH, F. (1928). The significance of pneumococcal types. *J. Hyg., Camb.*, **27**, 113.

HILLIER, J. (1950). *Electron microscopy.* In *Biophysical Research Methods*, ed. by F. M. Uber. New York: Interscience Press.

HILLIER, J., MUDD, S. & SMITH, A. G. (1949). Internal structure and nuclei in cells of *Escherichia coli* as shown by improved electron microscopic techniques. *J. Bact.* **51**, 319.

LARK, K. G. & MAALØE, O. (1954). The induction of cellular and nuclear division in *Salmonella typhimurium* by means of temperature shifts. *Biochim. biophys. Acta*, **15**, 345.

LARK, K. G. & MAALØE, O. (1956). Nucleic acid synthesis and the division cycle of *Salmonella typhimurium. Biochim. biophys. Acta* (in the Press).

LARK, K. G., MAALØE, O. & ROSTOCK, O. (1955). Cytological studies of nuclear division in *Salmonella typhimurium. J. gen. Microbiol.* (in the Press).

LEDERBERG, J. (1947). Gene recombination and linked segregation in *Escherichia coli. Genetics*, **32**, 505.

LEDERBERG, J. & LEDERBERG, E. M. (1953). Genetic studies of lysogenicity in *Escherichia coli. Genetics*, **38**, 51.

LOW, F. N. (1953). The preliminary alveolar epithelium of laboratory mammals and man. *Anat. Rec.* **117**, 241.

LURIA, S. E. & HUMAN, M. L. (1950). Chromatin staining of bacteria during bacteriophage infection. *J. Bact.* **59**, 551.

MAALØE, & LARK, K. G. (1954). In *Recent Developments in Cell Physiology*, ed. Kitching, J. A. London: Butterworths.

MAALØE, O., BIRCH-ANDERSEN, A. & SJÖSTRAND, F. S. (1954). Electron micrographs of sections of *E. coli* cells infected with the bacteriophage T4. *Biochim. biophys. Acta*, **15**, 12.

MURRAY, R. G. E. (1953). The problem of fixation for studies of bacterial nuclei. *Bacterial Cytology, Symp. 6th Congr. int. Microbiol., Rome*, p. 136.

MURRAY, R. G. E., GILLEN, D. H. & HEAGY, F. C. (1950). Cytological changes in *Escherichia coli* produced by infection with phage T2. *J. Bact.*, **59**, 603.

PALADE, G. E. (1952). A study of fixation for electron microscopy. *J. exp. Med.* **95**, 285.

PORTER, K. R. & BLUM, J. (1953). A study in microtomy for electron microscopy. *Anat. Rec.* **117**, 685.

PORTER, K. R. & KALLMAN, F. (1953). The properties and effects of osmium tetroxide as a tissue fixative with special reference to its use for electron microscopy. *Exp. Cell Res.* **4**, 127.

RHODIN, J. (1954). Correlation of ultrastructural organization and function in normal and experimentally changed proximal convoluted tubule cells of the mouse kidney. Thesis. Stockholm: Aktiebolaget Godvil.

RIS, H. & MIRSKY, A. E. (1949). The state of the chromosomes in the interphase nucleus. *J. gen. Physiol.* **32**, 489.

SJÖSTRAND, F. S. (1953a). The ultrastructure of the outer segments of rods and cones of the eye as revealed by the electron microscope. *J. cell. comp. Phys.* **42**, 15.

SJÖSTRAND, F. S. (1953b). A new microtome for ultrathin sectioning for high resolution electron microscopy. *Experientia*, **9**, 114.

SJÖSTRAND, F. S. & RHODIN, J. (1953). The ultrastructure of the proximal convoluted tubules of the mouse kidney as revealed by high resolution electron microscopy. *Exp. Cell Res.* **4**, 426.

STOCKER, B. A. D., ZINDER, N. D. & LEDERBERG, J. (1953). Transduction of flagellar characters in *Salmonella. J. gen. Microbiol.* **9**, 410.

WATSON, J. D. & CRICK, F. H. C. (1953). Molecular structure of nucleic acids. *Nature, Lond.*, **171**, 737.

ZINDER, N. D. & LEDERBERG, J. (1952). Genetic exchange in *Salmonella. J. Bact.* **64**, 679.

ZWORYKIN, V. K. *et al.* (1945). *Electron Optics and the Electron Microscope.* New York: John Wiley and Sons.

EXPLANATION OF PLATES

PLATE 1. Methacrylate embedding

Fig. 1. Fixation with 1 % OsO₄ for 10–15 min. (see p. 269, A. 3). Magnification, 21,000. Note grossly enlarged and torn cells with a few compact strings of 'nuclear material'.

Fig. 2. Fixation with 2 % formaldehyde for 2 hr. at 37° (see p. 270, C. 3. i). Magnification, 21,000. Note swellings in the vacuole regions, loose membrane and web-like nuclear material. The contrast, in this case obtained *without* OsO₄, may be compared with that of figs. 1 and 3.

Fig. 3. Fixation with 1 % OsO₄ for 2 hr. at 37° (see p. 269, A. 2. i). Magnification, 42,000. Note whole cells with slightly folded membranes, together with part of a greatly enlarged cell. The tube-like nuclear structures present here are rare in MET-embedded cells.

PLATE 2. Epoxy-compound embedding

Fig. 4. Fixation with 0·2 % OsO₄ for 2 hr. at 37°, followed by 1 % for 2 hr. at 27° (see p. 270, B. 2). Magnification, 21,000. *No* obvious signs of damage to cells, membranes smoothly attached. Vacuoles contain web-like structures which should be compared with corresponding structures in figs. 5 and 6.

Fig. 5. Fixation with 0·2 % OsO₄ for *c.* 10 min. at room temperature, followed by 1 % for 2 hr. at 37° (see p. 270, B. l. ii). Magnification, 21,000. Vacuoles contain both tubular structures and a few 'webs'.

Fig. 6. Fixation with 1 % OsO₄ for 2 hr. at 37° (see p. 269, A. 2. ii). Magnification, 42,000. Size and shape of cells and the smooth membrane attachment may be compared with Pl. 1, fig. 3. Nearly all nuclear structures tubular; note examples of tubes into which the EPO has not diffused and of tubes exhibiting uniform width over long stretches.

PLATE 1

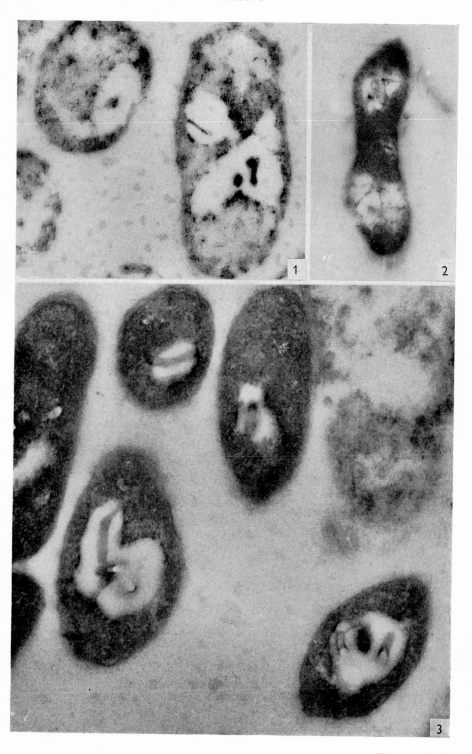

PLATE 2

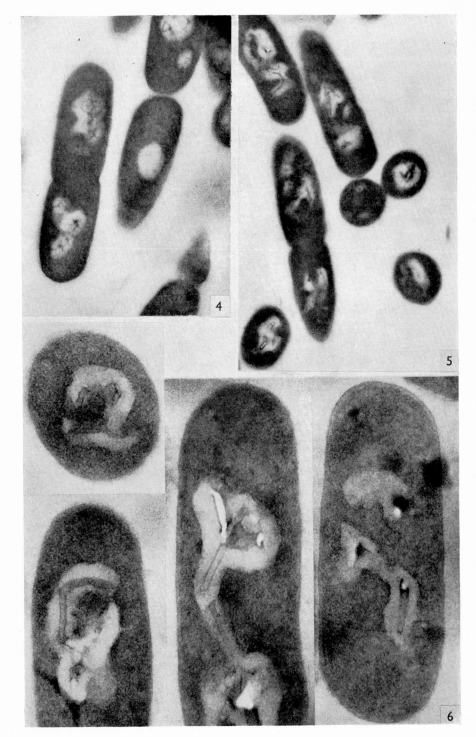

CHROMOSOMES IN MICRO-ORGANISMS

CHARLES G. ELLIOTT

Department of Genetics, University of Glasgow

The purpose of this contribution to the Symposium is to provide some comments on bacterial cytology by one having some familiarity with chromosomes in higher organisms. The study of the structure and behaviour of chromosomes is relatively easy in organisms with large chromosomes. In micro-organisms the analysis of chromosome behaviour is much more difficult. This is largely due to the inherent technical problems of dealing with very small structures, often at the limits of resolution with the ordinary light microscope. But one cannot escape the impression that the situation has been made more unsatisfactory by some lack of understanding of cytology, and more especially of genetics, on the part of some authors.

The discussion of bacteria will therefore be introduced by an account of some of the difficulties met with in fungi, which stand in ease of analysis between higher organisms with large chromosomes and bacteria where the nuclei are minute. It will be seen how improved technical methods and cognate genetical analysis can assist in the elucidation of cytological problems.

FUNGI

Brachymeiosis

The difficulties of cytological observations in fungi may be illustrated by a discussion of brachymeiosis.

It was originally claimed by Harper that in the development of the fruiting body nuclei fused in the ascogonium. This idea was accepted by Gwynne-Vaughan, who further believed that two diploid nuclei (arising from this first fusion) themselves fused in the ascus initial to give a tetraploid nucleus. In the course of the three divisions in the ascus the chromosome number was halved twice to give haploid ascospores; this process of double reduction was called brachymeiosis. For example, in *Peziza* (*Humaria*) *rutilans*, Gwynne-Vaughan (Fraser, 1908) observed 16 chromosomes during mitosis in the ascogenous hyphae (supposed diploid number), 16 bivalents at the first division in the ascus, and 16 chromosomes passing to each pole at the second division. She claimed that at the third division 8 chromosomes only passed to each pole at anaphase (supposed haploid number). Thus the first and third ascus divisions were reductional.

Similarly, the third ascus division was claimed to be reductional in *Patella* (*Lachnea*) *melaloma* (Gwynne-Vaughan, 1937) and *Ascobolus magnificus* (Gwynne-Vaughan & Williamson, 1932). It is odd, however, that in *Pyronema confluens* (*P. omphalodes*) the second reduction was believed to occur at the second division, the number of chromosomes being the same at second and third anaphase (Gwynne-Vaughan & Williamson, 1931). Gwynne-Vaughan's observations were made on sections stained with Heidenhain's haematoxylin or Fleming's triple stain.

The validity of these observations was denied by many mycologists. As Martens (1946) has shown, the evidence on which the claim for brachymeiosis was made was inadequate to substantiate a type of life cycle unknown in any other living organisms. The cytology of *Peziza rutilans* was reinvestigated in detail by Wilson (1937). This organism has exceptionally large nuclei for a fungus, and appears to be favourable cytological material, for Wilson claimed to see the four chromatids of diplotene bivalents. She found no evidence of brachymeiosis, 16 bivalents being observed at the first division, and 16 chromosomes in all other divisions. Thus 16 is the haploid number of chromosomes. Wilson's observations were made on sections stained with haematoxylin or crystal violet, or by the Feulgen technique.

More recently the cytology of other species claimed by Gwynne-Vaughan to show brachymeiosis has been examined using squash methods. *Patella melaloma* was investigated by Olive (1949b, 1950), *Pyronema confluens* by Hirsch (1950) and *Ascobolus magnificus* by Wood (1953). *Pyronema* has also been restudied by I. M. Wilson (1952), who used both squash methods and sectioned material. In all cases there was no evidence of brachymeiosis, the first division in the ascus being the reduction division, and the third a mitosis. Thus recent cytological analysis has rendered the concept of brachymeiosis untenable.

Chromosome numbers

At present, few counts of chromosomes in fungi can be considered reliable. Martens (1946) quotes the case of *Pyronema confluens*, in which up to that time seven different authors had counted five different numbers of chromosomes, ranging from 4 to 12. I. M. Wilson (1952) has now shown definitely that there are 12 chromosomes. Olive (1953) has indicated that a large number of the chromosome counts of *two* may be spurious because of the clumping of chromosomes together into two groups, especially at anaphase, with inadequate fixation or squashing (see Pl. 1, fig. 2*b*).

Using squash techniques, Fincham (1949) and Dodge, Singleton & Rolnick (1950) have made chromosome counts of several species of *Neurospora*; and C. M. Wilson (1952) and Emerson & Wilson (1954) have found a polyploid series in *Allomyces*. These are the first notable contributions to comparative cytological studies in fungi of a kind long known among higher organisms.

Squash methods which have been in use in higher organisms for some 25 years have been adapted for use in micro-organisms during the past 10 years. It is significant that the most important contribution to fungus cytology has been made not by a mycologist, but by a maize geneticist, Dr Barbara McClintock, who borrowed the technique she used in *Neurospora* from higher plants. It has been seen above that considerable advances have been made in fungus cytology with the use of such techniques.

Neurospora

The chromosomes of *Neurospora crassa* have been thoroughly mapped at pachytene by McClintock (1945) and Singleton (1953). By analysis of pachytene pairing McClintock (1954) has identified a reciprocal translocation known from genetical evidence to be present in one strain, and she found an extra segment in one chromosome of another. She also analysed the pairing behaviour at pachytene of a fragment present in a third strain. A large fusion nucleus, and exceptional technical ability, have permitted an accuracy in analysis approaching that possible in maize. However, both McClintock and Singleton have stated that the success of their preparations varies greatly with different strains. This is something which should be borne in mind in all studies of micro-organisms, and which may in part explain the unsatisfactory nature of much published work.

Sex in Hypomyces

In dealing with very small chromosomes, errors of interpretation can easily arise when there is no genetical control. A case in point is that of sex in *Hypomyces solani* f. *cucurbitae*. There are hermaphrodite, male, female and neuter strains. Hirsch (1949) found that in crosses between hermaphrodite strains four bivalents were present at first metaphase. In crosses between hermaphrodite and male or female strains she observed three bivalents and one univalent. Thus hermaphrodite strains have four chromosomes and male and female three each. One chromosome of the four was large, one very small, and two of intermediate size. The missing chromosome in male and female strains was one of the intermediate-sized ones. In crosses of male by female generally two bivalents and two univalents were present, but sometimes three bivalents. Thus she inferred that a different chromosome of the four was lacking in the male strain from that in the female, but that the chromosomes were partially homologous. Sex was determined by the differential segments of the two chromosomes. She inferred that the neuters have two chromosomes, and arose from non-disjunction of chromosomes 2 and 3, which would give hermaphrodites with a complete complement and neuters with chromosomes 1 and 4 only.

Unfortunately, this story does not agree with the genetic data of El-Ani (1954). He dissected asci of a cross between a male and a female strain, and found 23 asci with a 4:4 ratio of male to female, and 19 asci with a 2:2:2:2 ratio of male:female:hermaphrodite:neuter. On Hirsch's hypothesis one would expect a 4:4 ratio of hermaphrodite: neuter in non-disjunctional asci, which did not occur, and the four types in one ascus could not be predicted. El-Ani considers male and female sex to be determined by different loci on the one chromosome some distance apart, as had been suggested by Hansen & Snyder (1946). The true cytological picture is thus uncertain.

In the next section work will be discussed in which cytological and genetical investigation are done concurrently on the same material.

Aspergillus nidulans

The genetical evidence is conclusive for the existence of a 'parasexual' cycle in certain fungi, involving the formation of heterozygous diploids and the segregation somatically from them of diploid and haploid recombinants (Pontecorvo, 1954). In *Aspergillus nidulans* the diploids which arise by fusion of unlike nuclei in a balanced heterokaryon between two strains marked by biochemical deficiencies and other characters (Roper, 1952) are shown to be diploid by their phenotype and by the segregation somatically and in ascospores of the genetic markers present in the parental strains; furthermore, the diploids have a conidial diameter greater than that of the haploids. It has not been possible to make a cytological analysis of hyphal nuclei, and the evidence for the diploid state in vegetative tissues is genetical. Asci with 16 spores are found in diploids, and they have not been seen in haploids. However, 8-spored asci also occur, sometimes with high frequency, in perithecia arising on diploid strains (Pontecorvo & Roper, in Pontecorvo, 1953).

Pontecorvo & Roper found that ascospores of diploids with a high frequency of 16-spored asci were very infertile, less than 1 in 50 germinating, which precluded genetical analysis. They were therefore unable to show genetically whether in the development of the ascus there was fusion of two diploid nuclei followed by a tetraploid meiosis.

Cytological observations on both haploids and diploids were made by Pontecorvo (1953). In the haploids, the development of the ascus was followed and at first metaphase 4 bivalents were regularly observed. In the diploids, though numerous asci showing meiosis were seen, most of them subsequently degenerated. At first metaphase the chromosome configurations often appeared complicated and more than 4 in number. This was interpreted as evidence for a tetraploid meiosis.

This is not the place to discuss in detail the further observations which I have made, but the following points may be stated. In haploid wild type *Aspergillus nidulans*, after the fusion of nuclei in the ascus initial (Pl. 1, fig. 1*a*), the nucleus immediately undergoes meiosis. Early meiotic prophase in *Neurospora* shows seven contracted bivalents, which elongate while in the fully paired condition to give a typical pachytene appearance (McClintock, 1945; Singleton, 1953). No such process is evident in *Aspergillus*. Early prophases are shown in Pl. 1, figs. 1*b*, 2*a*, 3*a*. Pl. 1, fig. 3 shows two cells at diakinesis with 4 bivalents. Diakinesis and first metaphase are the only stages at which it is possible to count the chromosomes.

At first anaphase a stainable thread ('stem body') is seen between the separating chromosomes (Pl. 1, fig. 2*b*). This has often been remarked on in other fungi, and sometimes taken as evidence for the presence of heterozygosis for inversions, crossing-over in the inversion giving a bridge and fragment at first anaphase (e.g. Olive, 1949*a*). However, the strain used here has been repeatedly isolated as a single conidium or ascospore. In perithecia formed in these cultures, the fusion nucleus in the ascus must be homozygous for the structural arrangement of its chromosomes.

Observations have been made on a self-fertile diploid strain in which no 16-spored asci have been observed, in which respect it differs from the original diploids studied by Pontecorvo. Single random ascospores, isolated with a micromanipulator, gave 35 % germination. They were all haploid, and of the same types as those found in a cross between the two haploid strains from which the diploid arose. This suggests that simple meiosis of a single diploid nucleus included in an ascus initial had occurred. At first metaphase in this diploid, 4 bivalents are observed (Pl. 1, fig. 4). The chromosomes are larger than in wild type, but this may be a phenotypic expression of diploidy (cf. Thomas, 1936). Pl. 1, fig. 5, shows 3 bivalents and 2 univalents, and fig. 6, though of complicated appearance, is interpreted tentatively as 4 bivalents. The presence of more than 4 chromosomal structures in diploids may not necessarily indicate a tetraploid meiosis, for in the wild type, asci with apparently 8 univalents have been observed (Pl. 1, fig. 1 c).

Yeast

Yeast is a notoriously difficult cytological object. Not only is there controversy as to which structure in the cell is the nucleus, but even among authors who are agreed on that point, there is no agreement as to the number of chromosomes, or even whether they are visible at all. The only reliable information on the state of the cells is genetical. The situation in yeast is thus more akin to that in bacteria than to that in the fungi discussed in previous sections.

We should be cautious in accepting Lindegren's (1949) account of the cytology of *Saccharomyces cerevisiae*, as the chromosome behaviour he described is very different from the remarkably uniform behaviour known in higher plants and animals. The presence of chromosomes in a vacuole, and one end of them attached to the vacuolar membrane, with the free end 'waving around' in the vacuolar sap; their subsequent detachment from the membrane and vibration with rapid Brownian movement; and the formation of 12 chromosomes into a single pair of complexes is quite contrary to general cytological experience. The changes of size undergone by Lindegren's 'chromosomes' are remarkable. It is difficult to understand the results of some of his staining procedures, but structures which stain 'red-red' with fuchsin and are 'refractile' are not acceptable as chromosomes when the 'centrosome' stains 'purple-red', the colour which chromosomes are normally stained by the Feulgen technique. The 'centrosome' of Lindegren is regarded as the nucleus by most authors, e.g. Winge (1951), DeLamater (1950), Levan (1947) and Mundkur (1954). Levan claimed there were about 10 chromosomes, many more than other authors believe present. In support of his high count, he described small bodies apparently lagging on the spindle in 'polyploids' produced by treatment with organic substances, which are of the same size as the chromosomes of the diploid nucleus. DeLamater's photographs are unfortunately badly reproduced. He believes there are 4 chromosomes. Mundkur has examined material fixed by freeze-drying, subsequently sectioned and stained. He found that the nucleus is a uniform body both with Heidenhain's haematoxylin and Feulgen staining. There was no sign of any internal differentiation during division, which took place by simple constriction.

A convincing account of cytology of a yeast is that of Leitz (1951) on (*Zygo*)*Saccharomyces priorianus*. He found 3 chromosomes in haploid and 6 in diploid cells, and described meiosis. Meiosis in *Schizosaccharomyces octosporus* has been described by Widra & DeLamater (1955).

In crosses made by the mass-mating technique between apparent haploid strains of *Saccharomyces cerevisiae*, abnormal segregation ratios may occur, due to asci containing diploid ascospores (Roman, Hawthorne & Douglas, 1951; Lindegren & Lindegren, 1951). Presumably during the growth of the cultures to be crossed illegitimate hybridization of cells of like mating type takes place, giving diploid cells which fuse to give a tetraploid nucleus; this undergoes meiosis to give four diploid spores.

Lindegren & Lindegren (1951) have described the production of triploid and tetraploid strains of *Saccharomyces*. The diploid ascospores from irregular asci may be homozygous or heterozygous for mating type. The homozygotes may be crossed with haploids of opposite mating type, giving rise to some triploids, or with diploids homozygous for opposite mating type giving some tetraploid cells. The polyploid strains are identified by cell size and morphology. Mundkur (1954) has made a cytological study of a polyploid series made by Lindegren's technique, and he found a correlation between nuclear size and degree of ploidy. The cellular content of dry weight, DNA and RNA and metaphosphate, is claimed to show a correlation with ploidy (Ogur, Minckler, Lindegren & Lindegren, 1952), as does respiration rate (Ogur, 1954) and nitrogen content (Ogur, 1955).

Pomper & Burkholder (1949) described the isolation of prototrophic diploid strains, following the mixing of cultures of opposite mating type differing by several biochemical requirements. This process has been extended (Pomper, 1952) to the isolation of triploids as prototrophs, by mixing a diploid strain homozygous for genes determining several biochemical requirements, with a haploid with different biochemical requirements. Tetraploids may be produced by similar means. The genetical analysis of these triploids and tetraploids has been described by Pomper, Daniels & McKee (1954).

Latarjet & Ephrussi (1949) found that the survival curves of yeast cells irradiated with X-rays are characteristically different for haploids and diploids. This has been made use of by Pomper *et al.* (1954) to assist in determining ploidy of strains in the course of the analysis of their polyploid segregations.

Cytological studies of the polyploid segregations studied by Roman *et al.* (1951) and Pomper *et al.* (1954) do not appear to have been made. But in view of the difficulties of yeast cytology discussed above they would not be very profitable at present.

The abnormal segregation ratios interpreted in terms of a polyploid meiosis by Roman *et al.* (1951) have been interpreted in another way by Winge & Roberts (1954). In their material, the ascospores, originally haploid, undergo spontaneous diploidization. Abnormal segregation ratios occur when two haploid non-sister nuclei, resulting from an extra mitosis prior to spore delimitation, are included in a single ascospore, and these fuse to give a diploid heterozygote. Winge & Roberts published photographs demonstrating the supernumerary division of one or more nuclei, and also the failure of nuclei to be included in ascospores.

Documentation and interpretation of results

Some comment must be made here on the documentation of results of cytological studies. The use of photographs is essential, as they provide more objective evidence than drawings, which inevitably contain an element of interpretation. But what can be seen in a photograph varies greatly with quality of reproduction (cf. the same photographs in De-Lamater, 1953*a*, pl. 1; 1953*b*, pl. 2). Photographs are also necessary as a test of technical competence. However, in some cases it is difficult to assess from a photograph alone the reliability of an author's interpretation. The account of the cytology of *Eremascus albus* by DeLamater, Yaverbaum & Schwartz (1953) is lavishly illustrated by photographs, with many series of optical sections through single nuclei. However, it is difficult to see the difference between the interphase nucleus in their fig. 1 and the prometaphase and anaphase figures in their figs. 5, 6 and 8. The difference is not obvious between their figs. 77–81 (zygotene) and figs. 117–120 and 121–123 (diakinesis). Some drawings of these cells would have been most helpful; and without a drawing it is not possible to count the 12 leptotene chromosomes said to be shown in their figs. 60–62. Again, in the paper by Widra & DeLamater (1955) on *Schizosaccharomyces octosporus* it is difficult to see the difference between the stages shown in their figs. 14–17 and fig. 29 (said to be zygotene and first metaphase respectively!). The main sequence of stages illustrated in *Schizosaccharomyces* is, however, clear enough; but their interpretation in terms of the known behaviour of chromosomes in higher organisms seems to me far from evident. Despite Widra & DeLamater's remarks on the subject, it would be preferable to use such terms as early and late prophase, rather than zygotene and diakinesis to designate the various nuclear appearances.

BACTERIA

Problems of nuclear structure and division

Robinow (1945) studied the nuclei of bacteria and their division using mainly Piekarski's method of hydrolysis with N-HCl at 60° and staining with Giemsa solution. In such preparations, which agree in their results with specific staining methods for DNA, 'the basic chromatinic element is a more or less dumbbell-shaped rodlet which divides lengthwise in a plane more or less parallel with the short axis of the bacterium, one dumbbell giving rise to two whole daughter dumbbells' (Robinow, 1945, p. 359). Clifton & Ehrhard (1952) remark on the absence of dumbbell-shaped configurations in their time-lapse phase-contrast photographs. Division is seen to be initiated by the appearance of a break in the continuity of the chromatinic body on one side next to the cell wall, the break progressing across the body, generally yielding a U-shaped or less frequently a V-shaped structure before complete separation occurs.

Delaporte (1951) advocates careful comparison of all bodies present in the cell—lipid, metachromatic and glycogen granules and so on. She finds that the 'nuclear element' is a more 'fluid' body than any of these, and may be pressed out of shape and even fragmented by their presence. If such nuclei are to divide again, it is difficult to see how their structure is comparable to that of nuclei of higher organisms. (It should be mentioned that Mundkur (1954) believes that the nucleus of yeast may be pushed out of its spherical form by the vacuole.)

The most interesting results have come with the method of freeze-dehydration (Blank, McCarthy & DeLamater, 1951) of material hydrolysed and then stained with thionin or azure A in the presence of SO_2 (DeLamater, 1951; DeLamater & Mudd, 1951; DeLamater & Hunter, 1951). The techniques have been discussed by DeLamater (1953a). The magnificently reproduced photographs of *Bacillus megaterium* of DeLamater (1953b) leave no doubt that much more of the structure of the bacterial cell is revealed by this method than by those in use earlier. DeLamater considers his results show that bacteria have a nuclear structure and behaviour entirely comparable with that of higher organisms: 'It is felt that the intrinsic structures of the bacterial nucleus in all its phases, as indicated by this study, show its essential similarity to the nucleus of larger organisms. These findings tend to bring the bacteria cytologically into the general biologic economy where they already are biochemically, and where they certainly belong' (DeLamater & Mudd, 1951, p. 511). Nuclear division is believed to take place by an intranuclear mitosis (DeLamater, 1954). It is greatly to be hoped that De-Lamater's techniques will be extensively used and his observations repeated by workers independent of his school.

There is no need to discuss the various objections which have been raised to DeLamater's interpretations of nuclear structure and division, e.g. by Bisset (1953 and elsewhere)—indeed, it would be presumptuous for me to do so.

Beutner (1953) attempted to correlate the frequency of various types of nuclear configuration with the stage of growth of the culture, and found that 'mitotic' figures are most frequent during the early log phase of growth. This was held to indicate that the configurations in question are indeed those of nuclei in division. A more critical examination on these lines is possible in synchronized cultures. Maaløe & Lark (1954) found that when cultures of *Salmonella typhimurium* which have been growing at 25° are raised to 37°, nuclear division takes place simultaneously in most of the cells during the interval from 5 to 10 minutes after the increase in temperature. In the cytological studies on this organism reported by Lark, Maaløe & Rostock (1955), samples of the cultures were removed and fixed at intervals; the nuclear configurations seen in stained preparations were classified as dot, wedge, bar and dumbbell. It was shown that the times at which the configurations appeared after the rise in temperature indicate that the wedge, bar and dumbbell appearances are successive stages in the cycle of division of the nucleus, and that the dots are resting nuclei. Nuclear division is seen as 'a gradual transition from one compact body via the more irregular structures described as 'wedge', 'bar' and 'dumbbell' into two distinct round bodies' (p. 324), a scheme which 'would tend to agree' with that of Robinow. Nuclear configurations of the type claimed by DeLamater to be mitotic were observed occasionally, but they did not increase markedly in frequency during the period in which the number of nuclei was doubled. In *Bacillus megaterium*, Szybalski & Hunter-Szybalska (1955) found that exposure of actively growing cultures to a temperature of 15° for 30 minutes induces an accumulation of metaphase-like figures—condensed nuclei with distinct small granules located at their poles. The separation of sister chromosomes is observed soon after the cultures are returned to 34°, and thereafter division is synchronous, with metaphase-like figures visible during 'very short' intervals between the more dispersed and filamentous appearances of the resting stage. The use of synchronized cultures holds considerable promise for an experimental approach to problems of nuclear division which would be of great general interest.

Fitz-James (1954) has found that the DNA content of a culture rises continuously during the first few hours of germination, and he believes this to be evidence against mitosis. However, Walker & Yates (1952) have shown that the DNA content of the nucleus in dividing tissue culture cells rises continuously during interphase. In tissue cultures of higher animals, and in plant cells, the duration of mitosis is short compared to that of interphase (cf. Hughes, 1952). Evidence for a rapid mitosis and long interphase in bacteria may be found in Maaløe & Lark's (1954) observations, and in those of the Szybalskis (1955), on synchronized cultures. Since some lack of synchronization is to be expected in Fitz-James's cultures, his results can be accounted for as in no way evidence against mitosis.

Fitz-James (1954) states (p. 470): 'The chromatin structures seen in the initial stages of germination before the DNA has increased, appear in stained preparations as a triad of granules often connected on at least two sides by fine strands.' In White's (1954, p. 13) discussion of the structure of the resting nucleus, it is pointed out that in many cases the interphase chromosomes present an appearance in microscopical preparations bearing little or no resemblance to the structure they are believed to possess in the living cell. Connecting strands between chromosomes often appeared in older works on cytology, but were undoubtedly artifacts.

Beutner (1953) made the remarkable statement that 'the criterion for determining whether a nucleus divides mitotically rather than amitotically is the formation of a metaphase spindle' (p. 626). It is not the presence of a spindle but of a particular cycle of chromosome behaviour that is the essence of mitosis. We speak of 'endo*mitosis*' and 'colchicine-*mitosis*', because the chromosomes go through the cycle of contraction, centromere division, and elongation in the absence of a spindle (Painter & Reindorp, 1939; Levan, 1938).

Very interesting questions as to the organization of the bacterial nucleus are raised by the complex nuclear transformations found under various cultural conditions, or induced by ultraviolet irradiation or phage infection (Kellenberger, 1953) or antibiotics (Kellenberger, 1953; DeLamater, 1953b; DeLamater, Hunter, Syzbalski & Bryson, 1955). Kellenberger has described the process of recovery from the forms which the nucleus assumes under different cultural conditions to the normal form seen during the log phase of growth in broth. Several of the abnormal configurations break up into 'formes polychromosomiques', the 'chromosomes' of which regroup and proceed to divide in the manner observed in rapidly growing broth cultures. Axial rod forms undergo constriction to give normal nuclear structures. Kellenberger's interpretation of the normal nucleus is similar to Robinow's. According to DeLamater (1953 b) the recovery from antibiotic-induced 'polyploidy' involves the segregation of nuclear elements (viz. three chromosomes in *Bacillus megaterium*), while still within the nuclear membrane of the complex nucleus, which may then form resting nuclei, or proceed immediately to mitotic metaphase without intervening chromosome elongation.

Evidence for sexuality and meiosis in bacteria

Morphological evidence for sexuality in bacteria has been reviewed by Hutchinson & Stempen (1954). Such observations are very difficult, inasmuch as the events looked for are infrequent.

Klieneberger-Nobel (1951), from a study of phase contrast and stained preparations, believes that the formation of large bodies in the L-cycle is brought about by the fusion of small elements, and she states (p. 529) that when the bacterial phase is initiated from the giant bodies 'new races have arisen better adapted to the adverse conditions [that gave rise to the L-forms] than the mother organism'. The L-cycle is thus regarded as a sexual and regenerative process. This point of view is not confirmed by the evidence (Tulasne, 1953). The bacteria which arise from the L-forms reproduce all the morphological, physiological, biological, antigenic and pathogenic properties of the original organism. Nevertheless, it is admitted that nuclear transformations and genetic recombination might well take place during the L-cycle (Tulasne, 1953). Dienes (1946, 1947) observed that although contact between two antagonistic strains of *Proteus* is necessary for large body formation, the bacteria which arise from the large bodies have the antigenic and antagonistic properties of the original strains only. Stempen & Hutchinson (1951 a, b) investigated the development of large bodies in *Proteus* with phase-contrast time-lapse photography and staining methods. They could find no evidence of a sexual nature for the structures.

Webb & Clark (1954) found large cells in *Micrococcus pyogenes* which they believed to be diploid and to undergo meiosis. Lindegren (1942) studied what he believed to be meiosis in a micrococcus. De-Lamater (1953 b) illustrated cells in *Bacillus megaterium* in which he could count the diploid number of chromosomes, and other cells which were claimed to represent meiotic stages. DeLamater (1953 c) also described conjugation tubes between bacterial cells. His figs. 29 and 30 show a spirally coiled conjugation tube with large nuclei at each end; there may well be some justification for believing them diploid.

We agree with Hutchinson & Stempen (1954) who have stressed the desirability of following in the living state the development of structures believed to be sexual.

Conclusions. Observations on genetically known material

The alternatives, such as they are, to DeLamater's views on the bacterial nucleus and the mitotic nature of its division do not seem convincing. Lederberg & Tatum (1953) say, 'It is difficult for a geneticist to imagine how bacteria could get along without some sort of mitotic process, but its details require critical and objective definition'; and 'Although nuclear aggregates that are very suggestive of mitotic metaphases and anaphases can be found with a brief search, definitive interpretations of *E. coli* cytology depend for the most part on the validity of conclusions that have been drawn from technically superior material' (pp. 172–3). And Webb & Clark (1954), concerning *Micrococcus pyogenes*, remark: 'It does not appear probable that an amitotic division should occur since the genetic stability displayed by this organism indicates a regular reduplication and transference of genetic determinants to the daughter cells. On the basis of available evidence we believe that mitotic division does occur, but that there is no disintegration of the nuclear membrane during the prometaphase' (p. 94).

Technical improvements will lead to further advances, although DeLamater's (1951) techniques hold great promise, and their use should be extended. Robinow (1953), however, considers that the value of dehydrated and cleared material has been exaggerated.

Clearly much more work needs to be done, and especially in attempting to correlate cytological evidence with genetic phenomena. A very significant contribution to bacterial cytology is that of Lederberg, Lederberg, Zinder & Lively (1951), who observed consistent cytological differences between cells of *Escherichia coli* known from genetical evidence to be haploid and diploid. In the diploids the nuclei were larger and more 'dispersed' than in the haploids, and the chromatinic structures were generally of greater apparent complexity. Consistently correct classification of ploidy could be made cytologically, and in two cases the ploidy was predicted by cytological observation and confirmed genetically. These authors were most reserved in their interpretation of the cytology. 'The preparations so far studied do not admit of any clear interpretations in terms of doubled chromosomes, and it is not yet excluded that the differences reside principally in a better expansion and resolution of nuclear structure in the diploid cells' (Lederberg *et al.* 1951, p. 426). 'The determination whether the diploids show a doubling of the chromosome number is not yet subject to independent, objective verification' (Lederberg & Tatum, 1953, p. 173).

With the demonstration of genetic recombination in *Bacillus megaterium* (Szybalski, 1954; Yaverbaum & Hunter, quoted by DeLamater, 1953*b*), the study of bacterial cytology should enter a more precise and exciting stage.

REFERENCES

BEUTNER, E. H. (1953). The occurrence of mitosis in *Bacillus megaterium* and its relation to the growth cycle. *J. Bact.* **65**, 619.

BISSET, K. A. (1953). Do bacteria have mitotic spindles, fusion tubes and mitochondria? *J. gen. Microbiol.* **8**, 50.

BLANK, H., MCCARTHY, P. L. & DELAMATER, E. D. (1951). A non-vacuum freezing-dehydrating technic for histology, auto-radiography and microbial cytology. *Stain Tech.* **26**, 193.

CLIFTON, C. E. & EHRHARD, H.-B. (1952). Nuclear changes in living cells of a variant of *Bacillus anthracis*. *J. Bact.* **63**, 537.

DELAMATER, E. D. (1950). The nuclear cytology of the vegetative diplophase of *Saccharomyces cerevisiae*. *J. Bact.* **60**, 321.

DELAMATER, E. D. (1951). A staining and dehydrating procedure for the handling of microorganisms. *Stain Tech.* **26**, 199.

DELAMATER, E. D. (1953*a*). Aspects of bacteria as cells and as organisms. Part II. *Int. Rev. Cytol.* **2**, 158.

DELAMATER, E. D. (1953*b*). Structure and division of the bacterial nucleus. *Bacterial Cytology, Symp. 6th Congr. int. Microbiol., Rome*, p. 108.

DELAMATER, E. D. (1953*c*). Cytologic evidence for the occurrence of cellular and nuclear fusion in *Bacillus megaterium. Bull. Torrey bot. Cl.* **80**, 289.

DELAMATER, E. D. (1954). Cytology of bacteria. Part II. The bacterial nucleus. *Annu. Rev. Microbiol.* **8**, 23.

DELAMATER, E. D. & HUNTER, M. E. (1951). Preliminary report of true mitosis in the vegetative cell of *Bacillus megaterium. Amer. J. Bot.* **38**, 659.

DELAMATER, E. D., HUNTER, M. E., SZYBALSKI, W. & BRYSON, V. (1955). Chemically induced aberrations of mitosis in bacteria. *J. gen. Microbiol.* **12**, 203.

DELAMATER, E. D. & MUDD, S. (1951). The occurrence of mitosis in the vegetative phase of *Bacillus megaterium. Exp. Cell Res.* **2**, 499.

DELAMATER, E. D., YAVERBAUM, S. & SCHWARTZ, L. (1953). The nuclear cytology of *Eremascus albus. Amer. J. Bot.* **40**, 475.

DELAPORTE, B. (1951). Observations on the cytology of bacteria. *Advanc. Genet.* **3**, 1.

DIENES, L. (1946). Complex reproductive processes in bacteria. *Cold Spr. Harb. Symp. quant. Biol.* **11**, 51.

DIENES, L. (1947). Further observations on the reproduction of bacilli from large bodies in *Proteus* cultures. *Proc. Soc. exp. Biol., N.Y.*, **66**, 97.

DODGE, B. O., SINGLETON, J. R. & ROLNICK, A. (1950). Studies on lethal E gene in *Neurospora tetrasperma*, including also chromosome counts in races of *N. sitophila. Proc. Amer. phil. Soc.* **94**, 38.

EL-ANI, A. S. (1954). The genetics of sex in *Hypomyces solani* f. *cucurbitae. Amer. J. Bot.* **41**, 110.

EMERSON, R. & WILSON, C. M. (1954). Interspecific hybrids and the cytogenetics and cytotaxonomy of *Euallomyces*. *Mycologia*, **46**, 393.

FINCHAM, J. R. S. (1949). Chromosome numbers in species of *Neurospora*. *Ann. Bot., Lond.*, N.S., **13**, 23.

FITZ-JAMES, P. C. (1954). The duplication of bacterial chromatin. *J. Bact.* **68**, 464.

FRASER, H. C. I. (1908). Contributions to the cytology of *Humaria rutilans* Fries. *Ann. Bot., Lond.*, **22**, 35.

GWYNNE-VAUGHAN, H. C. I. (1937). Contributions to the study of *Lachnea melaloma*. *Ann. Bot., Lond.*, N.S., **1**, 99.

GWYNNE-VAUGHAN, H. C. I. & WILLIAMSON, H. S. (1931). Contributions to the study of *Pyronema confluens*. *Ann. Bot., Lond.*, **45**, 355.

GWYNNE-VAUGHAN, H. C. I. & WILLIAMSON, H. S. (1932). The cytology and development of *Ascobolus magnificus*. *Ann. Bot., Lond.*, **46**, 653.

HANSEN, H. N. & SNYDER, W. C. (1946). Inheritance of sex in fungi. *Proc. nat. Acad. Sci., Wash.*, **32**, 272.

HIRSCH, H. E. (1949). The cytogenetics of sex in *Hypomyces solani* f. cucurbitae. *Amer. J. Bot.* **36**, 113.

HIRSCH, H. E. (1950). No brachymeiosis in *Pyronema confluens*. *Mycologia*, **42**, 301.

HUGHES, A. F. (1952). *The mitotic cycle*. London: Butterworth.

HUTCHINSON, W. G. & STEMPEN, H. (1954). Sex in bacteria—evidence from morphology. In *Sex in Microorganisms*, ed. Wenrich, D. H., Lewis, I. F. & Raper, J. R. Washington: Amer. Ass. Advanc. Sci.

KELLENBERGER, E. (1953). Les formes caractéristiques des nucléoides de *E. coli* et leurs transformations dues à l'action d'agents mutagènes-inducteurs et de bactériophages. *Bacterial Cytology, Symp. 6th Congr. int. Microbiol., Rome*, p. 45.

KLIENEBERGER-NOBEL, E. (1951). The L-cycle: a process of regeneration in bacteria. *J. gen. Microbiol.* **5**, 525.

LARK, K. G., MAALØE, O. & ROSTOCK, O. (1955). Cytological studies of nuclear division in *Salmonella typhimurium*. *J. gen. Microbiol.* **13**, 318.

LATARJET, R. & EPHRUSSI, B. (1949). Courbes de survie de levures haploides et diploides soumises aux rayons X. *C.R. Acad. Sci., Paris*, **229**, 306.

LEDERBERG, J., LEDERBERG, E. M., ZINDER, N. D. & LIVELY, E. R. (1951). Recombination analysis of bacterial heredity. *Cold Spr. Harb. Symp. quant. Biol.* **16**, 413.

LEDERBERG, J. & TATUM, E. L. (1953). Sex in bacteria—genetic studies, 1945–1952. *Science*, **118**, 169.

LEITZ, K. (1951). Beitrag zur Hefecytologie. *Arch. Mikrobiol.* **16**, 275.

LEVAN, A. (1938). The effect of colchicine on root mitoses in *Allium*. *Hereditas, Lund*, **24**, 471.

LEVAN, A. (1947). Studies on the camphor reaction of yeast. *Hereditas, Lund*, **33**, 457.

LINDEGREN, C. C. (1942). Nuclear apparatus and sexual mechanism in a micrococcus. *Iowa St. Coll. J. Sci.* **16**, 307.

LINDEGREN, C. C. (1949). *The Yeast Cell, its Genetics and Cytology*. St Louis: Educational Publishers.

LINDEGREN, C. C. & LINDEGREN, G. (1951). Tetraploid *Saccharomyces*. *J. gen. Microbiol.* **5**, 885.

MAALØE, O. & LARK, K. G. (1954). A study of bacterial populations in which nuclear and cellular divisions are induced by means of temperature shifts. In *Recent Developments in Cell Physiology*. Editor, J. A. Kitching. London: Butterworth.

MCCLINTOCK, B. (1945). *Neurospora*. I. Preliminary observations of the chromosomes of *Neurospora crassa*. *Amer. J. Bot.* **32**, 671.

McClintock, B. (1954). Chromosome aberrations in *Neurospora*. *Yearb. Carneg. Instn*, **53**, 257.

Martens, P. (1946). Cycle de développement et sexualité des ascomycètes—essai critique. *Cellule*, **50**, 123.

Mundkur, B. D. (1954). The nucleus of *Saccharomyces*: a cytological study of a frozen-dried polyploid series. *J. Bact.* **68**, 514.

Ogur, M. (1954). Respiration in a polyploid series in *Saccharomyces*. *Arch. Biochem.* **53**, 484.

Ogur, M. (1955). The rapid estimation of ploidy in cultures of *Saccharomyces*. *J. Bact.* **69**, 159.

Ogur, M., Minckler, S., Lindegren, G. & Lindegren, C. C. (1952). The nucleic acids in a polyploid series of *Saccharomyces*. *Arch. Biochem.* **40**, 175.

Olive, L. S. (1949a). Karyogamy and meiosis in the rust *Coleosporium veroniae*. *Amer. J. Bot.* **36**, 41.

Olive, L. S. (1949b). Cytological evidence opposing the theory of brachymeiosis in the ascomycetes. *Science*, **110**, 185.

Olive, L. S. (1950). A cytological study of ascus development in *Patella melaloma* (Alb. & Schw.) Seaver. *Amer. J. Bot.* **37**, 757.

Olive, L. S. (1953). The structure and behaviour of fungus nuclei. *Bot. Rev.* **19**, 439.

Painter, T. S. & Reindorp, E. C. (1939). Endomitosis in the nurse cells of the ovary in *Drosophila melanogaster*. *Chromosoma*, **1**, 276.

Pomper, S. (1952). Isolation of triploid *Saccharomyces cerevisiae*. *Nature, Lond.*, **170**, 892.

Pomper, S. & Burkholder, P. R. (1949). Studies on the biochemical genetics of yeast. *Proc. nat. Acad. Sci., Wash.*, **35**, 456.

Pomper, S., Daniels, K. M. & McKee, D. W. (1954). Genetic analysis of polyploid yeast. *Genetics*, **39**, 343.

Pontecorvo, G. (1953). The genetics of *Aspergillus nidulans*. *Advanc. Genet.* **5**, 141.

Pontecorvo, G. (1954). Mitotic recombination in the genetic systems of filamentous fungi. *Proc. 9th Int. Congr. Genet.* (*Caryologia*, suppl.), p. 192.

Robinow, C. F. (1945). Nuclear apparatus and cell structure of rod-shaped bacteria. In Dubos, R. J. *The Bacterial Cell*. Cambridge, Mass: Harvard University Press.

Robinow, C. F. (1953). Observations on the nucleus of resting and germinating spores of *Bacillus megaterium*. *J. Bact.* **65**, 378.

Roman, H., Hawthorne, D. C. & Douglas, H. C. (1951). Polyploidy in yeast and its bearing on the occurrence of irregular genetic ratios. *Proc. nat. Acad. Sci., Wash.*, **37**, 79.

Roper, J. A. (1952). Production of heterozygous diploids in filamentous fungi. *Experientia*, **8**, 14.

Singleton, J. R. (1953). Chromosome morphology and the chromosome cycle in the ascus of *Neurospora crassa*. *Amer. J. Bot.* **40**, 124.

Stempen, H. & Hutchinson, W. G. (1951a). The formation and development of large bodies in *Proteus vulgaris* OX-19. I. Bright phase contrast observations of living bacteria. *J. Bact.* **61**, 321.

Stempen, H. & Hutchinson, W. G. (1951b). The formation and development of large bodies in *Proteus vulgaris* OX-19. II. Comparative cytology of bacilli and large bodies. *J. Bact.* **61**, 337.

Szybalski, W. (1954). Bacterial genetics and action of antimicrobial agents. *Report of the Biological Laboratory, Long Island Biological Association*, **64**, 27.

Szybalski, W. & Hunter-Szybalska, M. E. (1955). Synchronization of nuclear and cellular division in *Bacillus megaterium*. Communication to the 1955 Meeting of the Soc. of Amer. Bacteriologists (*Bact. Proc.* p. 36).

PLATE 1

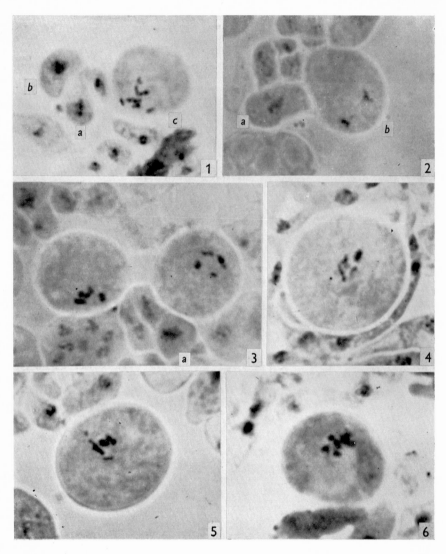

THOMAS, P. T. (1936). Genotypic control of chromosome size. *Nature, Lond.,* **138,** 402.

TULASNE, R. (1953). Le cycle L et les formes naines des bactéries. *Bact. Cytology, Symp. 6th Congr. int. Microbiol., Rome,* p. 144.

WALKER, P. M. B. & YATES, H. B. (1952). Nuclear components of dividing cells. *Proc. roy. Soc.* B, **140,** 274.

WEBB, R. B. & CLARK, J. B. (1954). Cell division in *Micrococcus pyogenes* var. *aureus. J. Bact.* **67,** 94.

WHITE, M. J. D. (1954). *Animal Cytology and Evolution,* 2nd ed. Cambridge: University Press.

WIDRA, A. & DELAMATER, E. D. (1955). The cytology of meiosis in *Schizosaccharomyces octosporus. Amer. J. Bot.* **42,** 423.

WILSON, C. M. (1952). Meiosis in *Allomyces. Bull. Torrey bot. Cl.* **79,** 139.

WILSON, I. M. (1937). A contribution to the study of the nuclei of *Peziza rutilans* Fries. *Ann. Bot., Lond.,* N.S., **1,** 655.

WILSON, I. M. (1952). The ascogenous hyphae of *Pyronema confluens. Ann. Bot., Lond.,* N.S., **16,** 321.

WINGE, Ö. (1951). The relation between yeast cytology and genetics. A critique. *C.R. Lab. Carlsberg,* ser. Physiol., **25,** 85.

WINGE, Ö. & ROBERTS, C. (1954). Causes of deviations from 2:2 segregations in the tetrads of monohybrid yeasts. *C.R. Lab. Carlsberg,* ser. Physiol., **25,** 285.

WOOD, J. L. (1953). A cytological study of ascus development in *Ascobolus magnificus* Dodge. *Bull. Torrey bot. Cl.* **80,** 1.

EXPLANATION OF PLATE

Photographs (all × 2250) of squashed contents of perithecia. Fixed in 1:3 acetic alcohol, hydrolysed for 5 min. at 60° in N-HCl, and stained in acetic-orcein.

Figs. 1–3. Wild-type haploid *Aspergillus nidulans.*

Fig. 1. *a,* ascus initial with two nuclei about to fuse; *b,* ascus with fusion nucleus in very early prophase; *c,* ascus with 8 univalents (diakinesis?) (cf. text-figure below).

Fig. 2. *a,* ascus with nucleus in early meiotic prophase; *b,* late first anaphase, showing 'stem body', and in the lower group of chromosomes, appearance suggesting two chromosomes only.

Fig. 3. Two asci at diakinesis showing 4 bivalents. At *a,* early meiotic prophase.

Figs. 4–6. Diploid strain of *Aspergillus nidulans.*

Fig. 4. First metaphase, showing 4 bivalents.

Fig. 5. First metaphase, with apparently 3 bivalents and 2 univalents.

Fig. 6. First metaphase of complicated appearance, but interpreted as 4 bivalents (cf: text-figure below).

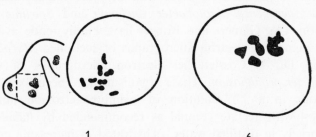

1   6

Interpretative drawings of Pl. 1, figs. 1 and 6.

ORGANIZATION OF BACTERIAL CYTOPLASM

J. R. G. BRADFIELD

Cavendish Laboratory, Cambridge

Of late three main methods have been employed in studies on the structure of bacterial cytoplasm: (*a*) light microscope observations, by phase contrast, or ultra-violet, or in conjunction with staining methods for metachromatic substances and for oxidative enzymes; (*b*) mechanical and chemical disintegration, followed by differential centrifugation and biochemical analysis of particle fractions; (*c*) electron-microscope studies, particularly on thin sections. Work in this laboratory has been mainly concerned with the latter approach, but an attempt will be made here to correlate the results of all three lines of investigation. Limitations of space unfortunately preclude mention of numerous recent contributions and permit only brief reference to those which are mentioned. The material to be discussed can conveniently be arranged in three main sections: (*a*) materials and methods used in the original work described here, and the general structural plan of bacterial cells; (*b*) detailed consideration of structures for whose existence in bacterial cytoplasm there is strong evidence; (*c*) structures important in the cytoplasm of animal and plant cells which have *not* so far been unequivocally demonstrated in bacteria.

MATERIALS, METHODS AND GENERAL PLAN OF BACTERIAL CELLS

The species which I have sectioned are as follows: *Staphylococcus aureus* (Oxford strain), *Streptococcus lactis*, paracolon bacillus D 201 H, *Aerobacter aerogenes*, *Azotobacter vinelandii* and *Spirillum serpens*. In addition, Drs Glauert and Brieger have kindly made available to me their numerous electron micrographs of sectioned *Mycobacterium phlei*, and Dr A. Cosslett her electron micrographs of sectioned *Chromobacter prodigiosum*. These organisms have been fixed for varying periods in a 1% solution of osmium tetroxide buffered to pH 7·2–7·4 with acetate veronal as recommended by Palade (1952), washed briefly in distilled water, dehydrated in increasing concentrations of ethanol and embedded in methacrylates (pure butyl or a mixture of three parts butyl and one part methyl). In the case of *Staphylococcus aureus* the effect of addition of sodium chloride to the fixative and washing fluid has been examined, and in the case of *Azotobacter* the fixative contained the same concentration of sucrose (2%) as was present in the culture medium.

Those familiar with bacterial cytology will doubtless shrink from the idea of drawing a 'typical' bacterial cell, for clearly none exists. Nevertheless, for purposes of reference in the following discussions it is convenient to reproduce diagrammatic sections through an imaginary bacillus and an imaginary coccus, showing some of the structures which they are believed to possess (Text-fig. 1). The coccus is shown in division.

The outstanding feature of electron-microscopic observations on sectioned bacteria to date is that they confirm that in general plan (though not in more detailed construction) bacteria are remarkably like simple animal and plant cells. They have a more or less central nucleus, containing most if not all the bacterial deoxyribonucleic acid (DNA), which is surrounded by cytoplasm possessing specialized surface layers, or cell membranes. So far no nuclear membranes have been detected in bacteria; and in bacilli the nucleus is often of very irregular shape, ramifying through the cytoplasm. The forces responsible for maintaining it as a separate structure distinct from the cytoplasm are unknown. Often in bacilli, such as young paracolon bacilli (Bradfield, 1954, fig. 6) it appears to fill a large part of the cell (nucleo-cytoplasmic ratio 1:2) so that the cytoplasm is confined to a thin cortical layer. In cocci, however, the nucleus is usually relatively smaller (Text-fig. 1b) and the nucleo-cytoplasmic ratio seldom exceeds 1:10. Considerable fibrous structure can often be seen in the nuclei (Pl. 1, fig. 1). The cytoplasm, on the other hand, shows little conspicuous structure apart from the numerous small granules (Text-fig. 1a, b; Pl. 1, fig. 1b) and the large volutin granules which are sometimes present. This state of affairs tends to be reversed during the preparation of homogenates for biochemical work, for the conspicuous nuclear fibrous structures are rather labile (their DNA being easily depolymerized, depending to some extent on the salt concentration of the homogenate fluid), whereas the cytoplasmic granules are quite stable and can be purified by differential centrifugation. The cell membranes contain at least two layers—an outer, mechanically important cell wall and an inner, osmotically important cytoplasmic membrane. During cell division these grow in towards the centre of the cell, preceded by elongation and nipping into two of the nucleus (Bradfield, 1956), without, so far as can be seen at present, anything akin to mitosis. Many bacilli carry flagella whose basal granules are embedded in the cytoplasm, inside the cell wall and cytoplasmic membrane. Notably absent from the cytoplasm of bacteria sectioned so far are the endoplasmic reticulum and mitochondria which are major features of the cytoplasm of animal and plant cells. The main categories of cytoplasmic structures are considered one by one in the following sections.

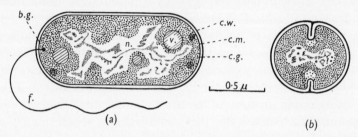

(a)   (b)

Text-fig. 1. (a) Diagram of idealized longitudinal section through a monotrichous bacillus showing cell wall (c.w.), cytoplasmic membrane (c.m.), 100–200 A. cytoplasmic granules (c.g.), basal granule (b.g.) of flagellum (f.), volutin granules (v.) and ramifying nucleus (n.) without a nuclear membrane. The cytoplasmic granules are arranged with varying density, as is observed in sections. The ground substance of the cytoplasm between the granules is not labelled and not considered here since, although it probably contains important chemical constituents such as dissolved enzymes, nothing definite can be added to the account given by Knaysi (1951). Only the most frequently occurring inclusions are shown. (b) Diagram of idealized longitudinal section through a dividing coccus. Cell wall and cytoplasmic membranes are as in the bacillus and both are represented in the ingrowing cross-walls. At the inner edge of the latter is a specialized zone of cytoplasm. The rest of the cytoplasm consists of fairly uniformly packed 100–200 A. granules, which surround a central nucleus. In cocci the non-dividing nucleus tends to be more nearly spherical than in bacilli. During division in cocci the nucleus becomes dumbbell-shaped, as shown here, but the chromatin remains fairly evenly distributed through it and is not noticeably more fibrous than in the non-dividing nucleus (though osmium tetroxide may preserve nuclear structure less satisfactorily than cytoplasmic structure). No centriole or spindle is shown since nothing which can be clearly identified as such has been seen by the author in bacteria.

STRUCTURES KNOWN TO EXIST IN BACTERIAL CYTOPLASM

(1) *Small granules* 100–200A. *in diameter*

All the studies in this laboratory (Bradfield, 1954, 1956) indicate that the major part of the cytoplasm in each of the species investigated consists of small granules about 100–200A. in diameter. In *Staphylococcus aureus* (Pl. 1, fig. 1), for example, the granules are very conspicuous, and we have never seen any other clearly defined cytoplasmic structure (apart from the vacuoles described in § (4) below). The granules are particularly apparent in cocci undergoing lysis (Pl. 1, fig. 1b)—as is the fibrillar nature of the nuclear contents. In *Aerobacter aerogenes* also the cytoplasmic granules are very conspicuous and often fill the whole of the cytoplasmic area in a section (Pl. 1, fig. 2). In the paracolon bacillus

D 201 H, *Spirillum serpens* and *Azotobacter vinelandii*, abundant granules of this order of size can again be identified (Pl. 1 and 2, fig. 3, 4, 5), though in these three species we sometimes see larger masses, which can in some cases be resolved into clusters of 100–200 A. granules and in some cases not. The sections of *Spirillum serpens* are rather hard to interpret, having very ill-defined nuclear areas and containing small, irregular amorphous masses about 500 A. across; yet the fixation is quite good judging from the integrity of the cell wall and cytoplasmic membrane and from the fact that neither is artificially separated from the cytoplasm by shrinkage or swelling—which we have found elsewhere to be a sensitive indication of damage. In the paracolon bacillus the larger bodies are seldom encountered, and then mainly in the polar regions. In most cases they can be resolved into clumps of smaller granules; whether these clumps are natural or artificial we cannot tell. Only in the paracolon bacillus have we made satisfactory comparisons between young (6 hr. agar slope) organisms and old organisms (grown for 2–3 weeks on an agar slope). The cytoplasmic granules of the old organisms (Pl. 1, fig. 3) appear to be distinctly larger (average 300 A.) than those of the younger organisms (average 200 A.) under identical conditions of fixation and embedding. The cytoplasm in the old bacilli also occupies a much larger proportion of the cell volume than in the young organisms (Bradfield, 1954).

Similar granular cytoplasm may be seen in the sections of *Bacillus cereus* published by Chapman & Hillier (1953), of *Escherichia coli* published by Birch-Andersen, Maaløe and Sjöstrand (1953), in the many electron micrographs of sectioned *Mycobacterium phlei* prepared by Glauert & Brieger (unpublished) and in the sections of *Chromobacterium prodigiosum* prepared by Cosslett (unpublished). The sections of myco-bacteria are hardest to interpret on account of the frequent occurrence of volutin granules and the convolutions of the nucleus; but at any rate it is clear that here, as in all the other bacterial sections seen by the author, a large part of the cytoplasm is composed of granules in the size range 100–200 A.

Most of the studies in this laboratory have been made using as fixative the 1 % solution of osmium tetroxide buffered to pH 7·2–7·4 with acetate-veronal, which has been recommended by Palade and found to be so excellent for preserving cytoplasmic (but not necessarily nuclear) structure in animal cells. However, cytoplasmic granules of approximately the same size as found after osmic fixation appear abundantly in *Staphylococcus aureus* after fixation in buffered 4 % formaldehyde solution, so that the granules are not particles of osmium, or osmium compounds.

Further evidence of the reality of the 100–200 A. cytoplasmic granules comes from ultracentrifugal analysis of bacterial homogenates. Schachman, Pardee & Stanier (1952) found that homogenates of *Escherichia coli*, *Micrococcus aureus*, *Clostridium kluyveri* and *Pseudomonas fluorescens* contained three main macromolecular components with sedimentation constants of about 40, 29 and 5 Svedberg units. Much the same pattern was found by Weibull (1953c) in *Bacillus megaterium*. Moreover, Schachman *et al.* found that the 40 S. granules contained much of the bacterial ribonucleic acid (RNA) and a similar correlation was made by Weibull, comparing RNA recovered with the calculated values for the percentages of granules thrown down after various periods of centrifugation. Schachman *et al.* took electron micrographs of the 40 S. granules and found them to be roughly spherical and of approximately 150 A. diameter, so that they seem to correspond to the granules seen in thin sections. These authors also refer to the paper of Sevag, Smolens & Stern (1941) on *Streptococcus pyogenes*, which contains an early electron micrograph taken by Anderson in which appear small dense particles of fairly constant diameter resembling in size those found in the cytoplasm of sectioned cocci. Particularly in bacteria such as cocci where these granules constitute almost the entire bulk of the cytoplasm (Pl. 1, fig. 1b), it is obviously very plausible that they contain much of the abundant RNA present in the growing bacteria. In electron microscopic studies of suspensions of 100–200 A. granules prepared by Dr Tissières from *Aerobacter* and *Azotobacter* we have observed not only isolated granules but also numerous clumps each containing 10–20 granules. During progressive centrifugation, as in Weibull's experiments, these clumps would come down faster than the isolated granules, and this is presumably the reason why, in the early stages of centrifugation, Weibull found more RNA coming down than would have been expected if the suspension had contained only single granules.

In enzyme studies on the granule fractions, Tissières (1952, 1954 and unpublished work) has found that cell-free suspensions of washed 100–200 A. cytoplasmic granules from *Aerobacter aerogenes* and *Azotobacter vinelandii* contain a major part of the succinoxidase activity of these organisms, including at least two of the cytochromes found in the intact cells. Those from *Azotobacter* will also oxidize fumarate and, with addition of final supernatant, washed particles of both organisms will carry out numerous stages of the Krebs cycle. Furthermore, Tissières & Slater (1955) showed that washed particles from *Azotobacter* carry out oxidative phosphorylation (with succinate, but not with fumarate; P:O ratio about 0·2). Unwashed particles give greater phosphate esterification (P:O ratio 0·8), so that there must be enzymes or co-factors sufficiently firmly held to withstand the long preparation, but loose enough to be removed by one wash (in 0·05 M-phosphate pH 7). Addition of supernatant produces more than additive increases in both oxygen uptake and phosphate esterification. Further evidence of the presence of oxidative enzyme systems in 100–200 A. cytoplasmic granules has been published by Stanier, Gunsalus & Gunsalus (1953), Billen & Volkin (1954) and Repaske (1954).

It is unfortunately impossible at present to answer the numerous questions which present themselves at this stage, for example: (a) are the RNA and succinoxidase in the same or in different particles? (b) are there several kinds of enzymically different particles? (c) is there, within limits, a continuous range of particle sizes with peak frequencies corresponding to the ultracentrifugal peaks, or are there only a few well-defined sizes? (d) are the particles self-reproducing or does each develop from a much smaller body formed elsewhere in the cell—possibly in the nucleus? The fact that the 40 S. component containing a large proportion of the RNA and succinoxidase is well defined in the ultracentrifuge suggests that both substances exist in the same granule. At any rate it is clear that these two substances, even if in separate granules, are in close proximity, unlike the condition in animal cells where the two kinds of granule have become localized on special membranes—the oxidative granules on the membranes (internal and/or external) of the mitochondria, and the RNA granules on the membranes of the endoplasmic reticulum.

Calculation of the hypothetical number of protein molecules per granule strongly suggests that there must be several enzymically different kinds of granule. Assuming that the specific gravity is 1·2, that protein makes up 50 % of the dry weight and that the latter is one-third of the wet weight, a granule 200 A. in diameter would accommodate about 14 protein molecules of molecular weight 35,000. This figure might be sufficient to provide one set of the molecules composing the bacterial succinoxidase system; but it could hardly include a second system and would be insufficient even for one set of the enzyme and carrier molecules composing the Krebs cycle. Of course there is considerable latitude in the data selected for such a calculation, but even assuming 100 % protein the granule would contain only about 28 molecules of the given molecular weight. This strongly suggests that there are numerous enzymically different types of granule. The total number of 200 A. granules in a bacillus 2μ long and 1μ wide, with nucleo-cytoplasmic ratio 1:2 and half its cytoplasm composed of the granules, would be about 10^5. For a

$\frac{1}{2}\mu$ diameter coccus with a nucleus occupying one-tenth of the cell volume and again half the cytoplasm composed of 200 A. granules, there would be only about 7×10^3 of the latter.

As regards size range and mode of origin, the RNA analyses of Billen & Volkin (1954) for *Escherichia coli* B/r are in keeping with a neo-Casperssonian view (Caspersson, 1950) of small RNA-rich particles (arising from the nucleus) growing by the formation or accumulation of enzyme proteins, there being a characteristic mature size represented by the 40 S. component. Whether or not the particles grow in this way, the results of Repaske (1954) certainly indicate that they can be broken down into smaller pieces by sonic vibration with the production of a soluble succinic dehydrogenase. Billen & Volkin also found that, under the conditions of their experiments, coarse particles had three times the succinoxidase activity of fine particles, but that only the latter could synthesize ATP. Taken at face value this implies granules which differ markedly both in chemistry and in size—the coarse ones not being clumps of the fine ones as suggested earlier. But Dr Tissières has informed me that washing (presumably by removal of inhibitors) can greatly increase the Q_{O_2} of such fine particle fractions so that the observed difference may not have been due to a difference in actual enzyme content. And it is possible that the ATP-synthesizing ability of the coarse fraction may have been neutralized by non-specific phosphatases present in the cell membrane, fragments of which this fraction would undoubtedly contain. Stanier *et al.* (1953) found similar enzyme activities (dehydrogenases for L-mandelic, malic and succinic acids) in both coarse and fine particles from *Pseudomonas fluorescens*, but since their coarse fraction was separated at only 22,000 g it seems likely that the fine fraction was composed mainly of 100–200 A. granules and not of finer particles as they imply. They state that electron-microscopic examination revealed particles 100–1000 A. in diameter in their coarse fraction, but judging from our own experience we should expect many of the large particles to consist of clumps of 100–200 A. granules. However, we have not examined their organism and the matter must remain open, pending more detailed electron-microscopic investigation.

In view of their size and nuclear content, the 'cell granules' prepared from a thermophilic bacterium by Georgi, Millitzer, Burns & Heotis (1951) seem to be very similar to whole protoplasts.

The study of the widely distributed 100–200 A. cytoplasmic granules of bacteria has only just begun, and unfortunately one line of approach—light microscope observations of living and of stained cells—is impossible on account of resolution limitations. But there is already considerable agreement between the electron microscope and the ultracentrifuge results, and further correlation of the enzymic activities of fractions with their electron microscopic appearance should prove interesting, particularly if it is possible to distinguish clearly between the enzyme activity of the granules and the enzyme activity (if any) of the cell wall and cytoplasmic membrane. The latter is likely to prove difficult, however, for it seems extremely probable that a 'ghost' obtained by lysis of a protoplast contains not only cytoplasmic membrane but also clumps of the 100–200 A. granules still adhering to it; and the cytoplasmic membrane appears (in sections) to be so tenuous that complete separation of it from these small granules will be no easy matter.

(2) Volutin granules

This subject constitutes one of the less highly controversial corners of bacterial cytology, for it is now clear that there is a frequent component of bacterial cytoplasm, often called volutin, which possesses the following properties: (a) it exists in the form of fairly smooth-contoured, approximately spherical granules, up to about 0.6μ in diameter; (b) it stains metachromatically with a variety of stains, or with Neisser's mixture of methylene blue (or crystal violet) and bismarck brown, and it stains at a lower pH than most other cell constituents; (c) it is the most electron-opaque material commonly encountered in bacterial cells—indeed, in many species cultured under suitable conditions it is easily the most conspicuous cell component—and under intense electron bombardment it absorbs so much energy as to volatilize or decompose, sometimes leaving an empty shell; (d) it contains important amounts of polymetaphosphate and probably of other phosphorus compounds.

König & Winkler (1948) demonstrated that the classical Babes-Ernst metachromatic granules of *Corynebacterium diphtheriae* are identical with the electron-opaque granules of the same organisms. Schmager & Kludas (1950), during their phase-contrast studies on living *C. diphtheriae*, appear to have observed the metachromatic granules, which suggests that the latter are genuine and not artifacts. Further evidence of the reality of metachromatic granules comes from the fact that they are clearly seen in Glauert & Brieger's many unpublished sections of mycobacteria and in our own sections of *Aerobacter*, all fixed in the best cytoplasmic fixative known at present (buffered osmium tetroxide solution). Artifacts there certainly are in any section, but not to the extent of the formation *de novo* of large, sharply defined, spherical granules half a micron in diameter. Glauert & Brieger (1955), photographing the same specimens of *Mycobacterium phlei* first in the light microscope, after treatment with Neisser's stain, and then in the electron microscope, produce further clear evidence that the metachromatic granules are the electron-opaque bodies. They observed no marked decrease in opacity after treatment with ribonuclease, unlike Minck & Minck (1949), who worked with *C. diphtheriae*. In the author's opinion, there is no foundation for the view that the metachromatic granules either are mitochondria, or are associated with mitochondria (Mudd, 1953, 1954), but this point will be discussed later. Certainly Glauert & Brieger found no clear correlation in *M. phlei* between supposed sites of oxido-reduction (tetrazolium salts and Janus green B) and the actual position of the electron-opaque granules; nor did Smith, Wilkinson & Duguid (1954), who obtained irregular results by using the same reagents on *Aerobacter* and state: 'Usually only a minority of the cells shows stained granules, and these did not correspond in number, size or situation with the volutin granules.' These authors give extensive results on the formation of volutin granules under a wide variety of cultural conditions, finding among other things that they appear during deficiency of nitrogen or sulphur, but not during deficiency of carbon, phosphorus or potassium. They show a striking parallel between poly-metaphosphate content and abundance of volutin granules, but estimate that volutin may be accounting for as much as 20% of the bacterial volume when only 1% of the dry weight is poly-metaphosphate, thus emphasizing that volutin contains much else beside metaphosphate.

Thus we have what appears to be a convincing correlation between the metachromatic volutin granules of the light microscope staining procedures and the large dense granules seen in the electron microscope. It remains to isolate and analyse more or less pure volutin granules by differential centrifugation, which ought not to be too difficult, with a suitable, volutin-rich starting culture, prepared, for example, in the light of the results of Smith *et al.*

(3) *Basal granules of flagella*

A bacterial flagellum is a long thread-like process often $3-4\mu$ long and about 100A. wide, constant in width over the greater part of its length. In many cases the flagellum has been clearly shown to pass at its proximal end through the cell wall and through the cytoplasmic membrane to end in a small basal granule about 400A. in diameter. Many excellent electron micrographs showing these features have been published by van Iterson (1953), and the fact that bacterial flagella originate within the cytoplasm has been confirmed by recent work on bacterial protoplasts (Weibull, 1953 b), where, in *Bacillus megaterium* for example, flagella remain firmly attached inside the protoplast after removal of the cell wall with lysozyme. Little is known about the function, structure and origin of the basal granule of bacterial flagella, though it is commonly supposed that, like the basal granules of animal cilia, these bacterial granules in some way regulate the activity of the flagella to which they are attached. No substructure comparable with that detected in animal cilia (Bradfield, 1955) has so far been observed in the basal granules and basal part of the flagellum of any bacteria observed in this laboratory (in work on unsectioned bacteria—no success having yet been achieved in tracing basal granules in sections). In all the groups examined by us (bacilli, spirilla, spirochaetes) the flagella are very much more resistant to tryptic digestion than is the general cytoplasm; the same is true of the basal granules, which, in *Spirillum serpens* for example, remain clearly visible, though perhaps reduced in size, after a digestion for 3 hr. In this species there is a collection of basal granules at the base of each of the two polar tufts of flagella forming quite a large, coherent clump at each end of the organism. During tryptic digestion the protoplasm shrinks greatly, drawing away from each pole and ending in a shrivelled remnant in the middle of the collapsed cell wall. In so doing the protoplasm draws with it the basal granule clump from each pole, and in one such digested cell (Pl. 2, fig. 4 c) we have observed a fibre passing from the basal granules into the centre of the cell. Isolated observations from such digested cells must obviously be treated with great caution, but it would not be surprising to find something akin to the internal fibre systems of ciliate Protozoa in these spirilla whose complex motility has been admirably illustrated by Pijper, Crocker, van der Walt & Savage (1953). Clear evidence has been obtained in this laboratory, and will shortly be published, that the flagella of *S. serpens* pass through the cell wall to end on basal granules in the cytoplasm and that they are not mere extensions of the cell wall as envisaged by Pijper *et al.*

(4) Cell wall, cytoplasmic membrane and structures associated with cell division

Little need be said regarding the cell wall since the subject is being separately considered by Salton in this Symposium. From the morphological point of view there are two main points of interest. (*a*) The cell wall is the outermost regularly occurring surface layer, varying from

100 to 300 A. in thickness, which in many cases confers on the bacterium its characteristic shape and which retains this shape after the cell contents have been removed by lysis—though it also of course possesses some degree of elasticity (Knaysi, 1951). (b) There has so far been no evidence from thin sections (except possibly in the case of spirilla) that bacterial cell walls contain two or more distinct layers in the way which can be so strikingly demonstrated for yeast (Northcote & Horne, 1952) and for the simplest algae (Pls. 2 and 3, figs. 6a, c and d).

A cytoplasmic membrane is believed to exist inside the bacterial cell wall. Bisset (1953) has stated that the cytoplasmic membrane is 'embarrassingly easy' to stain. In electron micrographs, on the contrary, the cytoplasmic membrane is embarrassingly difficult to see. All that can be said at present is that the outermost surface of the cytoplasm, lying against the cell wall, sometimes appears more smooth, continuous and uniformly dense over a thickness of about 50 A. (Pls. 1 and 2, figs. 1 c, 4a and b) than would be expected if there were no cytoplasmic membrane and the cytoplasm, after removal of the cell wall, consisted of a naked mass of granules, etc. This general conclusion applies to all the species studied here. Very often, of course, there is no trace of a cytoplasmic membrane and even the cell wall is hard to distinguish. This is presumably when the plane of the section passes at a glancing angle through the bacterial surface; one cannot hope to see any clear sign of a 50 A. membrane in a section unless the latter is approximately at right angles to the membrane. The cell wall very commonly becomes separated from the cell contents by the shrinkage of the latter; but the cytoplasmic membrane almost always remains attached to the cytoplasm and it is only very rarely that it can be demonstrated as a separate entity, as in the micrographs of Knaysi (1951) and of Robinow & Murray (1953). Even in these, the structure described as the cytoplasmic membrane may conceivably have been the latter plus a certain amount of adhering cytoplasm.

If, as seems likely, the cytoplasmic membrane is about 50 A. thick, far beyond the resolution limit with the light microscope, it is impossible to tell whether it can be stained alone without staining the adjacent cytoplasm: the 'embarrassingly easy' staining referred to by Bisset (1953) is almost certainly due to the staining of the surface layers of the cytoplasm, which is often rich in RNA. The author knows of no sound evidence to support the statement by Bissett (1953) that 'the entire cell membrane has a high content of nucleoproteins'. It is the cytoplasm, with its abundant 100–200 A. granules, which commonly has a high RNA content—though often in a bacillus the cytoplasm is confined by the large nucleus to a narrow cortical layer $0\cdot1-0\cdot2\,\mu$ thick, which might easily be confused with the cytoplasmic membrane under the light microscope. An interesting and valuable approach to the subject of staining the cytoplasmic membrane has been made by Robinow & Murray (1953), who show that with Victoria blue (alone of the dyes tested by them) staining can be limited to the cytoplasmic surface by leaving the organisms in contact with the very dilute stain for only 20–40 sec. and mordanting previously with mercury salts. On the basis of model experiments with gold films on thin glass fibres they reckon that the observed layer of Victoria blue staining in a $1\cdot5\,\mu$ thick *Bacillus mega-terium* is produced by a cytoplasmic membrane about 60A. thick, strikingly close to the figure of about 50A. arrived at by electron-microscopic observations and quite close to the 100A. advanced by Mitchell (1949).

It is presumed that the cytoplasmic membrane constitutes the surface layer of isolated bacterial protoplasts and is present in the 'ghosts' prepared from them. When, for example, *Bacillus megaterium* is treated with lysozyme in an appropriate concentration of sucrose (Weibull, 1953*b*), the cell wall upon which the rod-like shape depends is removed and the remaining protoplast rounds up into a sphere, which is pre-sumably bounded by the cytoplasmic membrane, though this has not been proved. Lysis of the protoplast, by suspension in buffer without sucrose, produces a suspension which is viscous (due to release of fibrillar DNA from the nuclei) and which contains ghosts together with 100–200A. cytoplasmic granules. Judging from Weibull's electron micrographs of ghosts, it seems that each of the latter consists of a cytoplasmic membrane with varying amounts of 100–200A. granules adhering to it, and that the oxidative activity which certain investigators have detected in the ghosts is due to the adhering small granules rather than to the presence of a very high concentration of oxidative enzyme systems in the tenuous cytoplasmic membrane itself.

Little can be said as yet regarding the special structures associated with cross-wall formation during cell division. Chapman & Hillier (1953), working with *Bacillus cereus*, first called attention to the ap-parent annular vacuole preceding the ingrowing cross-walls. Similar vacuoles have been observed in *Staphylococcus aureus* as indicated in Text-fig. 1*b*. There is no doubt that the details of fixation and washing affect the size of these vacuoles—as, indeed, they affect most other features of bacterial structure. But the fact that the vacuoles appear at all after the buffered osmic fixation, which produces more or less uniform granularity throughout the rest of the cytoplasm, shows that there is a marked local differentiation of the cytoplasm immediately in front of the advancing cell walls. Thin sections of *S. aureus* show no sign of the 'cell plate' described in *Micrococcus pyogenes* by Webb & Clark (1954), nor of a nuclear membrane of the kind which they assume.

The differentiation of cell wall and cytoplasmic membrane can be more clearly seen in the incomplete septa of a dividing blue-green alga filament (Pl. 2, fig. 6a). Similar but less easily reproducible electron micrographs have been obtained for *S. aureus* (Pl. 1, fig. 1c).

(5) *Miscellaneous metabolic granules including pigment granules*

By electron-microscopic study of homogenates of *Rhodospirillum rubrum*, Schachman, Pardee & Stanier (1952) observed well-defined chromatophores, approximately 400 A. in diameter and about 5000 per cell in number. Such chromatophores were absent from organisms grown in the dark. It would be interesting to know whether these chromatophores are homogeneous aggregates of the photosynthetic pigments, or whether they possess one or two lamellae of the kind found in the very much larger chloroplasts of flowering plants (Leyon, 1953; Steinman & Sjöstrand, 1955). Probably many photosynthetic bacteria possess similar bodies.

In addition to these and the structures considered in previous sections, there are numerous examples of cytoplasmic granules composed of intermediate or end-products of metabolism such as the poly-β-hydroxybutyric acid particles described in *Bacillus megaterium* by Weibull (1953c), the transient vacuoles of *Caulobacter vibrioides* rich in lipoid and RNA (Grula & Hartsell, 1954), various polysaccharide granules held to be glycogen on account of their staining with iodine, and the long-known sulphur granules and droplets of sulphur bacteria (Knaysi, 1951). The iron and manganese deposits of iron bacteria appear to be mainly in the sheaths of these organisms (Pringsheim, 1949).

STRUCTURES FOUND IN ANIMAL CYTOPLASM BUT NOT HITHERTO DEMONSTRATED IN BACTERIA

(1) *Endoplasmic reticulum*

An important contribution of electron microscopy to animal cytology has been the discovery that many cells with strongly basophilic cytoplasm contain a well-developed, complex apparatus appearing in sections as pairs of membranes, with lowered electron opacity between the members of each pair and abundant dense granules on the outer faces of each pair. The paired membranes seen in sections may result either from longitudinal sections of tubes or sections of much broader 'cisternae' shaped like flattened bags, the whole apparatus being named the endoplasmic reticulum by Palade & Porter (1954). There is considerable, but not as yet conclusive, evidence that the cytoplasmic RNA is located on this apparatus, probably in the granules. A few kinds of mammalian cells (e.g. intestinal epithelium) contain abundant dense granules not associated with membranes, but these same cells do nevertheless contain some endoplasmic reticulum with associated granules.

The 100–200 A. cytoplasmic granules of bacteria described above are reminiscent in size and RNA content of the endoplasmic reticulum granules (though they are more complex—individually or as a group—in that they contain important oxidative systems absent from endoplasmic reticulum). But bacteria have so far proved to be entirely without intra-cytoplasmic membranes comparable with those of animal endoplasmic reticulum. It is noteworthy that, as might therefore be expected, the phospholipid content of bacterial granules is low (Billen & Volkin, 1954) compared with that of animal microsomes, which are believed to contain (among other things) disintegrated endoplasmic reticulum, comprising both granules and membranes—the latter accounting for the high phospholipid content of microsomes (25%). The species investigated to date by the author include two cocci, three bacilli and a spirillum. Neither they nor the mycobacteria and chromobacteria studied by other workers in Cambridge contain either single or double intracytoplasmic membranes; but there are of course many other species awaiting investigation, including such relatively complex groups as the spirochaetes, which may prove more highly differentiated than the types studied hitherto. So far as the evidence goes at present, however, it appears that nothing akin to endoplasmic reticulum has been developed within bacteria. They are likewise devoid of a nuclear membrane, which, as Watson (1955) has shown, on account of its connexion with endoplasmic reticulum, might conceivably be regarded as a specialized branch of the latter enclosing the chromatin and nuclear sap.

On the other hand, in the blue-green algae—one of the groups most closely related cytologically to bacteria—we have found that something very similar to the endoplasmic reticulum of animal cells exists although a nuclear membrane is absent. Pls. 2 and 3, figs. 6 a, b, c, d, show longitudinal and oblique sections of filaments of Oscillatoria formosa fixed in 1 % osmium tetroxide solution buffered to pH 7·2–7·4. There appear to be two quite different sets of paired membranes: (a) a narrow set with membranes about 30 A. thick and 100–150 A. centre to centre; (b) a wider set with membranes about 90 A. thick and 300–500 A. centre to centre. There are dense granules, about 100A. in diameter, lying both between the membranes and free in the cytoplasm, which brings to mind the report of Schachman *et al.* (1952) that after centrifuging the homogenate of an unnamed blue-green alga for 1 hr. at 160,000 *g* they found the chlorophyll all in the pellet and most of the phycocyanin in the supernatant. Whatever may be the significance of the intracellular distribution of granules, however, the essential point is the demonstration of elaborate cytoplasmic membranes in one of the classes of organisms most closely related to bacteria cytologically. The blue-green algae appear to have quite rudimentary nuclear structures, more or less on a par with those of bacteria, but as regards the development of intra-cytoplasmic membranes the bacteria are very much the simpler of the two groups.

(2) *Mitochondria*

We come now to one of the most controversial topics in the study of bacterial cytoplasm, revolving mainly around the work of Mudd (1953, 1954) and his collaborators, who believe that mitochondria exist in a wide variety of bacteria. Their case can be summarized as follows. (*a*) If bacteria are treated under appropriate conditions with tetrazolium salts, or the Nadi reagent, or Janus green B, stained patches appear within the bacteria. (*b*) This is evidence of oxidation-reduction activity at the sites which become stained. (*c*) Since animal mitochondria contain many important oxidation-reduction systems, the stained patches in bacteria are mitochondria.

Several investigators have expressed considerable doubt regarding these conclusions. Without prejudice to any more clear and compelling evidence which may yet be produced, the author's view is as follows. (*a*) The structures so far described as bacterial mitochondria by Mudd and his collaborators in some cases do not exist (being either cytochemical artifacts, or 'optical' artifacts, resulting from resolution limitations of the light microscope); and in those cases where they do exist they are not mitochondria, but some quite different kind of structure such as volutin granules. (*b*) The structures in bacteria containing oxidation-reduction systems similar to those of animal mitochondria are the 100–200A. cytoplasmic granules, and it would be highly misleading and undesirable to call the latter mitochondria because they differ so profoundly from true mitochondria in shape, size and structure.

The case in favour of the existence of bacterial mitochondria depends on a number of assumptions, two of the most important of which are: (*a*) that the coloured products in each case appear and remain at their site of production; (b) that what appears as a stained patch in a bacterium under the light microscope represents a structural entity in the bacterium. There is much evidence that both these assumptions are unsound. Weibull (1953a), for example, has shown that the coloured formazans produced when *Bacillus megaterium* is allowed to reduce tetrazolium salts appear first as small granules dotted all over the organism and then aggregate to form the much larger secondary masses shown by Mudd and his collaborators in their photomicrographs. The coloured end-product of the Nadi reagent is well known to be preferentially absorbed by lipoid droplets, and this effect has been confirmed in a bacterium by Grula & Hartsell (1954) working on *Caulobacter vibrioides*. Tetrazolium salts and the Nadi reagent may be satisfactory *histo*chemically, but much rigorous testing of the kind specified by Danielli (1953) must be carried out with them, and with Janus green B, before any of these reagents can be regarded as satisfactory *cyto*chemically. Janus green B gives the least spectacular results of the three—indeed, several investigators have failed to obtain any positive results with it. Mudd and his collaborators report irregularities in the results with Janus green B; in many of their studies they have omitted to demonstrate two of the essential points about vital staining with this dye, which are reversible decolorization and inhibition by enzyme poisons. A structure in the presence of Janus green B may stain green and then turn red or colourless, simply because it absorbs the dye strongly and contains reducing substances. Even if reversible decolorization and inhibition by enzyme poisons can be demonstrated, it is still possible that marked differences in the amount of protein per square micron may strongly affect the intensity of staining with any of these dyes in whole bacteria.

Furthermore, even if methods can be so improved as to remove all these difficulties in the work on staining so-called bacterial mitochondria so that the reagents used can be relied upon to demonstrate unequivocally the sites of oxidation-reduction systems, there is still the stumbling block of assumption (b) above—the precise structural interpretation of the stained patches. Optical photomicrographs of bacteria are difficult to make, and those of Mudd and his collaborators are excellent so far as they go. But they cannot go further than the resolution limit of visible light, and in view of this and of the fact that the stained masses are near the resolution limit it is absurd to claim that: 'The bacterial mitochondria range from prolate ellipsoids and spheroids, similar in dimensions to the smaller mitochondria of mammalian cells, to spheroids well below the limits of microscopic resolution' (Mudd, 1953, 1954). With the exception of large volutin granules, there have been no structures in the bacteria sectioned in this laboratory which approached the size of small mammalian mitochondria; and the biochemical analyses of particle fractions, combined with the electron-microscope observations, make it extremely probable that the bacterial oxidation-reduction systems responsible for producing the mitochondrial stains are situated on 100–200 A. granules widely distributed throughout the entire cytoplasm. In the author's opinion the stained masses demonstrated by Mudd and his collaborators are in many cases artificially produced aggregations of bacterial cytoplasm containing large numbers of the 100–200 A. granules; and in other cases they consist of aggregations of stain (e.g. formazans) around volutin granules, as is suggested by the references to electron opacity, limiting membranes and metaphosphate content in the following definition of bacterial mitochondria: 'cytoplasmic granules, dense by electron-microscopic and phase-microscopic examination, possessing limiting membranes and possessing co-ordinated systems of oxidative-reductive enzymes; they contain phospholipoid and at least in certain cases metaphosphate' (Mudd, 1953, 1954). On the question of confusing volutin granules and mitochondria it should be noted (a) that careful comparisons of the sites of mitochondrial staining (whatever they may mean) with the positions of the electron-opaque volutin granules show that more often than not there is no correspondence between the two (Smith *et al.* 1954; Glauert & Brieger, 1955); (b) that if there is a correspondence then all the uncertainties of the staining procedures remain to be controlled; (c) that the electron-opaque volutin granules are in any case transient bodies, which may be completely absent from bacteria containing very active oxidation-reduction systems. It is always possible that future electron-microscopic observations may reveal cytoplasmic bodies identical in size and position with the centres of mitochondrial staining and which, in sections, prove to be discrete entities with limiting membranes instead of unorganized masses of small granules; but investigations to date have not done so.

It may of course be argued that the name 'mitochondrion' should be applied to the individual 100–200 A. granule in view of the statement: 'For the present at least, however, it seems better to refer to even the smallest cytoplasmic particles with the above morphological and biochemical properties as mitochondria rather than as microsomes' (Mudd, 1953, 1954). By all means let us avoid the word 'microsomes', which has acquired a certain amount of notoriety in the differential centrifugation studies on mammalian tissue homogenates (Bernhard, Gautier & Rouiller, 1954; Bradfield, 1953). But the use of 'mitochondrion' is even more undesirable. First, as to shape, a mitochondrion is essentially a thread-like object, as its etymology indicates, and the word was invented because animal mitochondria usually are thread-like; clearly it is unsuitable for describing a more or less spherical granule. Second, as to size, a small animal mitochondrion is at least 1000 times larger than a particle 200 A. in diameter. Third, as to structure, animal mitochondria have a most remarkable and characteristic structure, with a double external membrane, and internal membranes in the form of lamellae or tubes projecting in from the external membrane (Pl. 3, fig. 7). There may be a little structural variation (Beams, Tahmisian & Devine, 1955; however, many of the mitochondria in their micrographs look thoroughly typical), but the same basic plan has now been observed in very diverse cells and, in general, recent electron-microscopic observations, like the earlier biochemical work on isolated mitochondria, has served to confirm and emphasize the concept of the mitochondrion as a constant, characteristic and well-defined cell organelle. On the other hand, the 100–200 A. cytoplasmic granules of bacteria are not known to possess any membranes, external or internal, and, indeed, there is little room for them to do so as they are about equal in size to the larger granules lying between the internal membranes of an animal mitochondrion. It seems highly undesirable to stretch and distort the clear mitochondrial concept to include the bacterial granules which are so different in shape, size and structure. Indeed, it is desirable to emphasize the reverse point of view, that bacteria, so far as present investigations show, *do not possess mitochondria* (using the word in its precise and restricted sense); and that in bacteria, instead of the major parts of the oxidation-reduction systems being wrapped up inside complex organelles, they are instead located on very small granules 100–200 A. in diameter. The granules can easily be described thus by reference to their size, or to their sedimentation constants, or to their chemistry. Only if it could be shown that these granules are regularly combined together in substantial and coherent clumps, either enclosed in a membrane or arranged in some fairly constant and characteristic pattern, would the word 'mitochondrion' be justified; and to date there appears to be no evidence of this kind whatever.

SUMMARY

In their general plan bacteria resemble animal and plant cells in possessing nucleus, cytoplasm and cell membranes. Nucleo-cytoplasmic ratios vary at least from 1:2 to 1:10.

In bacterial cytoplasm the following structures have been detected: (*a*) small granules, 100–200 A. in diameter, containing succinic dehydrogenase, various cytochromes and Krebs cycle enzymes and the majority of the ribonucleic acid (RNA) and often forming the bulk of the cytoplasm; (*b*) so-called volutin granules which stain metachromatically, contain metaphosphate, are very opaque to electrons and vary in size from a few hundred A. up to $0\cdot5\mu$; (*c*) basal granules of flagella; (*d*) miscellaneous granules and vacuoles containing such substances as sulphur, glycogen, RNA and lipids including poly-β-hydroxybutyric acid; (*e*) an osmotically important cytoplasmic membrane, which is in some cases about 50A. thick, and an outermost cell wall varying from 100–300A. Components (*a*) and (*e*) occur in all six species sectioned by the author and probably in most bacteria; (*c*) has been shown to occur in many flagellate bacteria; (*b*) is fairly widespread, fluctuating according to cultural conditions; and the components listed under (*d*) vary greatly from species to species.

Bacteria have not so far been shown to contain structures similar to endoplasmic reticulum and mitochondria, which are both important structures in animal cells. On the question of mitochondria, it seems to the author on the basis of all the organisms examined to date: (*a*) that the structures described as bacterial mitochondria either (i) do not exist, or (ii) do exist, but are profoundly different structurally and chemically from true mitochondria; (*b*) that there are no bodies in bacteria structurally similar to true mitochondria; (*c*) that the structures chemically similar to true mitochondria (in their oxidizing enzyme content) are the 100–200A. granules and that it would be highly misleading and undesirable to name these mitochondria. In general, therefore, the most striking structural difference between bacterial cytoplasm and the cytoplasm of animals and plants is the absence from bacteria of all kinds of intra-cytoplasmic membranes: the oxidative granules are not wrapped in membranes to form mitochondria; the RNA-rich granules are not arrayed on membranes to form endoplasmic reticulum; and finally the cytoplasm as a whole is not separated from the nucleus by a nuclear membrane.

The author is much indebted to the Nuffield Foundation and to the Agricultural Research Council for supporting this work.

REFERENCES

BEAMS, M. W., TAHMISIAN, T. N. & DEVINE, R. L. (1955). Electron microscope studies on Malpighian tubes. *J. Biochem. Biophys. Cytol.* **1**, 201.

BERNHARD, W., GAUTIER, A. & ROUILLER, C. (1954). La notion de 'microsomes'. *Arch. Anat. micr. Morph. exp.* **43**, 236.

BILLEN, D. & VOLKIN, E. (1954). The effect of X-rays on the macromolecular organization of *Escherichia coli*. *J. Bact.* **67**, 191.

BIRCH-ANDERSEN, A., MAALØE, O. & SJÖSTRAND, F. S. (1933). High resolution electron micrographs of sections of *E. coli*. *Biochim. biophys. Acta*, **12**, 395.

BISSET, K. A. (1953). Bacterial Cell Envelopes. In *Bacterial Cytology, Symp. 6th Congr. int. Microbiol., Rome*.

BRADFIELD, J. R. G. (1953). New features of protoplasmic structure observed in recent electron microscope studies. *Quart. J. micr. Sci.* **94**, 351.

BRADFIELD, J. R. G. (1954). Electron microscopic observations on bacterial nuclei. *Nature, Lond.*, **173**, 184.

BRADFIELD, J. R. G. (1955). Fibre-patterns in animal cilia and flagella. In *Fibrous proteins and their biological significance*. Cambridge: University Press.

BRADFIELD, J. R. G. (1956). *Proc. 1st Int. Congr. Electronmicroscopy* (in the Press).

CASPERSSON, T. (1950). *Cell Growth and Cell Function*. London: Chapman and Hall.

CHAPMAN, G. B. & HILLIER, J. (1953). Electron microscopy of ultra-thin sections of bacteria. 1. Cellular division in *Bacillus cereus*. *J. Bact.* **66**, 362.

DANIELLI, J. F. (1953). *Cytochemistry*. London: Butterworth.

GEORGI, C. E., MILLITZER, W., BURNS, L. & HEOTIS, J. (1951). On the existence of a cell granule in a thermophilic bacterium. *Proc. Soc. exp. Biol.*, *N.Y.*, **76**, 598.

GLAUERT, A. M. & BRIEGER, E. M. (1955). The electron-dense bodies of *Mycobacterium phlei*. *J. gen. Microbiol.* **13**, 322.

GRULA, E. A. & HARTSELL, S. E. (1954). Intracellular structures in *Caulobacter vibrioides*. *J. Bact.* **68**, 498.

ITERSON, W. VAN (1953). Some remarks on the present state of our knowledge of bacterial flagellation. In *Bacterial Cytology, Symp. 6th Congr. int. Microbiol., Rome*.

KNAYSI, G. (1951). *Elements of Bacterial Cytology*, 2nd ed. Ithaca: Comstock.

KÖNIG, H. & WINKLER, A. (1948). Über Einschlüsse von Bakterien und ihre Veränderungen im Elektronenmikroskop. *Naturwissenschaften*, **35**, 136.

LEYON, H. (1953). The structure of chloroplasts. *Exp. Cell Res.* **4**, 371.

MINCK, R. & MINCK, A. (1949). Sur la constitution du bacille diptérique: Appareil nucléaire et granulations metachromatiques. *C.R. Acad. Sci., Paris*, **228**, 1313.

MITCHELL, P. (1949). The osmotic barrier in bacteria. In *The Nature of the Bacterial Surface*. edit. A. A. Miles & N. W. Pirie. Oxford: Blackwell.

MUDD, S. (1953). The mitochondria of bacteria. In *Bacterial Cytology, Symp. 6th Congr. int. Microbiol., Rome*.

MUDD, S. (1954). Cytology of bacteria. *Annu. Rev. Microbiol.* **8**, 1.

NORTHCOTE, D. H. & HORNE, R. W. (1952). The chemical composition and structure of the yeast cell wall. *Biochem. J.* **51**, 232.

PALADE, G. E. (1952). A study of fixation for electron microscopy. *J. exp. Med.* **95**, 285.

PALADE, G. E. & PORTER, K. (1954). Studies on the endoplasmic reticulum. *J. exp. Med.* **100**, 641.

PIJPER, A., CROCKER, C. G., VAN DER WALT, J. P. & SAVAGE, N. (1953). Flagellum and motility of *Spirillum serpens*. *J. Bact.* **66**, 628.

PRINGSHEIM, E. G. (1949). Iron bacteria. *Biol. Rev.* **24**, 200.

REPASKE, R. (1954). Succinic dehydrogenase of *Azotobacter vinelandii*. *J. Bact.* **68**, 555.

ROBINOW, C. F. & MURRAY, R. G. E. (1953). The differentiation of cell wall, cytoplasmic membrane and cytoplasm of Gram-positive bacteria by selective staining. *Exp. Cell Res.* **4**, 390.

SCHACHMAN, H. K., PARDEE, A. B. & STANIER, R. Y. (1952). Studies on the macromolecular structure of bacteria. *Arch. Biochem. Biophys.* **38**, 245.

SCHMAGER, A. & KLUDAS, M. (1950). Morphologischen Studien an Corynebacterien mit dem Phasenkontrastmikroskop. *Zentr. Bakt.* Abt. I. Orig. **156**, 502.

SEVAG, M. G., SMOLENS, J. & STERN, K. G. (1941). Pigmented heavy particles from *Streptococcus pyogenes*. *J. biol. Chem.* **139**, 925.

SMITH, I. W., WILKINSON, J. F. & DUGUID, J. P. (1954). Volutin production in *Aerobacter aerogenes* due to nutrient imbalance. *J. Bact.* **68**, 450.

STANIER, R. Y., GUNSALUS, I. C. & GUNSALUS, C. F. (1953). The enzymatic conversion of mandelic acid to benzoic acid. II. Properties of the particulate fractions. *J. Bact.* **66**, 543.

STEINMAN, E. & SJÖSTRAND, F. (1955). The ultra structure of chloroplasts. *Exp. Cell Res.* **8**, 15.

TISSIÈRES, A. (1952). Oxidation of glucose by a cell free preparation of *Aerobacter aerogenes*. *Nature, Lond.*, **169**, 880.

TISSIÈRES, A. (1954). Role of high molecular weight components in the respiratory activity of cell free extracts of *Aerobacter aerogenes*. *Nature, Lond.*, **174**, 183.

TISSIÈRES, A. & SLATER, E. C. (1955). Respiratory chain phosphorylation of *Azotobacter vinelandii*. *Nature, Lond.* (in the Press).

WATSON, M. L. (1955). The nuclear envelope. *J. Biochem. Biophys. Cytol.* **1**, 257.

WEBB, R. B. & CLARK, J. B. (1954). Cell division in *Micrococcus pyogenes* var. *aureus*. *J. Bact.* **67**, 94.

WEIBULL, C. (1953*a*). Observations on the staining of *Bacillus megaterium* with Triphenyltetrazolium. *J. Bact.* **66**, 137.

WEIBULL, C. (1953*b*). The isolation of protoplasts from *Bacillus megaterium* by controlled treatment with lysozyme. *J. Bact.* **66**, 688.

WEIBULL, C. (1953*c*). Characterization of the protoplasmic constituents of *Bacillus megaterium*. *J. Bact.* **66**, 696.

EXPLANATION OF PLATES

All figures except 4(*c*) and 5 show electron micrographs at 70 or 80 KV. of thin sections of organisms fixed in buffered 1 % osmium tetroxide solution and embedded in methacrylate.

PLATE 1

Fig. 1. *Staphylococcus aureus*. (*a*) Section showing more or less normal proportions of nucleus and cytoplasm. The central nucleus (much of which is less electron-opaque than the cytoplasm after osmic fixation) contains fibrous material and is surrounded by the granular cytoplasm. The dark patch in the latter is partly a sectioning artifact. (From Bradfield, 1954.) (*b*) Section including several organisms undergoing lysis with cytoplasmic granules more distinct and easily seen as they fall apart. (*c*) Section of organism prepared rather differently from those in (*a*) and (*b*), showing fairly clear distinction between outer cell wall and inner cytoplasmic membrane. The latter appears to be about 50 A. thick, though thickness in a print is, of course, very dependent on details of photographic processing. The cell shown is in division, and in the cross-walls three membranes can be detected. The upper and lower join at the inner edge of the cross-wall and are the cytoplasmic membrane; the central layer is the new cell wall, which later separates into two layers, one for each of the daughter cells.

Fig. 2. *Aerobacter aerogenes*. Glancing section through the edge of an organism showing cytoplasm entirely composed of granules 100–200 A. in diameter. The lifting off of the cell wall is accentuated by the fact that this is a glancing section.

Fig. 3. Paracolon bacillus D 201 H. Section of an organism from a culture 3 weeks old showing ramifying nucleus (the less opaque areas) and granular cytoplasm, some of the granules being rather more than 200 A. in diameter. (From Bradfield, 1954.)

PLATE 1

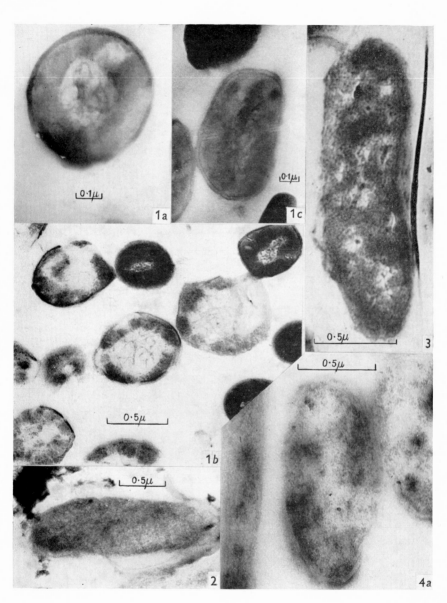

(*Facing p.* 316)

PLATE 2

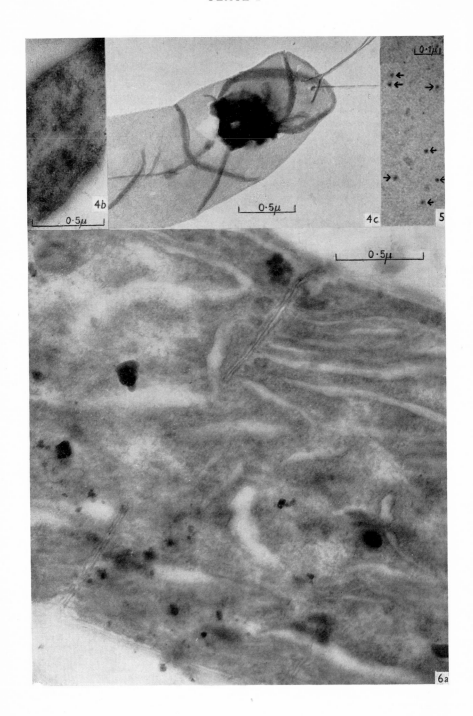

4b

0·5μ

0·5μ

0·1μ

4c

5

0·5μ

6a

PLATE 3

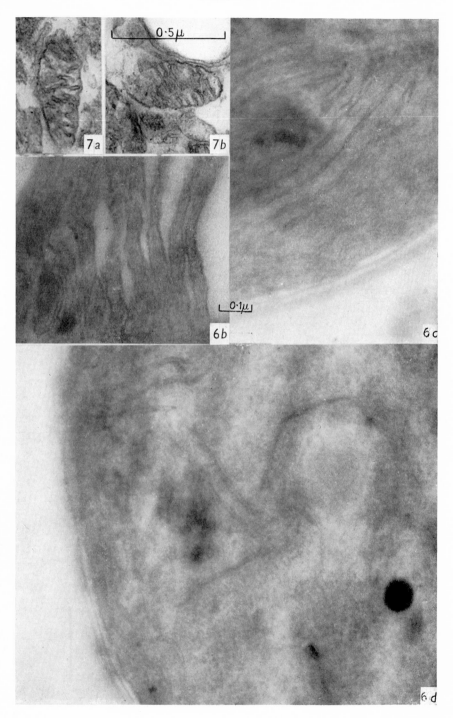

PLATE 2

Fig. 4. *Spirillum serpens*. (*a*), (*b*), Sections showing granular protoplasm. All that can be seen of a cytoplasmic membrane here is that the surface of the cytoplasm beneath the cell wall is in places rather more well defined and continuous than would be expected if the cytoplasm were a naked mass of granules. These places are presumably where the section passes more or less at right angles through a very thin cytoplasmic membrane. The section shown in fig. 1(*c*) is presumably equatorial, so that it cuts the cytoplasmic membrane more or less at right angles throughout its circumference. (*c*) One end of an unsectioned, trypsin-digested organism. All but three of the flagella have been lost. The large dense mass near the end of the organism is the mass of basal granules, as we know from electron micrographs of many similar, but less digested, organisms. The special interest of this organism lies in the apparent presence of a fibre running inward from the basal granule mass, traversing various folds in the flattened cell wall.

Fig. 5. *Azotobacter vinelandii*. Isolated unshadowed cytoplasmic granules (marked with arrows); diameter about 160 A. Preparation by Dr A. Tissières.

Fig. 6. *Oscillatoria formosa*. (*a*) Longitudinal section of one filament showing wide double membranes (400–900 A. centre to centre) in the cytoplasm, comparable with endoplasmic reticulum and containing large granules. The section also shows well-defined ingrowing cross-walls, containing rather thick (100–150 A.) cytoplasmic membranes above and below and a central layer, which eventually splits into the three distinct layers of the mature cell wall. (*b*) Another longitudinal section of the wide double membranes. (*c*), (*d*) Small areas from a transverse oblique section showing much narrower double membranes, only 100–150 A. centre to centre (and also showing the three layers of the mature cell wall).

PLATE 3

Fig. 7. (*a*), (*b*) Small animal mitochondria (from the salivary glands of *Chironomus* larvae) showing that the characteristic internal structure persists even in these small organelles, which are much more complex than anything yet found in bacterial cytoplasm.

INCLUSIONS IN BACTERIA

C. L. HANNAY

Science Service Laboratory, Department of Agriculture,
London, Ontario, Canada

This article is not concerned with lipid globules, volutin granules, glycogen, calcium carbonate concretions, droplets of sulphur in oil, which have often been described by bacterial cytologists, but with particular kinds of inclusion which are found in aerobic spore-forming bacilli at the time of spore formation. The matter is best introduced by a description of the author's experience with *Bacillus thuringiensis*. This organism is a variant, like *B. anthracis* and *B. mycoides*, of the ubiquitous *B. cereus*. It had previously been studied by Berliner (1911, 1915) and Mattes (1927), who both noticed that during sporulation a second body besides the spore was formed in each cell. This second body Berliner termed a 'Restkörper' or remaining body, and he suggested that it was formed from the materials in the cell which were not required for the formation of the spore. He described the *Restkörper* as initially spherical and then, as it increased in size, rhomboidal. Mattes confirmed Berliner's observations and added that the growth of the body changed the alignment of the spores so that the long axis no longer coincided with that of the whole chain of cells. This red herring—the spores lying obliquely in the cells—caught the attention of later workers and the *Restkörper* were forgotten. In 1946, Smith, Gordon & Clarke described *B. thuringiensis* as being identical with *B. cereus*, except that it was pathogenic for insects and that there was a tendency of the spores to lie obliquely in the cells, leaving two knobs of protoplasm after the sporangium had disintegrated. While examining the sporulation of a number of aerobic spore-formers which from their descriptions deviated cytologically from the normal, Hannay (1953) saw free diamond-shaped crystals in preparations of sporulating cultures of *B. thuringiensis*. It was then found that these crystals, many of them as large as the spores, were formed in the cells during sporulation and that each cell contained a crystal and a spore. The notation was different, but the *Restkörper* had been rediscovered. The significance attached to the presence of organic crystalline inclusions in these organisms will be discussed later. Perusal of the literature, followed by examination of a number of organisms, indicated that several species of aerobic bacilli form inclusions during sporulation. As the form of the inclusions varies considerably between species, some definitions are desirable. The term 'parasporal body' is used to denote an inclusion which lies alongside the spore and is formed during sporulation. Those inclusions which resemble crystals are called crystals; and those crystals which are known to be proteinaceous are called crystalloids. The different morphological forms of parasporal body range from the regular diamond-shaped crystals of *B. thuringiensis* and the ovoid membrane-enclosed medusal bodies to the rather amorphous-looking inclusions of *B. laterosporus*. These forms are illustrated diagrammatically in Text-fig. 1.

Detailed information is at present available about only one of them, *B. thuringiensis*, and this will be described first.

CRYSTALLOID PARASPORAL INCLUSIONS OF *BACILLUS THURINGIENSIS*

Microscopy

Under the light microscope, delineation of the fully formed parasporal bodies is easier and more accurate if use is made of their optical properties in preference to their staining characteristics. Robinow, realizing that the difficulty of staining mature spores within their cells had resulted in photographs of spored cultures being of a uniformly low standard, rejected direct-staining procedures and used the refractility of the spores in air-mounted nigrosin films to differentiate the spores from surrounding cell cytoplasm. Like the spores the parasporal bodies are highly refractile, and when viewed in air-mounted nigrosin films their sharp outline and their brilliance serve to differentiate them from other material. This technique contributed towards the discovery of the inclusions. Like all methods it has its limitations, and in the study of the parasporal bodies is most useful after sporulation has advanced to the point when the cytoplasm has decreased in optical density. Before this stage in the development of sporulation, excellent results can be obtained with phase-contrast microscopy, but even with this technique it is not possible to see the initial formation of the parasporal body. The morphology of the inclusions has been augmented by information obtained with the electron microscope, but a cytological study by the same means has not been completed.

Each sporing cell of *Bacillus thuringiensis* contains a spore and at least one parasporal body. The size of these inclusions varies greatly. The inclusions in most strains are regular diamond-shaped crystals (Text-figs. 1–3, Pl. 1, fig. 1), but Steinhaus (1954) has isolated strains in which the predominant form is rhomboidal to cuboidal. Both Berliner and Mattes described the *Restkörper* as being rhomboidal, and it was thought that the organisms as originally isolated by these authors might have formed inclusions similar to those described by Steinhaus. However, Mattes

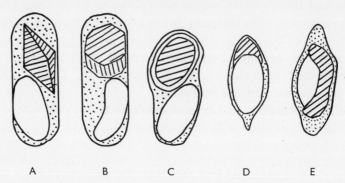

Text-fig. 1. Diagrams of different forms of inclusions associated with the spores of aerobic bacilli. The parasporal body has been shaded. A. Diamond-shaped parasporal body *Bacillus thuringiensis* Berliner. B. Cuboidal to rhomboidal-shaped parasporal body. *B. thuringiensis* isolated by Dr E. Steinhaus. C. Membrane-enclosed parasporal body. *B. medusa* isolated by Dr C. Robinow. D. Parasporal body. Variable shape. *B. popilliae* Dutky. E. Canoe-shaped parasporal body. *B. laterosporus* Laubach.

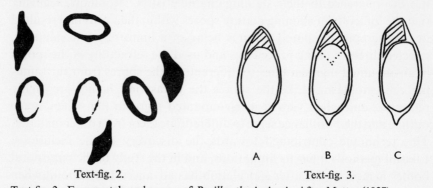

Text-fig. 2.   Text-fig. 3.

Text-fig. 2. Free crystals and spores of *Bacillus thuringiensis*. After Mattes (1927).

Text-fig. 3. A. Parasporal body and spore of *Bacillus popilliae*. After Dutky (1940). B and C. Two aspects of a parasporal body seen in preparations of *B. popilliae* isolated from infected insects.

included drawings of the *Restkörper*, which leave no doubt that his strain produced the diamond-shaped crystals and that the observations of Steinhaus are new. In the description of the bacilli, Hannay (1953) stated that each cell on sporulation contained only one crystal; Steinhaus (1954), however, reported that the occasional cell contained two inclusions but qualified his statement by saying that a freed inclusion might be superimposed on an inclusion-containing sporangium. The observation that cells may contain two inclusions has been confirmed. On Morton & Engley's medium (1945) *B. thuringiensis* does not spore, and by subculturing several times on this medium, growth was obtained free from spores and inclusions. A small amount of this growth was spread on the surface of nutrient agar and incubated until sporulation was well advanced but not until there were free crystals and spores. In films prepared from these plates a number of the bacilli contained two diamond-shaped crystals and one spore.

A curious phenomenon occurs on completion of sporulation; the spores remain within the exosporium but the majority of the crystals are free. A number of cells have been examined with the electron microscope, but the presence of a rent in the exosporium has not been established, and we are left uncertain whether the loose membrane in which the spore lies was synthesized during sporulation and never contained the crystal or whether the membrane is part of the old vegetative cell wall and the rent made by the crystal's departure has gone unobserved. Berliner's observation that some of the *Restkörper* are firmly attached to the spore has been confirmed.

The crystals stain readily with most biological dyes, but in particular they have some affinity for the acid stains. With Millon's reagent the crystals do not stain sufficiently for any colour to be seen under the microscope. With Ponceau de xylidine in N/10-HCl they stain a pale orange-red. The mercuric bromphenol blue reagent devised by Darrum (1950) for the staining of proteins and used according to the method of Mazia, Brewer & Alfert (1953) gave variable results. During treatment in dilute acetic acid most of the dye left the crystals, and it is uncertain whether the dye which remained was absorbed or whether it had reacted with the protein. The crystals were soluble in dilute alkali, and the material obtained was positive with the Millon's, biuret and xanthoproteic tests, but gave a negative Molisch test. The staining reactions and the chemical tests indicated a small number of free reactive groups in the intact crystal.

The diamond-shaped crystals were examined with the electron microscope by Hannay & Fitz-James (1955), and for full details their paper should be consulted. The crystals are regular in shape, are octahedra with a tetragonal form and lie on a plane surface with the tip of one pyramid projecting into the air (Pl. 1, fig. 5). In contrast, the rhomboidal to cuboidal inclusions formed in the new strain of *Bacillus thuringiensis* isolated by Steinhaus are irregular in shape (Pl. 1, figs. 6, 7).

The crystals were found to be very pliable and subject to considerable distortion in the electron microscope. The edges of many shadowed diamond-shaped crystals were serrated and the surface had a periodicity which was not seen on unshadowed inclusions. By changes in the beam intensity the crystals could be completely disintegrated, partially disrupted so that the striae seen on surface of the crystals were projected on to the supporting membrane, or affected so that a few of the crystals were almost reduced to shells. The best photograph of a shell is to be seen in the original paper; another example is illustrated in Pl. 2, fig. 8. The authors remarked that 'the serrated edges previously seen on the crystals are now resolved into parallel rows of material which extend round the corners of the crystal. The technique has failed to make it clear whether each pyramid is composed of the same number of rows; whether the pyramids have adjacent basal rows of equal dimensions or one basal row common to both; whether the rows extend throughout the crystal and whether they form a plate or a spiral about a dislocation in the crystal centre.' Despite the fact that the serrated surface was only seen on shadowed specimens, it was felt that the periodicity reflected a structural characteristic of the crystals rather than an artifact.

Treatment of the crystals with dilute sodium hydroxide solution disrupted them and the large striae, originally seen on the surface, disintegrated. No virus-like particles were seen amongst the alkali-dispersed protein.

The crystals of *Bacillus thuringiensis* are not covered with a membrane. It was stated that when crystals were treated with dilute alkali the crystals, while still retaining their shape, greatly increased in size, then lost their refractility and finally disappeared, leaving behind a shell or membrane (Hannay, 1953). In a more recent paper, Hannay & Fitz-James (1955) found that when a solution of sodium hydroxide was added to a water suspension of crystals they lost their refractility at pH 10–10·7, swelled to form ghosts at pH 10·7–11·8, and at pH 12·5 were completely disrupted. The authors said that the ghost forms (Pl. 2, fig. 12), which were found to contain all of the nitrogen of the crystal, had previously been mistaken for membranes.

Chemistry

Before any chemical analysis of the inclusions could be made, methods for obtaining sufficient material free from spores, debris and old vegetative cells had to be devised (Hannay & Fitz-James, 1955). The difficulties involved in separating the crystals by differential centrifugation necessitated the development of other methods. One method depended on the alkali fractionation of a sporulating culture and the separation of the alkali-dispersible crystal material from spores, vegetative cell debris and their alkali-soluble components. Two methods for obtaining intact crystals free from other substances were evolved: one depended on the mechanical disruption of the spores and the other on the germination and autolysis of the spores. After either method pure suspensions of crystals were obtained by repeated washing and differential centrifugation.

The purest preparations of crystalline material contained slightly more than 17% nitrogen and no phosphorus. Only α-amino acids were detected in an acid hydrolysate: arginine, lysine, aspartic, glutamic, glycine, histidine, alanine, proline, serine, tyrosine, valine, leucine, isoleucine, phenylalanine, threonine and methionine. No test was made for cysteine-cystine. Tryptophan was detected in an alkali hydrolysate.

This qualitative analysis of the crystal does not differ significantly from that of the amino acids found in *Escherichia coli* (Polson & Wyckoff, 1948), T_3 bacteriophage (Fraser & Jerrel, 1953), or botulinum toxin (Buehler, Schantz & Lamanna, 1947).

On addition of sodium hydroxide solution to a water suspension of the crystals, they were not completely dispersed below pH 12·2; above this pH they formed a colourless viscous solution and contained a substance precipitable with trichloracetic acid. When the viscous solution was centrifuged at 10,000 g a clear jelly-like pellet was formed which contained 84% of the total nitrogen; and of the 16% N remaining in the supernatant 89% was precipitated on the addition of an equal volume of 20% trichloracetic acid. The ultra-violet spectra of both the viscous solution of the whole crystals and the fraction which was not precipitated at 10,000 g were typical of proteins. Since the molecular weights of the two proteins were unknown it was convenient for comparison to express the ultra-violet absorption values as ϵ (N). The two fractions showed slight differences in the 280 and 290 mμ region. It was not known if the treatment of the crystals with sodium hydroxide produced two substances and attention was drawn to the need for some correlation between the method of dispersing the crystals and a biological test, such as toxicity to insect larvae or serological reaction.

Cytology

A cytological study of the inclusions in the cell has only just started. In the laboratory we have been bedevilled by the variability of sporulation on nutrient agar and a satisfactory formula has not yet been found for a synthetic medium which will give consistently good growth, synchronous sporulation with the formation of healthy spores, and parasporal bodies in all strains of *Bacillus thuringiensis*. The study of the formation of the crystals during sporulation would be much easier if it were possible to make comparisons with contemporary work on the cytology of sporulation of non-inclusion-forming strains of bacilli. The papers of Klieneberger-Nobel (1945) and Flewett (1948), while excellent, are not sufficiently comprehensive to be used for comparative purposes, and it is to be regretted that they did not continue to work in this field.

The mode of sporulation of these inclusion-forming strains differs according to the physiological conditions and the method of inoculating the medium. When nutrient agar plates have been inoculated from sporulating cultures, sporulation has been erratic and has taken place in cells containing four chromatinic bodies, as with the spore-formers described by the authors mentioned above. Recently a different method of inoculation has been found to give a more synchronous sporulation on nutrient agar, sporulation occurring in most cells when there are only two chromatinic bodies. The technique was as follows: the growth from a 6 hr. culture on nutrient agar was washed off with distilled water, washed twice by centrifugation, and resuspended in distilled water to give a fairly turbid suspension. Petri dishes containing 15 ml. of Difco nutrient agar were dried at 32° for 15 min. and the surface inoculated with 0·5 ml. of the washed bacterial suspension. The plates were not incubated until the water had been imbibed by the agar. Crystal and spore formation usually began within 16 hr. and was complete after 21 hr. incubation at 32°. The photographs of Text-figs. 1, 2 and 3, and Pl. 1, fig. 1 and Pl. 3, figs. 10 and 11 were of preparations grown in this way.

The cytological stage of sporulation at which crystal formation commences is different in cells containing four chromatinic bodies and in cells containing two chromatinic bodies. In those containing four chromatinic bodies the crystal can usually be seen as soon as a chromatinic body is beginning to develop into a spore at one end of the cell. The chromatinic body at this stage is relatively small, appears spherical, and has not as yet formed a visible ring-like structure. During sporulation in cells containing two chromatinic bodies, these retain their positions in the cell and the spore starts in the room of one of them. In these cells the crystals have not been seen until after the spore has reached a considerable size and the chromatinic body has already developed into a ring-like structure and the spore contents are about to stain as uniformly as those illustrated in Pl. 3, fig. 11. A further difference between the two modes of sporulation has been noticed in the staining reaction of those chromatinic bodies which do not appear to contribute to sporulation. In the cells containing four chromatinic bodies the latter rapidly lose their ability to take up stain as soon as sporulation begins. In the cells containing two chromatinic bodies the remaining body stains readily until sporulation is well advanced and the spore chromatin has already formed a ring structure. In summary, it may be said that under these conditions of growth the parasporal bodies can be formed in sporing cells which contain either two or four chromatinic bodies, and that the growth of the crystal appears to be more closely associated with the chromatinic bodies which do not contribute to sporulation than with any stage in the development of the spore. Association does not imply cause and effect; the loss in staining properties of the remaining chromatinic bodies may correspond to other changes in the cell directly concerned with the formation of the inclusions. The phrase 'growth of the crystal' has been used because the initial formation of the crystal has not been seen with the light microscope. The general question how a crystal grows should follow the more particular question, whether the chromatinic bodies which do not form spores are connected with crystal formation. At the stage of sporulation illustrated by Pl. 3, fig. 11, an unstained membrane can be seen with the light microscope, which besides covering the spore seems to extend under the crystal. The spore, together with these membranes, looks rather like a misshapen teardrop. There are now three problems in connexion with sporulation: the association of the crystals with the chromatinic bodies, the membranes which extend under the crystal and, as was mentioned much earlier, the adherence of some inclusions to the spore.

Visual evidence that these problems exist is provided by the electron micrograph of an ultra-thin section showing a cell containing a spore and a crystal (Pl. 3, fig. 10). Part of the spore is shown in the upper right-hand corner. The outer membranes of the spore in this particular cell are associated with a membrane which passes from the spore, under the crystal, to the end of the cell where it forms a loop. The chromatinic body which did not form the spore was expected to be found in the area occupied by the loop. The remnants of what may be a membrane can also be seen above the crystal. A light microscope picture of the same preparation before it was embedded in methacrylate is illustrated in Pl. 3, fig. 11.

THE SIGNIFICANCE OF THE INCLUSIONS IN RELATION TO TOXICITY AND PATHOGENICITY

Insect pathologists of several countries have been studying an endemic disease of larvae caused by an aerobic spore-forming bacillus. In each country the causal organism has been given a different name but it is now known that many of these organisms are *Bacillus cereus* variants which, in addition to possessing the physiological characteristics of *B. cereus*, are pathogenic to insect larvae and form crystalloid inclusions during sporulation. The three best known strains are *B. sotto*, *B. thuringiensis* and *B. cereus* var. *alesti*.

In Japan, Ishiwata (1902) isolated from diseased silkworm larvae (*Bombyx mori* L.) an organism which he named *Bacillus sotto*, 'sotto' meaning 'sudden collapse'. He showed that old cultures that had been grown on agar were toxic when eaten by larvae, whereas broth cultures were innocuous (1906). Aoki & Chigasaki (1915) noted that young vegetative cultures were neither toxic nor pathogenic when given orally but were pathogenic when injected into the body cavity. They concluded that old cultures contained a toxic substance which was not present in young cultures, and later they found that the toxic substance was associated with sporulating cultures and not with the medium on which they were grown. The toxic substance was destroyed by treating with iodine, mercuric chloride, formalin, alcohol or by boiling the cultures for 10 min. It is clear that by 1915 it was believed that old cultures of *B. sotto* were pathogenic and contained a toxic substance associated with the spores.

In Germany, Berliner (1911) isolated an aerobic spore-forming bacillus from diseased flour-moth larvae (*Ephestia kuhniella* Zell.). The disease he described as 'Schlaffseucht' (1911), and the causative agent as *Bacillus thuringiensis* (1915). Both Berliner (1915) and Mattes (1927), who confirmed Berliner's work, found that vegetative cells were only slightly pathogenic. They did not report the presence of a toxic substance associated with older cultures, or attach any significance to the *Restkörper* which they observed in sporing bacilli. Mattes (1927) stated that the growth of the *Restkörper* slightly changed the normal alignment of the spores so that the long axis no longer coincided with that of the whole chain of cells. The *Restkörper* was forgotten, but the angle at which the spores lay in the cells was remembered and quoted by later workers. Smith *et al.* (1946) classified *B. thuringiensis* as a variant of *B. cereus* because, apart from its pathogenicity for certain insects and the tendency for the spores to lie obliquely in the cells, the organism was indistinguishable from *B. cereus*. Steinhaus (1951) found in field trials that *B. thuringiensis* applied as a dried spore powder reduced the population of the alfalfa larvae (*Colias philodice eurytheme* Boisduval) to below the destructive level. Attention was drawn by Hannay (1953) to the presence of crystalline inclusions in sporing cells of *B. thuringiensis* and other insect pathogens related to *B. cereus*. It was speculated that the crystals might in some way be connected with the formation of a toxic substance inducing septicaemia of the insect larvae.

In France, Pasteur in 1870 wrote that the disease 'flacherie' of silk-worms was accompanied by multiplication of a spore-forming organism in the infected larvae and that powders containing the spores were still infective after storage for a year. Toumanoff & Vago (1951) isolated the causal organism and named it *Bacillus cereus* var. *alesti*. They described the progressive symptoms of the disease as sluggishness, paralysis and death; however, these symptoms varied with the amount of cultures ingested by the larvae (1952). Large doses produced a rapidly lethal effect which they called toxaemia, small doses killed more slowly with septicaemia. Toumanoff & Vago confirmed the work of Aoki & Chiga-saki (1951) when they found that in severe cases of toxaemia the ingested spores had failed to grow. They concluded 'Ils n'ont certainement pas le temps de s'y développer et la mort et l'intoxication doivent certainement être imputées à l'effet d'une substance toxique ou à une toxine soit sécrétée par les bacilles, dans le milieu, soit accumulée dans leur corps' (1953*a*). In a later paper during the same year (1953*b*), they reported that young cultures were not always toxic, but that sporulating culture produced toxaemia and that the toxic effects could be prevented by pre-heating the sporulating culture at 120°. The heated spores maintained their viability and pathogenicity. Attention was drawn to diamond-shaped crystalline inclusions in *B. cereus* var. *alesti* by Steinhaus (1954), and by Toumanoff & Vago (1954).

On the North American continent, Angus (1953, 1954*a*), working with *Bacillus sotto* and silkworm larvae, was the first to make use of the observations that sporulating cultures contained both a toxic substance and crystalline inclusions. Angus first confirmed the work of Aoki & Chigasaki (1915), then, with a pleasantly direct approach to the problem, he established a relationship between spore suspension and larval meta-bolism. A washed sporulating culture of *B. sotto* was suspended in silk-worm-gut juice and incubated at 28° for 6 hr., after which the mixture was centrifuged, the supernatant sterilized by filtration and the filtrate fed to larvae. The filtrate caused paralysis of silkworm larvae; a portion heated at 100° for 30 min. had no effect. Contrary to the findings of Toumanoff & Vago (1953*b*) a water extract of a sporulating culture was not toxic. Because silkworm-gut juice is normally very alkaline, pH 9·5–10, and on starvation the pH may rise to between 10 and 11, Angus extracted a spore suspension with dilute sodium hydroxide. The steri-lized extract caused paralysis. At about this time Angus received infor-mation that *B. thuringiensis* and some related strains formed alkali-soluble crystalline inclusions during sporulation, and a microscopic examination of *B. sotto* revealed that similar crystals were formed within this organism. Circumstantial evidence as to the role that crystalline inclusions might play in producing paralysis and inducing septicaemia was obtained by comparing the effects on larvae of a mixture containing crystals and spores, of spores freed from crystals and of an alkaline extract prepared from a suspension of spores and crystals. These fractions were tested on larvae by both feeding and injection into the body cavity. The results are given in Table 1. Further evidence which implicated the crystals as a source of toxic material was obtained when

Table 1. *The effect of feeding and injecting larvae of* Bombyx mori L. *with fractions of an alkali-treated culture of* Bacillus sotto (Angus, 1954 a)

Original culture	Method of dosing larvae	
	By feeding	By injection
Spores and crystals (1×10^5 spores per larva)	Paralysis within 4 hr.; septicaemia within 12 hr.	Septicaemia within 12 hr. No paralysis
Alkali-treated culture:		
(1) Spore fraction (1×10^7 spores per larva)	No effect	Septicaemia within 12 hr.
(2) Supernatant	Paralysis within 4 hr. No septicaemia	No effect
(3) Supernatant dialysed	Paralysis within 4 hr. No septicaemia	No effect
(4) Supernatant heated at 70° for 30 min.	No effect	No effect

Angus, after finding that the proportion of spores which autogerminated and lysed varied considerably between preparations, fed to larvae graded doses of suspensions containing different crystal-spore ratios. The toxicity varied directly with the crystal count and was independent of the spore content (1954*a*). Using a modification of one of the earlier methods developed by Hannay & Fitz-James (1955) for the separation of the alkali-dispersible crystal protein from spores, vegetative debris and their alkali-soluble components, Angus isolated a toxic protein from a sporulating culture (1954*b*). When administered orally, at a dosage rate of 0·5–1·0μg./g. larval weight, the protein caused paralysis within 6 hr. and death within 24 hr. but when injected into the body cavity the protein was non-toxic. Whereas a solution of the toxic compound was inactivated by heating at 55° for 15 min., a water suspension of intact untreated crystals still remained toxic after being heated for 1 hr. at 80°.

Investigation of the correlation between pathogenicity, toxicity and the possession of inclusions has been confined in the *cereus* group to a few bacilli already selected for their virulence and to test-species of insects selected for their susceptibility. The perspective was improved when Steinhaus (1954) tested fifty-one strains of spore-forming bacteria for both pathogenicity and the presence of inclusions. The fifty-one strains included *Bacillus thuringiensis*, *B. ephestia*, *B. laterosporus*, *B. alvei*, *B. sphaericus*, *B. subtilis*, *B. firmus*, *B. circulans*, *B. cereus* (from sources other than diseased insects), *B. megaterium*, *B. mycoides* and *B. pumilus*. The bacilli were fed and injected into groups of alfalfa caterpillars and buckeye caterpillars. Of these fifty-one strains of bacilli, the

Table 2. *The susceptibility of insect larvae with different midgut alkalinity to spored cultures and to toxin* (Angus, 1954*b*)

Insect species	Maximum pH of midgut	Relative susceptibility* following ingestion of	
		Whole organism	Toxin
Bombyx mori	10·0	+ + + +	+ + + +
Nymphalis antiopa	9·4	+ + +	+
Porthetria dispar	9·3	+ + +	+ +
Anisota rubicunda	9·3	+ + +	+ +
Anisota senatoria	9·6	+ + +	Not tested
Datana integerrima	9·0	+ + +	Not tested
Galleria mellonella	8·0	None	None
Diprion hercyniae	8·3	None	None
Neodiprion americanus banksianae	7·7	None	None
Neodiprion abietis	8·5	None	None
Neodiprion sertifer	8·2	None	None

* Graded from + + + + (highly susceptible) to + (slightly susceptible).

eleven strains of *B. thuringiensis* were the most virulent and were the only cultures related to *B. cereus* containing inclusions; spore-formers obtained from sources other than diseased insects were mainly non-pathogenic. Two hours after eating a sporulating culture of *B. thuringiensis* both species of insects showed signs of diarrhoea and vomiting; four hr. later they were suffering from partial paralysis and within 3 days the alfalfa caterpillars had died of general septicaemia; but the buckeye larvae were less susceptible to infection. The susceptibility of a wider range of insect species both to suspensions of *B. sotto* crystals and spores, and to partially purified inclusion protein was tested by Angus (1954*b*) (Table 2). These preliminary observations are indicative of a correlation of toxicity with insect species having a high gut pH. However, the toxicity of the alkali-dispersed crystal protein and that of the intact crystals and spores was confined to identical species, and it seems reasonable to suggest that an alkaline gut which disperses the crystals is therefore not the only condition required for the protein to be toxic.

Observations on the toxicity of the inclusions when administered as a crystal-spore mixture may be complicated by two factors which deserve closer attention. Toumanoff & Vago (1952) found that unfed larvae were more susceptible to toxaemia than were those that had just eaten, and Heimpel (1954) found that lecithinase produced by *Bacillus cereus* is toxic to many insects, particularly to those in which the midgut pH lies between 7 and 8. While the pH of the midgut of the silkworm is outside this range, the lecithinase might have some toxic effect if present in sufficient quantity or if fed with crystalline inclusions. Lecithinase prepared from *B. cereus* var. *alesti* was found by Toumanoff, Vago & Gladiline (1954) to be very toxic when injected into the silkworm larvae but only slightly toxic when taken orally.

It has been established that there is a triangle of variables: host, bacillus and inclusions. Because the limits of these variables have not as yet been clearly defined, and the number and extent of their interactions are unknown, it is difficult to assess the relative importance of any of them. There are variations within each variable which have to be considered.

Insect host. Species; age at time of contact with bacillus, spores and inclusions; feeding; enzymes present in the gut; gut alkalinity; susceptibility to inclusions and infection; general environmental conditions.

Bacillus. Strains; age; vegetative cells; sporing cells; spores; germinating spores; susceptibility of spores to autogermination and lysis; enzymes in vegetative cells, e.g. phospholipase; presence of uncrystallized toxic material; cultural medium; resistance to unfavourable conditions in the insect gut; virulence.

Inclusions. Source; effect of the cultural conditions of the bacteria on the chemical, physical and toxic properties of the inclusions.

Consideration of even a few of the variations presented by each component of the triangle reveals such a formidable array of interactions that the pathologist must plan his work knowing that he will need analysis of variance to help interpret his results.

For insects the most pathogenic members of the *Bacillus cereus* group are those variants which, while possessing the general physiological characteristics of the group, form crystalloid inclusions during sporulation. The emphasis has been shifted from the tendency of the spores to lie obliquely in the cells to the presence of inclusions. The significance of the inclusions needs to be assessed from two different but finally connected viewpoints. The first is the relationship of the inclusion to the bacterial cell, the reason for its being formed, and its connexion with other components of the cell; the second is the relationship of the inclusions to susceptible insect larvae, the possible alteration of the inclusions to a substance producing paralysis, and the relation of the toxic substance to invasion of the larval tissues by bacteria. Nothing concerning the relationship of the inclusion to the rest of the bacterial cell has been published, and the information regarding its relationship to larvae is as yet meagre and qualitative. When susceptible larvae are fed approximately 0.5μg. of the proteinaceous crystalline material per g. body weight they are paralysed after a few hours, and eventually killed. When the same material is given by injection into the body cavity the larvae continue to thrive. Since the crystalline material is the cause of paralysis it must be concluded either that the material when injected into the body cavity does not reach the proper site or that it is not toxic *per se*. Perhaps it has to undergo some change in the gut or surrounding cells before it is effective. That the dissolution of the crystals is not the only factor required to produce a toxic compound is also suggested in those experiments in which a correlation was formed between the toxicity of whole crystal, or even of dispersed crystalline material, and insect species with a high midgut pH. Those insects which have a high midgut pH may contain enzymes which break down the protein to a toxic substance, and it is unfortunate that Angus (1953), when he found that gut juice released a substance from a sporulating culture which was toxic when taken orally, did not inject a similar preparation into the body cavity. It is possible that the problem is more complex and that the protein has to be changed in the gut, the product having an affinity for some component of the enzyme systems in the gut epithelial cells and the muscles or nervous tissues consequently being affected by the metabolic changes. Pappenheimer & Williams (1952) showed that tissues of *Cecropia* silkworms containing certain cytochromes were susceptible to the action of diphtheria toxin, whereas those tissues containing other cytochromes were resistant. Later these authors examined the activities of a cytochrome which they isolated from the midgut of *Cecropia* silkworms and concluded that cytochrome b_5 probably accounts for much of the cyanide-, carbon monoxide- and antimycin-resistant DPNH oxidation (Pappenheimer & Williams, 1954).

It would be advantageous, and it is perhaps necessary, to answer two questions before studying any mechanism of inhibition: (1) the dispersal of the crystalloids *in vitro* may be accompanied by considerable denaturation. Does denaturation occur *in vivo* and what are the dispersing agents in the gut? (2) After the crystal protein is dispersed in the gut is it altered to a compound which is toxic when injected into the body cavity? Only when these processes in the gut have been elucidated will a direct approach to the nature of the toxicity be possible.

At present, the only information on the relationship of inclusions to the invasion of the larval tissues is that obtained by Angus (Table 1). The results obtained were unequivocal; crystals and spores caused paralysis and septicaemia, spores alone failed to infect the larvae. In these experiments it is possible that the high concentration of material administered killed the larvae or rendered them moribund before the spores germinated and the bacteria invaded the tissues. Under natural conditions it is unlikely that larvae would receive massive doses of crystals and spores and the question 'Is the crystal connected with the formation of a toxic substance inducing septicaemia of the insect larvae?' is unanswered. It would be of interest to know whether there is a dose of crystal material which, without killing the larvae, permits the invasion of tissues by the inclusion-forming bacteria and the related, non-inclusion-forming, *Bacillus cereus*, *B. mycoides* and avirulent *B. anthracis*.

The original tests on the pathogenicity and toxicity of vegetative cells and sporulating cultures were made before any significance was attached to the presence of inclusions. All the tests need repeating, particularly those in which spores were included. Angus has for some time past suspected that a considerably smaller dose of a mixture of spores and crystals was required to produce a given degree of paralysis than when crystals were used alone (personal communication). In the work of Aoki & Chigasaki and Toumanoff, in which large doses of spores (presumably a mixture of spores and crystals) caused paralysis without subsequent growth of bacteria, it is uncertain whether it was appreciated that many of the spores may have lysed or germinated but not grown into vegetative cells.

Until there is more integrated information of the role of inclusions in the host-parasite relationship, it will not be possible to see the problem in proper perspective.

Other forms of parasporal bodies

Canoe-shaped parasporal body

The spores of *Bacillus laterosporus* Laubach after lysis of the vegetative cell are seen cradled in a canoe-shaped parasporal body (Pl. 4, fig. 13). This parasporal body differs from those previously described in its staining properties and in its close intimacy with the spore. Robinow found that even after hydrolysis the parasporal bodies stained brilliantly with Giemsa. The order of formation of spore and body is not known, but the close intimacy could arise if at the beginning of sporulation the body developed preferentially and then the spore grew and matured within its embrace. The process of sporulation was described by Laubach, Rice & Ford (1916): 'as the organisms swell and assume the fusiform shape the spores appear as lightly staining globules. The protoplasm soon disintegrates but more on one side than on the other so that the free spores which are egg-shaped retain a rim of protoplasm on one side and present a characteristic appearance. As the spores mature they begin to lose their rim. Rarely small tags of protoplasm remain attached at the ends of the spores.'

That *Bacillus laterosporus* may not be the only species which is capable of forming canoe-shaped parasporal bodies was indicated by Smith *et al.* (1946) who wrote 'In the present work, however, certain other closely related species, especially *B. brevis* and *B. circulans*, at times formed spores showing this character, but the number of such spores in a smear was never very large.' These three organisms have in common the appearance of the cell during sporulation; in each case the cell becomes swollen and fusiform in shape. Of the three only *B. laterosporus* has been described as being associated with an insect disease.

Membrane-enclosed parasporal bodies

Dr Robinow some years ago isolated from cow dung an aerobic bacillus which is cytologically one of the more interesting members of the genus. This organism was called *Bacillus medusa*. On sporulation there is formed in the cells a highly refractile parasporal body and a refractile spore; usually the formation of one begins slightly before the other, but which starts first has not been determined. Unlike the spore, the parasporal bodies do not contain a chromatinic body nor do they germinate when placed on fresh medium, but like the spore they are covered with a thick membrane (Pl. 4, fig. 13) which Dr Robinow has shown with the electron microscope to be made up of several layers. Usually with the light microscope the material enclosed by the membranes appears to be homogeneous, but occasionally areas are seen which do not stain. Ponceau de xylidine in N-HCl stains many of the parasporal bodies; those which do not stain with this dye are resistant to most staining methods. The proportion of bodies stained appears to depend on the medium on which the organisms have been grown. Strictly speaking, the parasporal bodies are not alkali-soluble. However, the bacteria when grown on some media produce bodies that, when immersed in N-

NaOH solution, swell and burst, spilling their contents, but when the bacteria are grown on other media the bodies are resistant to treatment with 10 N-NaOH solution. From microscopical observation it is felt that the parasporal bodies, which are ultimately larger than the spores, continue to grow after the spores have matured, and that during growth there is a competition between the two bodies for available materials from a common pool. Most media appear to favour the growth of the parasporal body with the result that many bean-shaped spores are formed, and in extreme cases the spores may lyse before they are completed or, even if completed, may autogerminate.

On nutrient or heart-infusion agar the bacterial cells are inordinately long as compared with those of *Bacillus cereus*; they grow in chains in the wildest disorder associated with varying degrees of lysis, cell size, fat content, dissociation and secondary colony formation. The diagrams of *B. medusa* in Text-fig. 1C and the photograph in Pl. 4, fig. 13, were prepared from bacteria grown on a semi-synthetic medium on which the growth is more controlled. The surface of the cells is covered with a slimy layer which sloughs off more readily than would be expected of the usual bacterial capsule. Like *B. thuringiensis* this bacillus produces substances at the time of sporulation that are inimical to the satisfactory growth of the subculture.

If *Bacillus medusa* is grown in a large volume of broth and after a week's incubation plated out, the colonies exhibit a variety of characteristics. The cells of some colonies contain inclusions which resemble those of *B. thuringiensis*. Usually in these cells the rest of the contents have lysed and no spores are seen.

Although many of the physiological characteristics of *Bacillus medusa* have been determined, no relationship to other members of the genus has been established. While in some respects it resembles *B. cereus* it does not produce lecithinase in egg-yolk broth. The identity of this organism may be obscured by its ability to form inclusions and a parent strain free from such bodies might possess physiological characteristics which would relate it to a classified member of the genus. Alternatively, it may be aberrant and not conform to the pattern of an existing species.

Another organism which, if its parasporal body is enclosed in a membrane, may be closely related to *Bacillus medusa* was described in a communication by Fowler & Harrison to the American Society of Bacteriologists in 1952. They reported that they had isolated an 'aerobic spore-forming bacillus resembling *Bacillus cereus* in its size, growth, spore germination pattern and biochemical tests, which during sporulation develops an extra, less refractile, globular body that adheres to the spore throughout its subsequent germination and, having taken no visible part in germination, often remains attached to the spore coat'.

The chemical composition of these parasporal bodies is not known, but the presence of protein is indicated by the staining properties of the parasporal bodies of *Bacillus medusa*. Neither organism is known to be an insect pathogen.

The inclusions of Bacillus popilliae

The inclusions of *Bacillus popilliae* Dutky vary in shape from hemispherical to subconical, but this form may be imposed on them by their growth within the limiting confines of the cell. Through the courtesy of Dr Steinkraus of Cornell University, I have been able to examine slides of this organism and have found that a few of the spored bacilli contained diamond-shaped crystals which are illustrated in Pl. 1, fig. 1 *b* and *c*. Unlike any of the cultures of *B. thuringiensis* that I have seen, the crystals were squeezed between the spore and the cell wall.

Dutky (1940) described the formation of the spores and parasporal body within the cell, 'When the cell begins to swell, the spore becomes visible as a slightly refractile vacuole equal in size to the mature spore. As sporulation proceeds, the vacuole becomes more refractile until a definite spore is observed. At this time the cell has a pronounced spindle shape and the spore is located somewhat terminally. One end of cell broadens, and the cell becomes more pyriform than spindle-shaped. A granule is now observed at the broadened end, which grows until it is about half the size of the spore. With the development of the granule the spore assumes a more central position; the cytoplasm about the spore becomes increasingly refringent.' Dutky found that the parasporal bodies were resistant to most methods of staining, but that with Dorner's spore stain both the spore and the parasporal body were stained. He also noted that the refractile bodies were resistant to immersion in 10% sodium hydroxide solution.

Bacillus popilliae was isolated by Dutky (1940) and was found to be the organism causing milky disease of the Japanese beetle *Popillia japonica*. A closely related bacillus causing a milky disease of *Odontria zealandica* was isolated by Dumbleton (1945). It was reported that this species formed a spherical parasporal body.

GENERAL REMARKS

A number of different species of aerobic spore-forming bacilli have been shown to form parasporal bodies on sporulation. Of the four species forming parasporal bodies, *Bacillus thuringiensis*, *B. popilliae*, *B. laterosporus* and *B. medusa*, the first two are known insect pathogens, the third has been associated with an insect disease, and the fourth still provides a happy hunting ground for microbiologists. The form of the parasporal bodies may vary both within and between species of bacilli. The general chemical composition of the bodies is as yet unknown but there are indications that some are proteinaceous. The parasporal bodies of *B. thuringiensis* are highly toxic to some species of insect larvae, and as a result of these toxic effects the bacilli are able to invade the larval tissues. The relation of the parasporal bodies to pathogenicity in other species of bacilli is not known.

Each form of parasporal body and each species of inclusion-forming bacteria may possess different salient features. When viewed collectively, these suggest questions that are of fundamental importance. The salient features noticed and the questions asked will depend upon the inclinations of the observer. Unfortunately, the amount of information on the inclusions and their formation is woefully inadequate and there is a danger that the author, in clutching straws, has developed a bias in the wrong direction and has finally asked the wrong question.

The spores and inclusions of *Bacillus thuringiensis* are formed within a period of 5 hr. The production of proteinaceous crystals within that period of time is not exceptional. Charcot-Leyden crystals described by Charcot & Robin (1853) and Leyden (1872) are proteinaceous crystals formed from eosinophils and are believed to be products of the nuclei. These crystals are larger than the bacterial inclusions and measure from $7-21\mu$. in length and occasionally lengths of 96μ. have been recorded (Ayers, 1949; Dawe & Williams, 1953). While, normally, the crystals are formed as a result of bacterial action over a period of days, they can be induced *in vitro* within a few minutes or hours with synthetic detergents or wetting agents. That bacteria can transform one crystalline protein without serious damage into another crystalline protein was shown by Linderström-Lang & Ottesen (1947). Within 5 hr. 90% of a solution of ovalbumin needle crystals was converted by an extracellular protease from *B. subtilis* into a modified protein which crystallized in the form of rectangular plates. No reference in the literature has been found to bacteria producing enzymes which will change their own protein into a crystalline form, but recently there has been work which indicates that bacteria produce substances which act specifically on their own species. Greenberg & Halvorson (1955) found that medium in which strains of *B. cereus* or strains of *B. polymyxa* were grown contained an autolytic substance at the onset of sporulation. These autolytic substances possessed marked species specificity and lysed only the species from which they had been derived. If all of the materials for the synthesis of the spore can be obtained from the vegetative cell, these autolytic substances may play an important role in providing for the growth of the spore. I am assuming that as the developing spore appears to be surrounded by refractile walls any substance of high molecular weight within the spore will have been synthesized from compounds of lower molecular weight capable of passing through the spore walls. The crystalline inclusions, on the other hand, are either synthesized from small units or they are formed by a change in an existing protein in the cell. As far as we know, either alternative might apply to the inclusions of *B. thuringiensis*, but with the inclusions of *B. medusa* the case is slightly different. The parasporal body of *B. medusa* grows rapidly within a thick membrane. It is difficult to believe that the fully formed constituents pass through the membranes, and it seems more reasonable to suppose that its substance is synthesized within the membrane and that the body continues to grow until the synthesizing mechanism for some reason stops. The only other body within the bacillus which is actively synthesizing materials and is covered with a membrane is the spore; the obvious association leads to the speculation that the parasporal body was itself once an incipient spore. It is then logical to ask this question about all spore-formers: why, when the cells at the time of sporulation contain several chromatinic bodies, does only one spore develop in each cell? Vegetative cells that are about to spore may be in a situation analogous to that in a tree branch when the buds are expanding. The developing terminal bud inhibits the growth of the other buds on the branch, and if the terminal bud is removed the other buds immediately grow. The effect of the terminal bud can be reproduced by removing it and applying indolacetic acid to the cut surface of the branch. In vegetative bacillus cells when the conditions are correct for sporulation one chromatinic body may develop a spore ahead of the others and set up a concentration gradient of substances which inhibit the formation of spores from other bodies. As spores are composed of a variety of compounds a number of enzyme systems must be engaged in synthesizing the compounds, and the inhibition of some processes might, in the inclusion-forming strains, still permit the functioning of others, and an inclusion might develop from a partially inhibited chromatinic body. We do not as yet know whether the medusal body develops from a chromatinic body, but supposing that it does, what bearing would this have on the formation of crystal inclusions in *B. thuringiensis*? A similar process might occur, but, in addition, the surrounding membranes might disintegrate or in fact not be formed and the protein might be modified by enzymic action so that it crystallized in the cell. One would have to assume that the protein formed is related to proteins formed within the spores.

Some of these speculations are difficult to test. The problem should be regarded first as cytological rather than as biochemical and the cyto-logical changes in a sporing cell of the inclusion-forming strains should be carefully observed. The important hypothesis could probably be tested in any laboratory: can non-inclusion-forming strains of bacilli be induced to form either inclusions or spores from every chromatinic body within the cell? Thus the discussion ends, as it began, with a cytological problem.

REFERENCES

ANGUS, T. (1953). Studies of *Bacillus* spp. pathogenic for silkworm. *Progress Rep. Canada Dept. Agric., Science Service, Forest Biol. Div.* 9 (6), 1.

ANGUS, T. (1954a). A bacterial toxin paralysing silkworm larvae. *Nature, Lond.,* 173, 545.

ANGUS, T. (1954b). Some properties of a bacterial toxin affecting insect larvae. *Progress Rep. Canada Dept. Agric., Science Service, Forest Biol. Div.* 10, (4), 2.

AOKI, K. & CHIGASAKI, Y. (1915). Ueber die Pathogenität der sog. Sotto Bacillen (Ishiwata) bei Seidenraupen. *Mitt. med. Fak. Tokio,* 13, 419.

AYERS, W. W. (1949). Production of Charcot-Leyden crystals from eosinophils with aerosol M.A. *Blood,* 4, 595.

BERLINER, E. (1911). Über die Schlaffsucht der Mehlmottenraupe. *Z. ges. Getreidew.* 3, 63.

BERLINER, E. (1915). Über die Schlaffsucht der Mehlmottenraupe. (*Ephestia kühniella*, Zell.) und ihren Erreger, *Bacillus thuringiensis*, n.sp. *Z. angew. Ent.* 2, 29.

BUEHLER, H. J., SCHANTZ, E. J. & LAMANNA, C. (1947). The elemental and amino acid composition of crystalline *Clostridium botulinum* type A toxin. *J. biol. Chem.* 169, 295.

CHARCOT, J. M. & ROBIN, C. (1853). Observation de leucocythemie des SG. et *Mem. de Soc. de Biol.* 5, 44.

DARRUM, E. L. (1950). A microelectrophoretic and microiontophoretic technique. *J. Amer. chem. Soc.* 72, 2493.

DAWE, C. J. & WILLIAMS, W. L. (1953). Histochemical studies of Charcot-Leyden crystals. *Anat. Rec.* 116, 53.

DUMBLETON, L. J. (1945). Bacterial and nematode parasites of soil insects. *N.Z. J. Sci. Tech.* 27, 76.

DUTKY, S. R. (1940). Two new spore-forming bacteria causing milky disease of Japanese beetle larvae. *J. agric. Res.* 61, 57.

FLEWETT, T. H. (1948). Nuclear changes in *Bacillus anthracis* and their relation to variants. *J. gen. Microbiol.* 2, 325.

FRAZER, D. & JERREL, E. A. (1953). The amino acid composition of T_3 bacteriophage. *J. biol. Chem.* **205**, 291.

GREENBERG, R. A. & HALVORSON, H. O. (1955). Studies of an autolytic substance produced by an aerobic sporeforming bacterium. *J. Bact.* **69**, 45.

HANNAY, C. L. (1953). Crystalline inclusions in aerobic sporeforming bacteria. *Nature, Lond.*, **172**, 1004.

HANNAY, C. L. & FITZ-JAMES, P. (1955). The protein crystals of *Bacillus thuringiensis* Berliner. *Canad. J. Microbiol.* **1**, 694.

HEIMPEL, A. M. (1954). Investigations of the mode of action of strains of *B. cereus* Fr. and Fr., pathogenic for the larch sawfly (*Pristiphora erichsonii* Htg.). Thesis, Queen's University, Kingston, Ontario, Canada.

ISHIWATA, S. (1902, 1906). Quoted by Aoki & Chigasaki (1915).

KLIENEBERGER-NOBEL, E. (1945). Changes in the nuclear structure of bacteria, particularly during spore formation. *J. Hyg., Camb.*, **44**, 99.

LAUBACH, C. A., RICE, J. L. & FORD, W. W. (1916). Studies on aerobic sporebearing non-pathogenic bacteria. *J. Bact.* **1**, 493.

LEYDEN, E. (1872). Zur Kenntnis des Bronchial-Asthmas. *Virchows Arch.* **54**, 324.

LINDERSTRÖM-LANG, K. & OTTESEN, M. (1947). A new protein from ovalbumin. *Nature, Lond.*, **159**, 807.

MATTES, O. (1927). Parasitäre Krankheiten der Mehlmottenlarven und Versuche über ihre Verwendbarkeit als biologisches Bekämpfungsmittel. *Ges. Beförd. gesam. Naturw. Sitzber., Marburg*, **62**, 381.

MAZIA, D., BREWER, P. A. & ALFERT, M. (1953). The cytological staining and measurement of protein with mercuric bromphenol blue. *Biol. Bull., Woods Hole*, **104**, 57.

MORTON, H. E. & ENGLEY, F. B. (1945). The protective action of dysentery bacteriophage in experimental infections in mice. *J. Bact.* **49**, 245.

PAPPENHEIMER, A. M. & WILLIAMS, C. M. (1952). The effects of diphtheria toxin on the *Cecropia* silkworm. *J. gen. Physiol.* **35**, 727.

PAPPENHEIMER, A. M. & WILLIAMS, C. M. (1954). Cytochrome b_5 and the dihydrocoenzyme l-oxidase system in the Cecropia silkworm. *J. biol. Chem.* **200**, 915.

PASTEUR, L. (1870). *Études sur la maladie des vers à soie (flacherie)*, pp. 226–240. Gauthier-Villars. Quoted by Toumanoff (1954).

POLSON, A. & WYCKOFF, R. W. G. (1948). The amino acid content of bacteriophage. *Science*, **108**, 501.

SMITH, N. R., GORDON, R. E. & CLARKE, F. E. (1946). Aerobic mesophilic sporeforming bacteria. *Misc. Publ. U.S. Dep. Agric.* no. 559. Issued 1952 as *Aerobic sporeforming bacteria*, U.S. Dep. Agric., Agricultural Monograph no. 16.

STEINHAUS, E. A. (1951). Possible use of *Bacillus thuringiensis* Berliner as an aid in the biological control of the alfalfa caterpillar. *Hilgardia*, **20**, 359.

STEINHAUS, E. A. (1954). Further observations on *Bacillus thuringiensis* Berliner and other sporeforming bacteria. *Hilgardia*, **23**, 1.

TOUMANOFF, C. & VAGO, C. (1951). L'agent pathogène de la flacherie des vers à soie endémique dans la région des Cevénnes; *Bacillus cereus* var. *alesti* var.nov. *C.R. Acad. Sci., Paris*, **233**, 1504.

TOUMANOFF, C. & VAGO, C. (1952). La nature de l'affection des vers à soie due à *Bacillus cereus* var. *alesti* et les modalités d'action de ce bacille. *Ann. Inst. Pasteur*, **83**, 421.

TOUMANOFF, C. & VAGO, C. (1953a). Étude histopathologique des vers à soie atteints de *Bacillus cereus* var. *alesti*. *Ann. Inst. Pasteur*, **84**, 376.

TOUMANOFF, C. & VAGO, C. (1953b). Recherches sur l'effet toxique de *Bacillus cereus* var. *alesti* vis-à-vis des vers à soie. *Ann. Inst. Pasteur*, **84**, 623.

TOUMANOFF, C. (1954). A propos d'un caractère différentiel de *Bacillus cereus* var. *alesti* Toum. et Vago, agent pathogène de la flacherie infectieuse des vers à soie. *Ann. Inst. Pasteur*, **87**, 486.

TOUMANOFF, C., VAGO, C. & GLADILINE, C. (1954). Recherches sur l'effet toxique de *Bacillus cereus* var. *alesti* vis-à-vis des vers à soie. *Ann. Inst. Pasteur*, **86**, 438.

EXPLANATION OF PLATES

PLATE 1

Figs. 1–4. Crystal and spores in cells of *Bacillus thuringiensis*. Each cell contains one refractile spore and one refractile crystal. Phase contrast. Photographs by Dr C. Robinow. × 3600.

Fig. 5. Free crystals and spores of *B. thuringiensis*. Negative print from an electron micrograph of a gold-shadowed specimen. × 7500.

Fig. 6. Cell containing a spore and a cuboidal crystal. *B. thuringiensis* strain no. 16-1-1, isolated and described by Dr E. Steinhaus (1954). Negative print from an electron micrograph of a gold-shadowed specimen. × 7500.

Fig. 7. Free cuboidal and rhomboidal crystals produced by *B. thuringiensis* strain no. 16-1-1. Negative print from an electron micrograph of a gold-shadowed specimen. × 7500.

PLATE 2

Fig. 8. Shell of protein crystal. *Bacillus thuringiensis*. Positive print from an electron micrograph of a palladium-shadowed specimen. × 54,000.

Fig. 9. Protein crystal after treatment with 0·02 molar sodium carbonate solution. Negative print from an electron micrograph of a uranium-shadowed specimen. × 25,500.

PLATE 3

Fig. 10. An electron micrograph of an ultra-thin section of *Bacillus thuringiensis* showing a portion of a cell containing a crystal and a spore. Part of the spore is shown in the upper right-hand corner. The outer membranes of the spore in this particular cell are closely associated with a membrane which passes from the spore, under the crystal, to the end of the cell where it forms a loop. The chromatinic body which did not form the spore was expected to be found in the area occupied by the loop. The cell suspension was fixed with osmium, embedded in methacrylate resin and sectioned with the Porter-Blum microtome. × 94,000.

Fig. 11. Light microscope photograph of the same preparation before embedding in methacrylate. Cells of *B. thuringiensis* in an advanced stage of sporulation. Spore contents uniformly stained. One crystal developing alongside each spore. Osmium, HCl, Giemsa, undifferentiated. × 3600.

PLATE 4

Fig. 12. Chains of cells containing unstained refractile spores and heavily stained, membrane-enclosed parasporal bodies. In each cell there is one parasporal body and one spore. Bacillus grown on a semi-synthetic medium. *Bacillus medusa* isolated by Dr C. Robinow. Dilute carbol-fuchsin. × 3600.

Fig. 13. *B. laterosporus* spores and parasporal bodies. Each unstained refractile spore is cradled in a metachromatically stained, canoe-shaped parasporal body. Preparation and photograph by Dr C. Robinow. Giemsa. × 3600.

PLATE 1

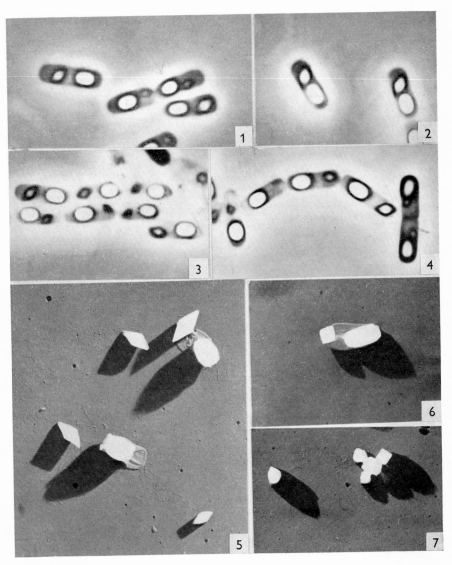

(*Facing p.* 340)

PLATE 2

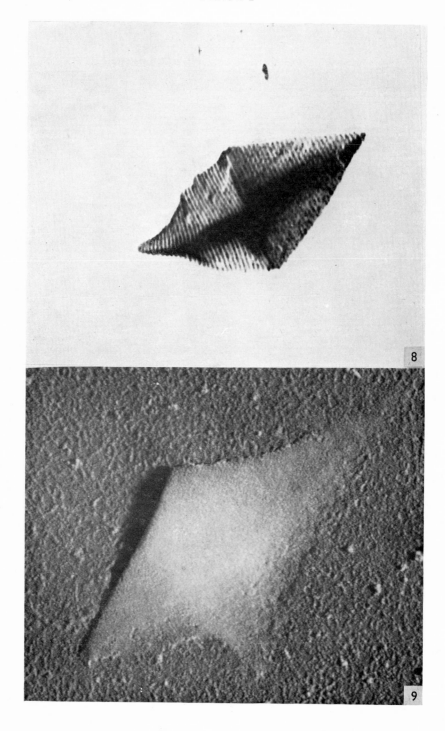

8

9

PLATE 3

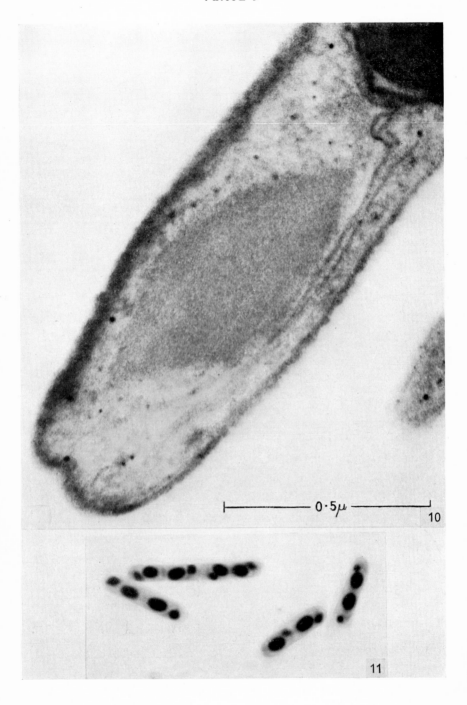

├───── 0·5μ ───────┤

PLATE 4

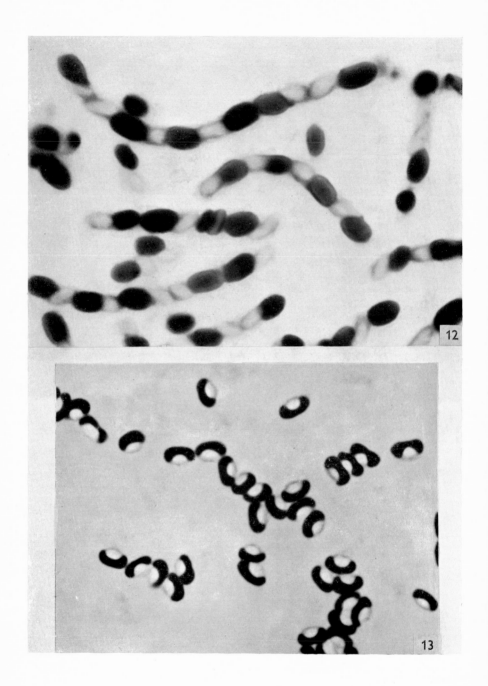

THE STRUCTURE AND DEVELOPMENT OF THE INDUCED LONG FORMS OF BACTERIA

W. H. HUGHES

WITH ELECTRON MICROSCOPY BY C. E. CHALLICE

Wright-Fleming Institute, St Mary's Hospital, London

The existence of microbes differing in appearance from the type has been recognized and recorded by many hundreds of workers. It is impossible here to review any of the earlier work, and this has already been done in the greatest detail by Lohnis (1921). These earlier workers were divided into two groups, those who regarded the variations in morphology as evidence for a life cycle in bacteria and a minority (e.g. Fischer, 1903) who regarded them purely as involutionary. These two schools of thought still persist and no bridge has yet been built between them. Ainley Walker & Murray (1904) were among the first to recognize that it was possible to induce the changes, usually described as spontaneous, by acting on the typhoid bacillus with methyl violet. Many other controllable agents have since been found to be active, and this aspect of the work has been reviewed by Dienes & Weinberger (1951). The position in the period between the review of Lohnis and that of Dienes is covered adequately by Wahlin & Almaden (1939).

Owing to the current confusion in nomenclature it is essential to define exactly what a 'long form' is and what may fairly be called an L-form. Although *Streptobacillus moniliformis* has rather the same appearance as abnormal forms in other organisms, it is desirable to exclude it from this discussion, since too much attention to it disturbs perspective. It is unfortunate that in the past many including the writer have misunderstood Klieneberger-Nobel's use of the term L-form, treating it as synonymous with 'large body'. The correct usage (Pulvertaft, 1952) is for 'L-form' to be restricted to those forms of the *S. moniliformis* and other organisms which remain permanently in the cycle and to describe abnormal forms which revert as long forms or large bodies, keeping to descriptive terms throughout. It will be seen from the reference, however, that L-form and long form are used as synonyms in many recent papers germane to our subject, and it is necessary to establish to which particular school of nomenclature each author belongs.

Even the descriptive 'long form' needs definition, since variations in size will be encountered in the normal development of a culture. The difference between a long form and a cell which is merely large but otherwise normal is reflected morphologically in their method of division. The large normal cell in a favourable environment will be seen to divide into two equal daughter cells; under suitable conditions a long form may divide at more than one point giving, instead of two, a number of cells which usually differ from one another in size—an appearance not unlike plasmotomy in Protozoa. Differentiation is not absolute and this criterion must be applied intelligently. The presence of one or two abnormal cells in a culture, particularly when freshly isolated, is quite usual. Similarly, in every predominantly abnormal culture, however bizarre the majority of the cells may be, a residue of normal organisms can often be found. This steady gradation from normal to abnormal is due to the variation in the responses of individual cells in a pure culture, even when they are closely related (Hughes, 1953b, 1955b). When Duguid (1948) encountered this mixture of abnormal and normal bacilli he referred to the cultures as intermediate.

A very wide range of organisms has been recognized as giving long forms. Table 1 gives a representative sample from recent literature. The Coccaceae can be included, but the modified response of these genera make them less attractive to work with. Large forms are certainly present in enterococci, and Dienes, who at first failed to show anything equivalent in streptococci, has now succeeded (1953). This list, taken with that of Lohnis (1921), shows that almost all members of the Schizomycetes are included.

INDUCING AGENTS

Table 1 also shows that there are three main classes of agents which cause long forms to appear in culture: (1) a variety of poisons, including the antibiotics, (2) starvation and (3) physical traumata. In the first class the earliest example is probably the action of methyl violet on the typhoid bacillus (Ainley Walker & Murray, 1904), the most recent example is mainly the antibiotics (Pulvertaft, 1952; Dienes & Weinberger, 1951). In the second class, deprivation of nitrogen (Duguid, 1948; Knaysi & Baker, 1947) appears equally as effective as the antibiotics. It is not always clear which of two possible agents are responsible for the presence of any particular long form. It is probable that most workers have inadvertently employed mixed stimuli. Even when antibiotics are used, and certainly in much of the earlier work, it is emphasized that the long forms appear most readily on poor media or after prolonged cultivation without subculture or on drying media. Here much of the

Table 1. *Methods of inducing long forms in various organisms*

Organism	Provoking agent	Author
Escherichia coli	penicillin, streptomycin, aureomycin, chloromycetin and terramycin	Pulvertaft (1952)
	bacteriophage	Gorrill & Challice (1955)
	sodium ricinoleate	—
	amino acids	Rowley (personal communication)
	ultra-violet light	Challice and Gorrill (1954)
	chloramphenicol and antiserum	Voureka (1951)
	streptomycin	Stubblefield (1947)
E. coli-communis	pH changes	Wahlin & Almaden (1939)
Aerobacter aerogenes	phosphorus and nitrogen deficiency; presence of calcium carbonate; pH change to acid	Duguid (1948)
	2 % lithium chloride	Wahlin & Almaden (1939)
Salmonella typhi	methyl violet, fuchsin, methyl green and methylene blue	Ainley Walker & Murray (1904)
	pH changes	Wahlin & Almaden (1939)
	penicillin	Dienes (1948*a*)
	antibody and complement	Dienes, Weinberger & Madoff (1950)
	carboxylmethoxylamine glycine	Dienes, Weinberger & Madoff (1950)
	heavy-water medium	Chance & Wendell (1946)
S. typhimurium	furazolidone	Hobson (personal communication)
Other salmonellae	pH changes	Wahlin & Almaden (1939)
	amino acids	Dienes & Zamecnic (1952)
	fresh isolation	Weinberger, Madoff & Dienes (1950); Taylor & Hughes (unpublished)
Shigella	fresh isolation	Weinberger *et al.* (1950)
S. sonnei	pH changes; nitrogen-deficient	Wahlin & Almaden (1939)
S. flexner	media; glycerin	
Proteus vulgaris	penicillin	Fleming, Voureka, Kramer & Hughes (1950)
	penicillin, streptomycin, aureomycin, chloromycetin	Pulvertaft (1952)
	penicillin	Tulasne (1949)
	1 %–2 % carbolic acid	Moltke (1927); Braun & Solomon (1918)
Vibrio cholerae	glycine and alanine	Gordon & Gordon (1943)
	penicillin	Fleming *et al.* (1950)
	low temperature and drying media	Almquist (1922)
Bacillus mycoides	nitrogen-free medium	Knaysi & Baker (1947)
B. cereus	penicillin, streptomycin, aureomycin and chloromycetin	Pulvertaft (1952)
Clostridium welchii	penicillin	
	magnesium deficiency	Gardner (1940); Webb (1948)
C. tetani and others	penicillin	Dienes (1950)
Brucella abortus	2 % lithium chloride	Wahlin & Almaden (1939)
Haemophilus influenzae	amino acids	Dienes & Zamecnic (1952)
	solid media	Dible (1924)
Corynebacterium diphtheriae	drying medium	Almquist (1922)
Bacterioides	penicillin	Dienes (1948*b*)
Streptococcus haemolyticus	concentration of NaCl 0·25–0·1 M and other electrolytes	Sharp (1954)
S. viridans	penicillin	Dienes (1953)
Haemophilus pertussis	immunity	Wittler (1952)
Bacterium lactis aerogenes	resorcinol, M-cresol sodium ricinoleate and γ-rays	Spray & Lodge (1943) Henrici (1925), Lea *et al.* (1937)

effect may be due to the depletion of nitrogen. In other cases substances are added which might act as inhibitors for one organism while
being energy sources for others. Glycerin is a good example of this
(Wahlin & Almaden, 1939). The amino acids are particularly interesting. Rowley (1953) has shown that on a chemically defined medium
certain of the amino acids inhibited strains of *Escherichia coli* and that
this action could be counteracted by the addition of minute amounts of
other amino acids. He did not, however, draw attention to the fact that
the inhibited strains were converted into long forms during exposure to
the amino acids concerned, and that they reverted to normal bacilli when
favourable conditions were restored. Amino acids follow the antibiotics
closely in the ease with which they induce long forms. Gordon &
Gordon (1943), using glycine and alanine, produced long forms in *Vibrio
cholerae*, while Dienes & Zamecnic (1952) found glycine, methionine,
phenylalanine, tryptophan and tyrosine effective with various organisms.

The third group of less specific traumata includes physical agents. An
alteration in pH to the alkaline side causes long forms in *Shigella sonnei*
and to the acid side in *Salmonella typhi* (Wahlin & Almaden, 1939).
Refrigeration is also effective (Dienes, 1942; Klieneberger-Nobel, 1951*b*),
and so is irradiation with β and γ-rays (Lea, Haines & Coulson, 1937).
Ultra-violet light (Gorrill & Challice, 1954; Challice & Gorrill, 1954)
must be considered separately, since it has two actions. It is effective
alone, but it may also induce production of bacteriophage which also
causes long forms to appear. Morphologically the long forms caused
in one way are indistinguishable from those caused in the other or in
both together. Then, again, complement and antibody have this effect
on *S. typhi* (Dienes, Weinberger & Madoff, 1951) as also have antigen-
antibody reactions.

Little attention appears to have been paid to the presence of long
forms in fresh pathological material. They are frequent in pus, sputum
and urine in the untreated patient as well as after antibiotic therapy,
when their presence might be anticipated. They appear in the urine of
patients with pyelitis and cystitis after the administration of autogenous
vaccines and are more readily phagocytosed than the normal bacteria.
Dienes & Weinberger (1951) survey the evidence that a culture in the
long phase is much less virulent than the parent strain.

All the treatments causing long forms are more or less damaging, but
it is important to realize that some long forms also appear in the early
stages of culture on artificial media usually regarded as adequate. In
the salmonellae, for instance, Weinberger, Madoff & Dienes (1950)
report a proportion of such cells in newly isolated strains. Dienes &

Weinberger (1951) thinks that they are rare among the salmonellae. This does not agree with my own observations, for even in strains transformed in the laboratory, e.g. S. 2297/53 made by Stocker, early platings show a proportion of such forms (Hughes & Taylor, unpublished). They are certainly easy to obtain by chemical treatment (Ainley Walker & Murray, 1904; Almquist, 1922; Wahlin & Almaden, 1939; Dienes & Zamecnic, 1952). In *Escherichia coli* the number of naturally occurring long forms that are present can be increased by selective breeding (Hughes, 1953a). In more recent experiments (Hughes, 1955a) it was found that if poorly growing colonies of *E. coli* were selected with the micromanipulator it was possible to obtain a strain which could hardly grow at all in the cultural conditions provided. Not only are the colonies very small as compared with those of the parent strain, but many cells fail to develop into colonies at all and grow into true long forms. These, however, resumed normal growth on removal to broth from the nutrient agar blocks in the oil chamber where they had developed.

The assumption was made above that some long forms arose spontaneously in young cultures under normal conditions. It does not follow that because a particular strain of organism can be persuaded to grow readily on a medium the nutritional properties of that medium are optimal for every individual cell in the strain. Throughout the literature on this subject, references will be found to variation in behaviour between individual cells. This has been made the basis of a study of variation in single cells, and it can readily be shown that on the division of a cell the two daughter cells will react differently to the same degree of stress (Hughes, 1955b). The appearance of long forms in newly isolated strains need not be regarded as any more normal than when a medium has been deliberately made inadequate for the majority of cells in a culture. An excellent illustration of this argument is given when streptomycin is withheld from a streptomycin-dependent strain (Paine & Finland, 1948). Here again many of the cells become long, yet ordinarily streptomycin-free agar would not be regarded as an unsuitable medium.

It seems reasonable to suppose that the presence of any long forms in a culture is a measure of the inadequacy or toxicity of the medium, and that the number of these forms is proportional to that inadequacy or toxicity. Where this is a transitory phenomenon and the long forms are not detected in subcultures they will have been eliminated by selection and the strain as a whole may be considered to be adapted by the death of the sensitive cells. When it is considered desirable to study the presence of long forms in cultures it is important that repeated examination should take place during the first few hours of growth, since lysis and overgrowth with normal small forms will obscure the picture. It is untrue that long forms are not produced in liquid media; they are, however, very rapidly replaced by small, well-adapted forms and become inconspicuous and ultimately lyse.

The swarmers of *Proteus vulgaris* need special consideration. This organism is particularly suitable for the study of the induced long forms and large bodies, since it responds so readily to a variety of agents. This was described by Hauser (1885). It is difficult, if not impossible, to detect any differences in morphology between induced long forms and spontaneous swarmers. Among the latter a proportion of bulbs will be found. It has been suggested that the swarmers are induced by the accumulation of the products of the colony's metabolism or by the depletion of nitrogen in the medium. The growth cycle for this organism would accordingly be as follows: small forms multiply to form a colony which reduces the available nitrogen and excretes metabolites; the environment is now less favourable and susceptible cells develop into long forms which are motile on agar or other solid medium, they move away from the colony until they reach a fresh site where the environment corresponds to the original one; here they break down to small forms again which then start a fresh cycle. The degree of abnormality exhibited by the swarmers will depend on their individual susceptibility and the concentration of metabolites. A particular variant of this behaviour is seen when two incompatible strains swarm towards one another (Dienes, 1949). Here long forms and bulbs are produced where the two strains approach each other.

Moltke (1927) reached two conclusions about the swarmers. First, that they were not able to multiply and would ultimately die and that the multiplication of the colony depended on a reserve of small forms which accompanied them from within the colony. The second conclusion was that the medium did not become toxic since a colony would spread across an agar block which had previously been covered by growth, cleared of organisms, washed and remounted surrounded by fresh medium.

These two conclusions need re-examination. The viability of the cells in the culture is not constant. If those from a young broth culture are tested, 95% or more will grow out into colonies. If the swarmers from the colony developing on agar are examined their mortality is much higher, as the following experiment shows.

A young broth culture of *Proteus vulgaris* was planted on well-dried nutrient agar plates and on to agar blocks and incubated. The numbers of organisms dividing, growing but failing to divide or showing evidence of lysis were determined under the microscope. At intervals further blocks were prepared by removing part of the edge of the colony, suspending the organisms in broth and spreading this on the blocks. These were also incubated and counted in the same way. The results are shown in Table 2.

This does not mean that there is no reserve of small cells in the swarm but only that the viability of long cells falls steadily throughout. It happens also that the least viable cells are deposited by the swarm at its edge and are the most obvious features under the microscope.

During the stage of swarming division is constantly taking place and small relatively normal forms are arising from the swarmers deep in the colony, so that at the end of the swarming phase only the cells whose division is inhibited are recognized as long, the better adapted having already divided.

Table 2. *Viability of swarmers of* Proteus vulgaris *at various stages of growth*

	Percentage		
	Dividing	Not dividing	Lysing
Normal small forms	92	7	1
18 hr. swarmers	19	26	55
48 hr. swarmers	1	—	99

The presence of a toxin similarly needs reconsideration. If the organisms are grown on cellophane disks on agar plates and the growth is stripped off after swarming it is possible to reinoculate the plate and obtain growth where the disks were, or to allow the swarm to spread back from the edge. On filter-paper the results are different and the tendency is for swarming to be inhibited where growth has previously taken place. The technique is not so satisfactory as with a more uniform membrane, since organisms pass through the paper and remain scattered on the otherwise cleared area. Moreover, swarming is well known to be inhibited by high agar concentrations; with my strain, 4·5% agar will stop all spreading, and in all experiments in Petri dishes some gradual drying and concentration of the medium will take place. Swarming can only be detected on dry medium with concentrations of agar between 1 and 4% after drying. Simple spreading without formation of long forms takes place on media containing less than 1% agar. With more than 4% agar, though long forms appear, they cannot move to give the characteristic appearances of a 'swarm'. There seems little doubt that swarming Proteus are under the influence of an adverse environment and that they are examples of induced long forms.

In the interpretation of experiments in which long forms are induced in culture we are in a more favourable position than were the earlier workers, and the techniques used today allow proof to be substituted for some of the speculation. The early methods depended on stained preparations made at intervals after plating. The abnormal forms, particularly the bulbs and the long forms with bulbous enlargements, are extremely fragile, and methods of making smears similar to those used in routine bacteriological investigation destroy many of them and give a false picture of the culture as a whole. The modification of this method, the coverslip impression technique of Ledingham, Klieneberger-Nobel and others, was a great improvement, but such preparations give a static picture, and although repeated impressions may be made and their order carefully recorded, there is no reason to assume that the forms found late in a series are derived from those seen earlier, unless the generation time is known and the age of the original implant is also checked; the specimens taken after 5 hr. incubation may show younger forms than those taken after 20–30 min. The second disadvantage of the older methods is that the killing, fixing and staining of the cells involves shrinking the cytoplasm, which may be more affected than the cell wall or septa; the loss in diameter may be as much as 30 % for the whole cell and even more for the contents, which may draw away from the wall. Ross (1953) studied shrinkage during fixation in mammalian cells with similar results. Thirdly, in bacteria it is difficult to establish with certainty which cells in the culture were alive and which dead or dying before they were stained. Finally, since cells in a culture normally divide at different rates, stained impression preparations show all the stages at the same time. Attempts to synchronize division in all the cells of a culture have been made by Birch-Andersen, Lark, Maaløe & Sjöstrand (1954).

DEVELOPMENT OF LONG FORMS

Continuous observation of the developing cell dates mainly from the work of Ørskov. With the coming of modern phase-contrast equipment it has been possible for other workers to develop his method and to take serial photographs or time-lapse cinemicrographs and so to establish directly the sequences in single cells or in small groups (Fleming, Voureka, Kramer & Hughes, 1950; Klieneberger-Nobel, 1951 b; Pulver-taft, 1952; Hughes, 1953 a, b). The stages of development of the various abnormal forms from the small organisms appear not to have been studied systematically in this way by other workers, and the description which follows is based largely on these papers and unpublished work of my own. Most of the observations are drawn from *Proteus vulgaris* acted on by penicillin.

Development of Proteus vulgaris *in critical concentrations of antibiotic*

When a young culture is transferred to an unfavourable environment the events which follow depend on a number of factors. The provoking agent (or the deficiency in the medium) must be so adjusted that some growth can take place; some agents, penicillin especially, can be used over a wide dilution range, but with others, concentration is critical, a little too much being lethal from the start, while concentrations which are a little too low show no effect. Such low concentrations, showing no effect at first, may become effective as the culture ages, being reinforced by changes in the medium.

With *Proteus vulgaris*, even when the culture has been recently derived from one single cell, variation can be shown between the individual cells (Hughes, 1953*a*, *b*, 1955*a*, *b*). While some of these develop into typical long forms, some will lyse and some may be relatively unaffected. For this reason the method of sampling a culture at intervals is not recommended as a substitute for concentrating attention on a small group of cells and following their individual development.

(a) Stage of elongation

When *Proteus vulgaris* in critical concentrations of antibiotic is watched under the microscope, the first change seen will be continuous elongation. Increase in girth is less obvious. At such concentrations division seldom occurs, except in some cells which may have been on the point of dividing when transferred from normal medium.

The elongating organism is motile, and, if transferred to normal medium, will develop normally. Under phase contrast it is either uniformly opaque or banded. Flagellar activity, even of motionless cells, is revealed by the movement of small particles or 'dead' organisms near them, especially when these lie trapped between the coils of a long-coiled filament: the coil rotates in one direction, the disturbed particles in the opposite direction. Freely swimming forms sometimes gather their flagella into bundles which can be seen easily for a few moments under the light microscope, especially when one organism passes between two others which are stationary, or when a coiled cell rotates with only a small space between the coils. The movement of the flagella is faster than the undulation of a free-swimming organism (Fleming *et al.* 1950; Fleming, 1950).

(b) Bulb formation

The next development is the bulbous enlargement of part of the filament. The bulb is a thickening either at one end or in the length of the organism, the position being entirely random, and the optical density differing not at all from that of the rest of the thread. Usually the whole organism, including the swelling, is viable on removal from the antibiotic. In normal medium the thread with its bulb, like all other viable forms, breaks down into a number of units which thereafter each divide normally, becoming shorter at each division until they are indistinguishable from the cells of the original parent strain from which the long forms were derived. When the bulbous enlargement is situated in the length of the thread one of the first divisions passes through the middle of it to give two club-shaped daughter cells, and for some time afterwards these can be distinguished from the rest.

(c) Stage of degeneration

Further development is accompanied by certain irreversible changes which may hold the key to the phenomenon. The bulbs enlarge and become progressively less opaque, showing a reticular structure. Strands develop from the contents of the cell and are separated from one another by transparent areas, forming a reticulum which may be replaced by coarse granules. It is this appearance which has attracted so much interest in stained preparations and has been interpreted as part of a life cycle, the bulbs being fruiting bodies, sporangia or some other reproductive structure. Several workers, including Knaysi (1951), have collected series of photographs or have drawn diagrams illustrating the stages of formation of the bulbs by the looping of a thread, the fusion of the overlapping sides of the loop, the development of this ring into a bulb and the production of small forms in the bulb. I have failed to confirm this in serial photographs and films. Instead, the bulbs develop from a thickening in the length of the thread and no coiling need take place. If the thread, with the large bulbs attached, is transferred to normal medium it will divide rapidly as before but the bulb will burst, liberating the contained material as amorphous debris. All normal cells in the culture thereafter can be seen to arise from the opaque threads, and none has ever been seen by our methods to arise from the wreckage of the bulb. Any bulb which has developed a reticular structure is dead or dying. In salmonellae, Vadasz & Juhasz (1955) report that normal organisms can arise from fully developed bulbs.

In cells still exposed to adverse influences, the bulbs continue to enlarge and multiple swellings, not necessarily all in the same stage of development, may appear in a single filament. The small opaque form and the large reticulated one may be linked by a thread only a little wider than normal. The organism is still motile as a whole and its flagella are co-ordinated. It may break apparently by the lysis of a segment, not necessarily one containing a bulb, rather than by normal division. If a bulb bursts, the contents of the thread may also spill out and the whole be killed.

Certain of the threads will show reticulation similar to that of the bulbs, associated with a uniform increase in girth. Such threads, like the bulbs, are not viable on transfer and will eventually lyse. Cells without opaque areas fail to divide, and any normal organisms appearing in the subculture can be traced to surviving opaque segments. Although the bulbous enlargements and the transparent threads lyse rapidly on transfer to normal medium and will eventually lyse if left where they are, and though they are extremely fragile, yet they may not all be described as dead, since flagellar movement may persist for many hours after ability to reproduce has been entirely lost. Completely spherical organisms, with only a few dots of material representing the original structure of the internal cell, may have flagella beating rhythmically, or gathering into bundles like plaits of hair and undulating to propel the doomed cell.

I am convinced that in the cultures I have studied no cell showing a transparent reticulated pattern of internal structure by phase contrast has been wholly viable, and that the presence of such structure is evidence of irreversible degeneration.

Cells which are opaque may be ruptured mechanically or with alkali and the contents will run out to form an irregular pool of opaque fluid, the residual cell wall being then transparent. In the fluid from such cells no structure can be resolved by the light microscope; there is no nucleus with a defined membrane nor other formed element.

STUDIES WITH THE ELECTRON MICROSCOPE

It was hoped that the electron microscope might reveal structures beyond the resolving power of light microscopy. Smith, Mudd & Hillier (1948) have already reported their observations on cultures of *Streptobacillus moniliformis*, and their sections of normal organisms serve as a control for our own observations (1954). We consider that they and Sjöstrand (Birch-Andersen *et al.* 1954) have so far produced the truest picture of the internal structure of bacteria. The methods we have used include thin sections as well as shadow-cast preparations of whole cells (Challice & Hughes, 1954; Challice, 1954).

The least affected cells differ in no way from the normal short forms except in length (Pl. 1, figs. 5, 6); when shadow cast they are shown to have the same depth as width. The more affected long forms, if the bulbs are still optically opaque, also show long shadows, giving a depth corresponding to the width. The bulbs and the segments of threads corresponding to the transparent ones in the living preparations are seen to be collapsed, and the cell contents are reticulated or broken into fragments. After shadow-casting they are shown to be flattened on to the supporting membrane (Pl. 1, fig. 7).

Sectioning of the bacteria reveals further details. Satisfactory results can only be obtained if very great care is taken to avoid shrinkage arti-facts. We consider that a true picture can be best obtained if a suspension of organisms, whether originally in broth or on solid medium, is washed free from the protein and the polypeptides of the media by centrifuging in isotonic buffered saline and then fixed in bulk with an isosmotic solution of osmium tetroxide (Palade, 1952). With this method there will be no gross difference between the appearances under the electron micro-scope and under phase contrast, and there is good agreement with the stained impression preparations of Klieneberger-Nobel or the coverslip cultures of Fleming. We have found that the more carefully cells are fixed the less structure they exhibit in section and the better the contents fit the cell wall.

Glancing cuts and oblique sections show that there is a potential space between the cell wall proper and what is usually called the inner limiting membrane. This space is greatly increased by inferior fixation methods and has, we believe, been misinterpreted as being a cytoplasmic space. It is not seen in living organisms but can readily be produced both in the dried films and in wet preparations by acid treatment. Normal sections pass through the cell contents, the more superficial cuts showing material filling the cell completely (Pl. 2, fig. 9). Cuts passing through the middle of the cell often expose an irregular area transparent to the rays. This is an important feature of the pictures of both Hillier and Sjöstrand. This space or vacuole is seen under phase contrast; it represents the lighter band in the pattern of young long forms. Nothing correspond-ing to it has been reported in stained material. A similar appearance is to be seen with the interference microscope (Dodds, personal communication). Sectioned long forms, both from swarming cultures and those treated with inhibitors, show features corresponding closely to shadow-cast whole organisms and with living phase-contrast preparations. The long forms which would be uniformly opaque by phase contrast have the same internal structure as normal bacilli. Those that would be banded show a repeat pattern of the light and dark areas and suggest a spiral organization (Pl. 2, fig. 10). Those with translucent bulbs or segments show fragmentation of the cell contents, the strands and nodules of opaque material being separated by spaces in which nothing can be found (Pl. 2, fig. 11). The most advanced stages of bulb formation are frequently associated with rupture of the wall of the cell and only the empty skin is seen. It is noteworthy that there is little particulate debris left behind when this has occurred, and nothing is visible which might be interpreted as mitochondria, nuclei, or any other formed structures.

The most important evidence from the sections is on the cell wall itself. In healthy control cells and in the long forms which would be viable this wall is uniformly dense and smooth, but in the bulbous enlargements and in non-viable segments there is an appearance of roughness, lamination or fraying (Pl. 2, fig. 12). We believe that the essential difference between a cell which is viable and one which is irreversibly damaged is here. The wall in the non-viable cell ceases to be an effective osmotic barrier and all the structures that appear, the stranding and nodulation of the contents, represent a hydration, and these changes are of the same nature whether the damage is caused by antibiotics and other chemicals, by starvation, by phage or by X-rays or with ultra-violet light. That this is so might also be deduced from a comparison of the morphological changes seen and described in long forms and large spheres with those reported under the name of plasmolysis and plasmoptysis. Fischer (1900) shows typical large forms produced by the action of acetic acid. When the acid was neutralized they disappeared. This work was confirmed by Garbowski (1907) and by Raichel (1928), who both used hypotonic solutions and distilled water (see review by Knaysi, 1951). Although these authors regard their phenomenon as due to osmotic effects it was noted that with normal potassium nitrate the bulbs were produced only after an interval of 15–20 min. Stapp & Zycha (1931) obtained similar results with magnesium sulphate. Variation in the resistance of individual cells to the same osmotic concentration offers a close parallel to their resistance to antibiotics.

The observations of Weibull (1953) with lysozyme may be interpreted as another example of the effect of weakening the cell wall. The protoplasts which he has photographed, and to which flagella are still attached, have the same appearances as cells exposed to distilled water, or as the more advanced spherical forms given by penicillin.

It is probable that had Dienes (1949) been interested in plasmolysis and not in L-forms and long forms he would have reported the effect of tap water on *Proteus* as an example of the former rather than the latter phenomenon. There seems little reason to doubt that the overcoming of the osmotic barrier of the cell wall, whether primarily by the direct action of hypotonic solutions or secondarily by damage to the wall by chemicals and other agents, causes morphological changes in the organism which are indistinguishable from one another.

SPONTANEOUS RECOVERY OF CULTURES EXPOSED TO ANTIBIOTICS

In the later stages of culture most authors have noted the appearance of small cells. Various explanations have been offered for their appearance; those authors who have discerned a life cycle in the development of long forms and spheres consider the small cells to be its completion. Serial photographs or time-lapse cinemicrographic techniques, however, show the following sequence. In old cultures, when many of the long forms have developed bulbs and degenerated and others are only empty husks, some will be left which contain segments still opaque by phase contrast and still viable if transferred. These segments, even if they are left under adverse conditions, will separate from one another, not by normal division but by the lysis of the intervening parts. One of two things may now happen. If the toxic agent is unstable, as penicillin is, its concentration will fall until it is no longer inhibitory for the remaining selected segments, which will resume growth as though they had been transferred to a more favourable medium and will soon outnumber the dead cells present with them. If, however, the toxic agent is stable, although its concentration will not fall, some of the surviving elements will possess a resistance high enough to allow them to grow, and these will multiply until they dominate the picture, less resistant cells gradually disappearing by lysis.

During the development of small forms in old cultures fortuitous arrangements provide support for the theories of life cycles, provided only that the sequence of events has not been followed closely and that only stained preparations are available. A first example of this is shown in Pl. 1, fig. 4. This is part of a series of photographs taken to follow the recovery of cells after removal from penicillin (Fleming *et al.* 1950). It would be reasonable to suppose, if this were a fixed preparation and there were no other evidence to go on, that a large bulb had burst, liberating a number of small rods. Nevertheless, all these rods developed from a short thread attached at the end of the bulb (Pl. 1, fig. 1). This very misleading appearance is common in all cultures which are recovering. A second example would be even more difficult to interpret if fixed and stained. This is where small forms are actually contained inside a large bulb. It is not possible to explain this away as due to the small forms lying either under or over the bulb, as I have been able to observe it on several occasions in living preparations with the small forms motile within the bulb and their movement limited by its wall. Long forms may also be seen rotating continuously within bulbs. In the case of the small forms this occurs in an old culture in the stage of recovery. The tails of bulbs separate and form small cells and, while some of the bulbs themselves lyse, others remain as empty shells with holes in them through which it is possible for the small forms to find access. This is not dependent on the randomly swimming small forms passing by accident through a relatively small opening, but on a particular characteristic of recently separated cells in growing cultures. Immediately after division it is the rule for the cells to move in relation to one another and to the rest of the colony. Normally the movement results in two cells which have separated moving from a line-ahead to a line-abreast position. When there is a long form or a bulb present next to them, this post-divisional movement is deflected and they follow the new surface that is presented. The colony they form is no longer compact and round but stretched out. This tropism for surfaces will lead them towards any breach in the bulb wall and they turn into it at the next division. Thereafter division will take place within the bulb and, in motile cultures, those outside will sooner or later move away while those inside will be trapped. The rotating long form in a bulb may arise in the culture at any time and is probably a more common phenomenon. Anyone acquainted with agar block preparations will know how slight an obstacle is necessary to deflect the long forms. They always follow the line of least resistance, and show the same inclination to pass along any surface presented to them. If the fore-end of a long form is deflected to meet the hind end, it will pass along itself to form the well-known spiral and may rotate for hours or days on end. Any long form that encounters a spherical form which has burst will pass along its surface and, turning into any breach, be trapped in the interior.

THE LONG-FORM COLONY

There is finally the long-form colony. It is not easy to dogmatize about this, since no one has so far followed its development from a single cell. The appearance of the colony is shown in Pl. 2, fig. 13, and compared with the small-form colony in Pl. 2, fig. 14, from the same culture and an adjacent field. It will be seen to be composed of long and bulbous forms; it has obviously differed in sensitivity from the rest of the culture which has produced large colonies of normal small forms. When subcultured in broth it will revert to small forms, but colonies of this type in the hands of Tulasne, of Dienes and of Klieneberger-Nobel have been made to breed true even when away from penicillin and other provoking conditions. It is legitimate at this stage to interpret these colonies as a selected culture which has been bred to be sensitive to the conditions on the agar. That some organisms maintain a long-form colony on agar alone is not surprising, since it is possible to select organisms which are badly adapted to solid media. These true-breeding colonies are the only true L-cultures. Their chief characteristic is that they do not revert to normal morphology on repeated subculture.

The presence of long forms and large bulbs in a culture is a measure of the inadequacy of the medium for the support of some or all of the culture. We are watching in a microcosm the laws of selection and adaptation at work. In our implant are a number of individuals unable to survive on the artificial medium; these lyse and are not usually seen and reported. A further number can grow but cannot divide; these are the long forms. In the filaments to which they give rise are individual segments which differ in resistance from one another; the better adapted form the nucleus of future growth and revival, the worse adapted give rise to the degenerate bulbs. In the implant also are cells adequately adapted from the start; these grow away as small forms and rapidly overrun the culture. The threads which are formed early soon become inconspicuous, and subcultures are unlikely to contain them unless a special single-cell technique is employed, when they can be made to yield a strain growing very poorly and mainly composed of long forms like themselves.

In spite of the primarily toxic nature of the changes and the fact that the bulbs and transparent forms are definitely degenerative (Heilman, 1941) it may be that there is an advantage to the organism in being temporarily in the long phase, since this may well increase the natural rate of variation in the culture, so giving every possible chance for resistant individuals to appear.

SUMMARY

Long and large forms are found in nearly all bacteria. This may mean either that they are stages in a life cycle or that they are formed following injury. The latter view is supported here and traumata having this effect may be classified as due to chemical agents, nutritional deficiencies or physical conditions. Organisms and individual cells vary in susceptibility to any particular injury.

Electron micrographs of thin sections support the view that degeneration of the wall and hydration of the contents of the cell is the essential lesion which allows the development of the large forms. This change is irreversible.

The resumption of normal growth in the cultures and the production of healthy short forms depends on the presence in the long threads of segments with higher resistance which are able to survive. From these the culture regenerates.

REFERENCES

AINLEY WALKER, E. W. & MURRAY, W. (1904). The effect of certain dyes upon the cultural characters. *Brit. med. J.* ii, 16.

ALMQUIST, E. (1922). Variation and life cycles in pathogenic bacteria. *J. infect. Dis.* **31**, 483.

BRAUN, H. & SOLOMON, R. (1918). Die Fleckfieber Proteusbazillen. *Z. Bakt.* **82**, 243.

BIRCH-ANDERSEN, A., LARK, K. G., MAALØE, O. & SJÖSTRAND, F. S. (1954). A study of sections of bacteria undergoing synchronous nuclear division. *Proc. int. Congr. Electronmicroscopy, London*, 1954.

CHALLICE, C. E. & GORRILL, R. H. (1954). Some observations on the morphological changes in *E. coli* accompanying induction by ultraviolet light. *Biochim. biophys. Acta*, **14**, 482.

CHALLICE, C. E. & HUGHES, W. H. (1954). *Proc. int. Congr. Electronmicroscopy, London.*

CHALLICE, C. E. (1954). The electron microscope, with particular reference to its use in biological research. Part II. Histological techniques for electron microscopy. *Lab. Practice*, **3**, 279.

CHANCE, H. L. & WENDELL, C. A. (1946). The influence of heavy water on the growth, morphology and fermentative reactions of *Eberthella coli*. *J. Bact.* **51**, 547.

DIBLE, J. H. (1924). The haemophilic bacteria of the normal throat: their types and incidence. *J. Path. Bact.* **27**, 151.

DIENES, L. (1942). Significance of large bodies and development of the L-type of colonies in bacterial cultures. *J. Bact.* **44**, 37.

DIENES, L. (1948 a). Isolation of L-type colonies from typhoid bacilli with the aid of penicillin. *Proc. Soc. exp. Biol., N.Y.*, **68**, 589.

DIENES, L. (1948 b). The isolation of L type cultures from *Bacteroides* with the aid of penicillin and their reversion into the usual bacilli. *J. Bact.* **56**, 445.

DIENES, L. (1949). The development of Proteus cultures in the presence of penicillin. *J. Bact.* **57**, 529.

DIENES, L. (1950). Isolation of L type cultures from Clostridia. *Proc. Soc. exp. Biol., N.Y.,* **75**, 412.

DIENES, L. (1953). L type cultures isolated from streptococci. *Proc. Soc. exp. Biol., N.Y.,* **83**, 579.

DIENES, L. & WEINBERGER, H. J. (1951). The L-forms of bacteria. *Bact. Rev.* **15**, 248.

DIENES, L., WEINBERGER, H. J. & MADOFF, S. (1950). The transformation of typhoid bacilli into L-forms under various conditions. *J. Bact.* **50**, 755.

DIENES, L. & ZAMECNIC, P. C. (1952). Transformation of bacteria into L-forms by amino acids. *J. Bact.* **64**, 770.

DUGUID, J. P. (1948). The influence of cultural conditions on the morphology of *Bacterium aerogenes*, with reference to nuclear bodies and capsule size. *J. Path. Bact.* **60**, 265.

FISCHER, A. (1900). Die Empfindlichkeit der Bakterienzelle und das baktericide serum. *Z. Hyg. InfektKr.* **35**, 1.

FISCHER, A. (1903). *Vorlesungen über Bakterien*, 2nd edit. Jena: G. Fischer.

FLEMING, A. (1950). Further observations on the motility of *Proteus vulgaris* grown on penicillin agar. *J. gen. Microbiol.* **4**, 457.

FLEMING, A., VOUREKA, A., KRAMER, I. R. H. & HUGHES, W. H. (1950). The morphology and motility of *Proteus vulgaris* and other organisms cultured in the presence of penicillin. *J. gen. Microbiol.* **4**, 257.

GARBOWSKI, L. (1907). Gestaltsänderung und Plasmoptyse. *Arch. Protistenk.* **9**, 53.

GARDNER, A. D. (1940). Morphological effects of penicillin on bacteria. *Nature, Lond.,* **146**, 837.

GORDON, J. & GORDON, M. (1943). Involution forms of the genus *Vibrio* produced by glycine. *J. Path. Bact.* **55**, 63.

GORRILL, R. H. & CHALLICE, C. E. (1955). Further observations on the electron microscope changes following induction of *E. coli* K. 12. *Biochim. biophys. Acta,* **16**, 82.

HAUSER, G. (1885). Über Fäulnisbakterien und deren Beziehungen zur Septicaemie, p. 99. Leipzig: Tag.

HEILMAN, F. R. (1941). A study of *Asterococcus muris*. *J. infect. Dis.* **69**, 32.

HENRICI, A. T. (1925). On cytomorphosis in bacteria. *Science,* **61**, 644.

HUGHES, W. H. (1953*a*). The origin of the L-form variants in anaerobic cultures of *Bacterium coli*. *J. gen. Microbiol.* **8**, 307.

HUGHES, W. H. (1953*b*). In *Adaptation in Micro-organisms*, p. 250. Edit. E. F. Gale & R. Davies. Cambridge: University Press.

HUGHES, W. H. (1955*a*). The inheritance of differences in growth rate in *Escherichia coli*. *J. gen. Microbiol.* **12**, 265.

HUGHES, W. H. (1955*b*). The differences in antibiotic sensitivity of closely related single cells of *Proteus vulgaris*. *J. gen. Microbiol.* **12**, 269.

KLIENEBERGER-NOBEL, E. (1951*a*). Filterable forms of bacteria. *Bact. Rev.* **15**, 77.

KLIENEBERGER-NOBEL, E. (1951*b*). The L-cycle: a process of regeneration in bacteria. *J. gen. Microbiol.* **5**, 525.

KNAYSI, G. & BAKER, R. F. (1947). Demonstration, with the electron microscope, of a nucleus in *Bacillus mycoides* grown in a nitrogen-free medium. *J. Bact.* **53**, 539.

KNAYSI, G. (1951). *Elements of Bacterial Cytology*, 2nd ed. New York: Comstock.

LEA, D. E., HAINES, R. B. & COULSON, C. A. (1937). The action of radiation on bacteria. *Proc. Roy. Soc.* B, **123**, 1.

LOHNIS, F. (1921). Studies upon the life cycles of bacteria. *Mem. nat. Acad. Sci.* **16**, 335.

MOLTKE, O. (1927). *Contributions to the Characterisation and Systematic Classification of* Bact. proteus vulgaris (*Hauser*). Copenhagen: Levin and Munksgaard.

PAINE, T. F. & FINLAND, M. (1948). Observations on bacteria sensitive to, resistant to and dependent upon streptomycin. *J. Bact.* **56**, 207.

PALADE, G. E. (1952). A study of fixation for electron microscopy. *J. exp. Med.* **95**, 285.

PULVERTAFT, R. J. (1952). The effect of antibiotics on growing cultures of *Bacterium coli. J. Path. Bact.* **64**, 75.

RAICHEL, B. (1928). Ueber den Einfluss osmotisch wirksamer Mittel auf die Bakterienzelle. *Arch. f. Protistenk.* **63**, 333.

ROSS, K. F. A. (1953). Cell shrinkage caused by fixatives and paraffin wax embedding in ordinary cytological preparations. *Quart. J. micr. Sci.* **94**, 125.

ROWLEY, D. (1953). Inhibition of *E. coli* strains by amino acids. *Nature, Lond.* **171**, 80.

SHARP, J. T. (1954). L colonies from haemolytic streptococci: new technique in the study of L forms of bacteria. *Proc. Soc. exp. Biol., N.Y.*, **87**, 94.

SMITH, W. E., MUDD, S. & HILLIER, J. (1948). L-type variation and bacterial reproduction by large bodies as seen in electron micrograph studies of *Bacteroides funduliformis. J. Bact.* **56**, 603.

SPRAY, G. H. & LODGE, R. M. (1943). The effects of resorcinol and of M-cresol on the growth of *Bact. lactis aerogenes. Trans. Faraday Soc.* **39**, 424.

STAPP, C. & ZYCHA, H. (1931). Morphologische Untersuchungen an *Bacillus mycoides*: ein Beitrag zur Frage des Pleomorphismus der Bakterien. *Arch. f. Mikrobiol.* **2**, 493.

STUBBLEFIELD, E. (1947). Globulus and stranded forms of *B. coli* on streptomycin agar. *J. Bact.* **54**, 81.

TULASNE, R. (1949). Existence of L-forms in common bacteria and their possible importance. *Nature, Lond.*, **164**, 876.

VADASZ, J. & JUHASZ, I. (1955). Plasma globules of *Salmonella enteritidis* (var. *danysz*) arising under the influence of penicillin and their reversion to the original bacillary forms. *Nature, Lond.*, **176**, 169.

VOUREKA, A. (1951). Production of bacterial variants *in vitro* with chloramphenicol and specific antiserum. *Lancet*, i, 27.

WAHLIN, J. G. & ALMADEN, P. J. (1939). Megalomorphic phase of bacteria. *J. infect. Dis.* **65**, 147.

WEBB, M. (1948). The influence of magnesium on cell division. *J. gen. Microbiol.* **2**, 275.

WEIBULL, C. (1953). The isolation of protoplasts from *Bacillus megaterium* by controlled treatment with lysozyme. *J. Bact.* **66**, 688.

WEINBERGER, H. J., MADOFF, S. & DIENES, L. (1950). The properties of L forms isolated from *Salmonella* and the isolation of L forms from *Shigella. J. Bact.* **59**, 765.

WITTLER, R. G. (1952). The L-form of haemophilus in the mouse. *J. gen. Microbiol.* **6**, 311.

EXPLANATION OF PLATES

PLATE 1

Figs. 1–4. Recovery of large forms on removal from the influence which provoked them. Phase contrast, Electronmicrograph, × 600. The bulbous enlargement degenerates; normal cells are produced from the more normal element in the tail.

Fig. 5. Normal bacilli for comparison with affected forms in figs. 6–8. Electronmicrograph, × 7000.

Fig. 6. Long forms of *Escherichia coli* B induced by ultra-violet light, showing dense structure of viable cells. Electronmicrograph, × 7000.

Fig. 7. Penicillin-induced forms showing collapse of non-viable cells. Electronmicrograph, × 10,000.

Fig. 8. Collapsed long form with bulbous segment in the middle and apparently viable tip. Electronmicrograph, × 10,000.

PLATE 2

Figs. 9–12. Electronmicrographs.

Fig. 9. Section of control normal cells, × 7000.

Fig. 10. Section of swarmer of *Proteus vulgaris* showing alternating pattern of more and less dense material, × 7000.

Fig. 11. Penicillin-induced forms showing the development of reticulation, × 10,000.

Fig. 12. Degenerating forms showing lamination of cell wall and the breaking-up of the contents, × 7000.

Fig. 13. Large-form colony on agar, × 120.

Fig. 14. Small variant colony, consisting of normal forms and edge of normal colony, × 120.

PLATE 1

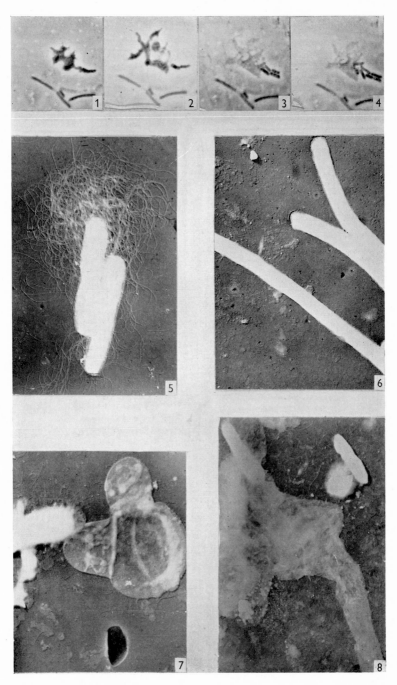

PLATE 2

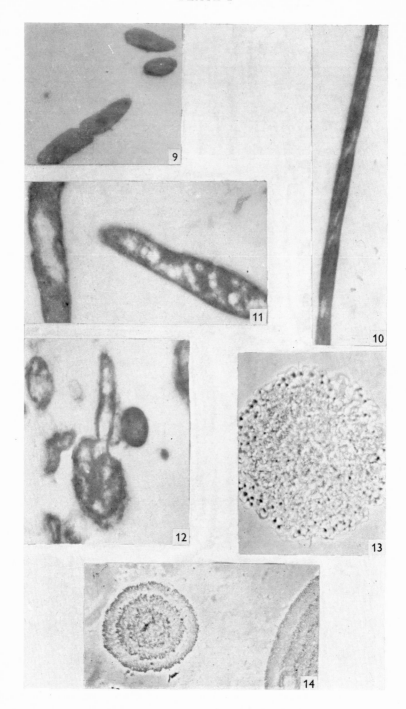